Mathematics
Intermediate Course A

Purposeful Design Publications
A division of ACSI
Dr. Ken Smitherman, President
Post Office Box 35097 Colorado Springs, CO 80935-3509
www.acsi.org

purposeful design
p u b l i c a t i o n s

To enable Christian educators and schools worldwide to effectively prepare students for life

For additional information, write Purposeful Design Publications, PO Box 35097, Colorado Springs, CO 80935-3509.

Scripture taken from the New King James Version of the Bible. Copyright © 1982 by Thomas Nelson, Inc. Used by permission. All rights reserved.

Cover image © Samuel Monnier. Please visit www.p-gallery.net. Used by permission.

Ribbits!™ is a trademark of Focus on the Family. Copyright ©2002. Used by permission. For additional information about Focus on the Family and the *Ribbits!*™ video series, please visit their website at www.family.org or call 800-A-FAMILY.

UNO® is a registered trademark of Mattel, Inc. Used with permission. ©2002 Mattel, Inc. All Rights Reserved.

MONOPOLY® & ©2002 Hasbro, Inc. Used with permission.
CLUE® & ©2002 Hasbro, Inc. Used with permission.
SCRABBLE® is a registered trademark of J.W. Spears & Sons Limited, a subsidiary of Mattel, Inc. Used with permission. ©2002 Mattel, Inc. All rights reserved.

Burt's Bees® images on pages 140 and 141 used by permission.

GPS image on page 66 used by permission from Garmin International.

Wooden clock image on page 190 used by permission. Please visit www.wooden-clockworks.com for additional information.

Slinky® is a registered trademark of POOF Products/James Industries, Inc. Used by permission.

NOTE: References to books, computer software, and other ancillary resources in this series are not endorsements by ACSI. These materials were selected to provide teachers with additional resources appropriate to the math concepts being taught and to promote student understanding and enjoyment.

Printed in the United States of America

Purposeful Design Intermediate Mathematics
ISBN 1-58331-195-5 Student Textbook - Catalog #7222
ISBN 1-58331-196-3 Teacher Edition - Catalog #7223

Mathematics
Intermediate Course A

Authors
Mae Branda
Sharon Bruce
Fran Burdick
Jessica Waggener

Grade Level Editor
Dr. Gary Kimball
Managing Editor
Paula Redfield
Senior Content Editor
Dr. James Schwartz

Editorial Team
Suzanne Clark
Anita Gordon
Stephen Johnson
Christy Krenek
Solly Thomas

Design Team
Susanna Garmany
Phil Lear
Kristopher Orr

Table of Contents

11 Probability

12 Statistics

13 Solid Geometry

14 Coordinate System

15 Cumulative Review

Chapter Theme:
Infinity

1 Chapter

Number Sense

Construct Meaning

We serve an infinite God who has no beginning and no end. If you tried to think of the most distant time past, God existed even before that time. Whether we consider the most distant time past or future, God exists.

Can you express the least or greatest possible numbers?

No matter what number is expressed, a number that is less or greater can be found. Not only can counting continue infinitely, but two finite numbers, such as 0 and 10, have an infinite amount of numbers between them. The number line indicates that numbers extend into infinity in either direction.

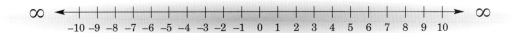

∞ ← +—+ → ∞
    −10 −9 −8 −7 −6 −5 −4 −3 −2 −1 0 1 2 3 4 5 6 7 8 9 10

The position of each digit in a finite number indicates its value. The numbers are divided into groups of three digits called **periods**.

billions			millions			thousands			hundreds			decimal fraction				
hundred billions	ten billions	billions	hundred millions	ten millions	millions	hundred thousands	ten thousands	thousands	hundreds	tens	ones	tenths	hundredths	thousandths	ten-thousandths	hundred-thousandths
						6	2	5	9	0	7 .	6	2	7		
				2	0	0	0	0	0	0	0 .					
											4 .	0	1	5	6	8
								5	3	9	9 .	0	0	6		

Check Understanding

a. Read each number in the chart. List the numbers from greatest to least.

b. In a number such as 55,555, the value of each digit is multiplied by 10 as you move to the left. How does the value of each digit change if you move right to the next digit?

c. Compare the value of 7 in the ones place to 7 in the thousandths place.

d. If the model shows 2.35, explain how 2.3 would be shown.

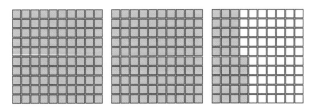

e. What is the greatest number that can be written on the place value chart above?

Practice

1. Using each digit only once, write the greatest possible whole number with the digits 3, 9, 5, and 2. What is the least possible whole number formed by these digits?

2. Using each digit only once, what pair of two-digit numbers can you form that have the greatest possible difference? Use 8, 4, 1, and 6.

3. Is $3,567,320 greater than or less than a billion dollars?

4. Is 0.2197 greater than or less than three-hundredths?

Apply

5. Compare the unit costs and order the snacks from least expensive to most expensive.

    Kreamy Kookies: 16.10 cents per ounce
    Super Snacks: 16.11 cents per ounce
    Crumble Cakes: 16.2 cents per ounce
    Primo Pretzels: 16.01 cents per ounce

6. The goal of Rapid Running Gear, Inc., is to make a six-digit annual profit. If the total profit was $85,500 by October, find the minimum additional profit that must be earned by the end of the year to meet the goal.

7. The Appalachian Trail is approximately 2,160 miles long. Ian and Fiona plan to hike an average of 12 miles per day. Without performing calculations, state whether or not it is reasonable that they could hike the entire length of the trail in three months. Explain your reasoning.

8. A person is considered to have lead poisoning if a blood sample shows lead levels greater than 0.00010 grams per liter. Use the information below to determine which patients may need treatment for lead poisoning.

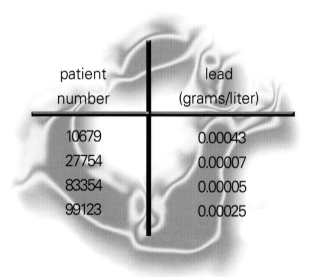

patient number	lead (grams/liter)
10679	0.00043
27754	0.00007
83354	0.00005
99123	0.00025

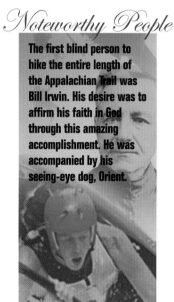

Noteworthy People

The first blind person to hike the entire length of the Appalachian Trail was Bill Irwin. His desire was to affirm his faith in God through this amazing accomplishment. He was accompanied by his seeing-eye dog, Orient.

Exponents

Construct Meaning

When exponents are used to express amounts, only a few numbers are needed to show increase. An **exponent** determines the number of times the **base** is used as a factor. A number expressed in this way is in **exponential notation**.

Even a professional weightlifter, who might lift more than 200 pounds, will never progress to lifting the number of pounds equal to 10^3.

$$10^4 \leftarrow \text{exponent}$$

base 10^4 is read "ten to the fourth power."
$10^4 = 10 \times 10 \times 10 \times 10 = 10,000$

Use exponents to think of the amount of weight a person is capable of lifting.

$10^1 = 10$ pounds
$10^2 = 100$ pounds
$10^3 = 1000$ pounds
$10^4 = 10,000$ pounds
$10^5 = 100,000$ pounds

The four by four array represents 4^2 (four squared). A number is squared when it is multiplied by itself. $4^2 = 4 \times 4 = 16$

How can connecting cubes be used to model 4^3 (four cubed)?

Find the value of x if $4^x = 1024$.

think How many times does the base need to be multiplied by itself to result in the given product?

Find the value of x if $x^5 = 32$.

think What number multiplied by itself five times results in the given product?

If 5 students in 5 classrooms each have 2 boxes of 2 pens, what is the total number of pens?

$$5 \times 5 \times 2 \times 2 = 5^2 \times 2^2 = \square \times \square = \square \text{ pens}$$

Check Understanding

Write >, < or = .

a. $12^2 \bigcirc 6^3$ **b.** $1^7 \bigcirc 6^1$ **c.** $2^4 \bigcirc 4^2$ **d.** $10^5 \bigcirc 12,000$

Review the list of numbers in exponential notation.

e. What is the pattern in the products as the exponent decreases?

f. Use the pattern to determine the value of 5^0.

$$5^3 = 125$$
$$5^2 = 25$$
$$5^1 = 5$$
$$5^0 = \square$$

g. Explore with patterns to find the value of any base number raised to the zero power.

Practice

Evaluate.

1. 8^3 **2.** Seven cubed   **3.** 3^4 **4.** Eleven squared

Solve for x.

5. $3^2 \times 4^3 = x$ **6.** $6^0 \times 243 = x$ **7.** $x^3 = 1000$ **8.** $5^x = 625$

9. Use your calculator to find 23^4.

Apply

10. If six campers in six cabins at Mount Holy Cross Center each have a six-pack of bottled water for each day of a six-day retreat, what is the total number of bottles?

11. $A = s^2$ is the formula used to find the area of a square. Suppose the 24-foot square cabins at Mount Holy Cross Center are divided into six equal-sized rooms. Use the formula to determine the total area of one cabin. Next, find the area of each room.

12. $V = s^3$ is the formula used to find the volume of a cube. The volume of the bear-proof food locker at camp is 27 cubic feet. What is the length of each side of the locker?

13. Dominic's counselor, Mr. Copernicus, offered a reward to the first camper who could tell which summer had a greater food expenditure. He said the amount spent in 2001 was equal to 200^2 dollars and the total for 2002 was 6^6 dollars. Compare the amounts to see which was greater.

1.3 Square Roots

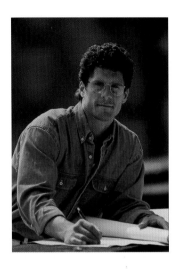

Construct Meaning

Mr. Diversion, who designs games for a living, needs to make a square game board with an area of 144 square inches. What are the dimensions needed for the game board?

Use $A = s^2$.
144 sq in. $= s^2$

What number multiplied by itself equals 144?
$s \times s = 144$ sq in.

think.

$s = 12$ in.

Another way to solve the problem is to find the square root of A. The **square root** of a given number is a number which, when multiplied by itself, results in the given number.

Finding the square root of a number:

If $A = 144$ sq in., then 144 sq in. $= s^2$.

Write the radical sign $\sqrt{}$
on both sides of the equation.

$\sqrt{144}$ sq in. $= \sqrt{s^2}$

Find the number that equals
144 when it is squared.

$\sqrt{12 \text{ in.} \times 12 \text{ in.}} = \sqrt{s \times s}$
12 in. $= s$

A **perfect square**, such as 144, is the number that results when a whole number is multiplied by itself. Name another number that is a perfect square.

Mr. Diversion's supervisor advised him to reduce the size of the game board to about 132 square inches to save production costs. Is 132 a perfect square?

Mr. Diversion considered the two closest perfect squares.
$\sqrt{121} = 11$ $\qquad\qquad$ $\sqrt{132}$ $\qquad\qquad$ $\sqrt{144} = 12$
$\sqrt{132}$ is between 11 and 12.

He refined his estimate.
$11.2 \times 11.2 = 125.44$ $\qquad$ $11.4 \times 11.4 = 129.96$ $\qquad$ $11.5 \times 11.5 = 132.25$
11.5 is a close estimate for $\sqrt{132}$.

He used a calculator to find the exact number. $\sqrt{132} = 11.489125$
Mr. Diversion decided to make the board 11.5 inches on each side.

6

Check Understanding

Find each square root.

a. $\sqrt{49}$ **b.** $\sqrt{169}$ **c.** $\sqrt{10,000}$ **d.** $\sqrt{0.81}$

e. The square root of 200 is between what two consecutive whole numbers?
f. Is the square root of 150,000 closer to 300 or 400?

Practice

Use the graph of numbers and their squares to find the square root. If the number is not a perfect square, round to the nearest tenth. Check your answers with a calculator.

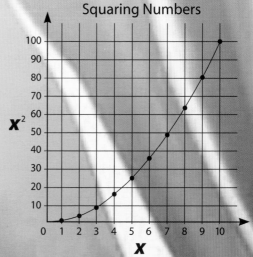

Squaring Numbers

	Graph	Calculator
1. $\sqrt{64}$		
2. $\sqrt{55}$		
3. $\sqrt{40}$		
4. $\sqrt{16}$		
5. $\sqrt{89}$		

Apply

6. Patriot's Park is a square having a grassy area of 159,775 square yards surrounding a square pavilion displaying flags. The pavilion measures fifteen yards by fifteen yards. What is the length of the side of Patriot's Park?

7. The Americana Basket Company ships their products in square boxes. The bottom of the new square Betsy Ross Basket has an area of ninety-five square inches. What is the minimum size of the shipping box that may be used if the sides of the shipping boxes are in whole numbers of inches?

8. George said that the square root of $\frac{1}{9}$ is $\frac{1}{3}$.
   a. Explain how he found this answer.
   b. How can the square root of a fraction be greater than the given fraction?
   c. Will the square root of a given whole number ever be greater than the given number?

Scientific Notation

Construct Meaning

The Sahara in northern Africa is the largest desert in the world. It covers 3,500,000 square miles, stretching from the Atlantic Ocean past the Red Sea. It consists of rocky plains, vast sandy expanses, and irrigated fields that produce bountiful crops. Can you count the grains of sand in the Sahara? Is it an infinite number?

Scientific notation is a way to express a number as a decimal between 1 and 10 multiplied by a power of 10.

$$3{,}500{,}000 = 3.500000 \times 10 \times 10 \times 10 \times 10 \times 10 \times 10$$
$$= 3.5 \times 10^6$$

Notice that the exponent of 10 is equal to the number of places the decimal point is moved to the left.

In order to change a number from scientific notation to **standard notation** (the usual way to express numbers) simply do what the operations symbol indicates—multiply.

$$7.32 \times 10^4 = 7.32 \times 10 \times 10 \times 10 \times 10$$
$$= 73200.$$

Each time the number is multiplied by ten, the decimal point is moved one place to the right.

Copy and complete the table.

World's Largest Deserts

Desert name	Approximate size in square miles	
	Standard notation	Scientific notation
Sahara	3,500,000	3.5×10^6
Arabian	1,000,000	
Australian	570,000	
Gobi		5.0×10^5
Kalahari		2.2×10^5

A scientific calculator can be used to enter numbers in scientific notation. Find the sum of the areas of the Gobi and Kalahari deserts using scientific notation.

$$\boxed{5} \; \boxed{\cdot} \; \boxed{0} \; \boxed{\text{EE}} \; \boxed{5} \; \boxed{+} \; \boxed{2} \; \boxed{\cdot} \; \boxed{2} \; \boxed{\text{EE}} \; \boxed{5} \; \boxed{=} \qquad \boxed{720000.}$$

The total area is 7.2×10^5 square miles.

Check Understanding

a. If a calculator gives an answer in scientific notation, how can you change it to standard notation?

Determine the missing exponent.

b. $16,300 = 1.63 \times 10^{\square}$ **c.** $9,000,000 = 9.0 \times 10^{\square}$ **d.** $7350 = 7.35 \times 10^{\square}$

e. Change 56,760,000 to scientific notation.

f. Change 4.59×10^3 to standard notation.

Practice

Express each number in scientific notation.

1. 3,560,000   **2.** 97,000   **3.** 860,000   **4.** 19,500,000

Express each number in standard notation.

5. 2.5×10^4 **6.** 5.9×10^6 **7.** 1.0×10^3 **8.** 8.437×10^9

Apply

Use a scientific calculator to solve the following. Use scientific notation for your answers.

9. How much larger is the Arabian than the Australian desert? Use the numbers from the table on the previous page. Write your answer in scientific notation.

10. Is the Sahara more than five times the size of the Gobi desert?

11. Add 3.1×10^5 and 2.4×10^5. Multiply 3.11×10^5 by 2.4×10^5. What do you notice about the exponent in your answers?

12. Is a desert area of 6.1×10^4 square miles greater than or less than an area of six hundred thousand square miles?

13. Why would it be easy to find the combined areas of the Sahara and Arabian deserts in scientific notation without a calculator? Find the combined area using mental math.

Order of Operations

Boats of Saintes-Marie
by Vincent Van Gogh

Construct Meaning

At the Van Gogh Art School, there are two young adult classes. The thirty students in the evening class each made five pieces of pottery during the spring session. Each of the twenty-five students in the morning class completed three paintings during the term. What is the total number of items that can be displayed at the end-of-term art show?

Art items from evening class   Art items from morning class   =   Total art items
30×5 $+$ 25×3

An **expression** is a mathematical phrase containing operation symbols and numbers and/or variables. A **variable** is a letter that represents a numerical value. It is important to follow the **order of operations** to correctly evaluate an expression when there is more than one operation.

> ### Order of Operations
> 1. Complete operations inside parentheses and above or below a division bar.
> 2. Simplify exponents.
> 3. Multiply and divide from left to right.
> 4. Add and subtract from left to right.

Evaluate the expression using the order of operations to find the total number of art items.

$$30 \times 5 + 25 \times 3$$
$$150 + 75$$

225 art items can be displayed.

Evaluate $160 - 2^4(3) + 10$.

Simplify the exponent.	$160 - 16(3) + 10$
Multiply.	$160 - 48 + 10$
Add and subtract from left to right.	$112 + 10 = 122$

> **Remember:**
> Multiplication may be shown as:
> $5 \times a$
> $5 \cdot a$
> $5(a)$
> $5a$

Complete and evaluate the expression for finding the total number of helpers if half of the class of 30 and 4 families of 3 people helped set up the art show.

$$\frac{\square}{2} + \square \cdot \square = \square$$

Knowledge of the Commutative, Associative, and Distributive Properties is helpful for writing and solving equations.

Commutative Property of Addition	$8 + 2 = 2 + 8$	$a + b = b + a$
Commutative Property of Multiplication	$5 \cdot 4 = 4 \cdot 5$	$ab = ba$
Associative Property of Addition	$7 + (7 + 3) = (7 + 7) + 3$	$a + (b + c) = (a + b) + c$
Associative Property of Multiplication	$6 \cdot (2 \cdot 2) = (6 \cdot 2) \cdot 2$	$a(bc) = (ab)c$
Distributive Property	$3 \cdot (9 + 1) = 3 \cdot 9 + 3 \cdot 1$	$a(b + c) = ab + ac$

Check Understanding

a. Which properties state that grouping does not matter in addition or multiplication?

b. Which properties state that order does not matter in addition or multiplication?

c. The ☐ Property states that multiplying a given number by the ☐ of two numbers is equal to multiplying the given number by each of the two numbers and ☐ the products.

d. Select the correct equation and explain your choice.

$100 + 10 \times 2 - 3^2 = 111$ or $100 + 10 \times 2 - 3^2 = 221$

Practice

Write the order of operations for each problem.

example

$3 + (8 + 8) \div 2$
parentheses, divide, add

1. $100 - 5^2 \times 3$ **2.** $40 \div 2(4 + 1)$ **3.** $8^2 \div \frac{6 \times 4}{12}$

Use the order of operations to evaluate each expression.

4. $(9 - 1) - 6 \div 2$ **5.** $4^2(2) \div 4 - 1$ **6.** $5^0 + 6 \times 9$

7. $30 \div 5 + 8 \div 2$ **8.** $20 - 10 + 182$ **9.** $100^2 \div \frac{10}{5}$

Copy each equation and insert parentheses to make it true.

10. $20 + 10 \div 5 + 1 = 7$ **11.** $20 + 10 \div 5 + 1 = 5$

Write the property being shown.

12. $30(12) = (12)30$

13. $14 + (5 + 5) = (14 + 5) + 5$

14. $9 \cdot (3 \cdot 2) = (9 \cdot 3) \cdot 2$

15. $20 \cdot (7 + 4) = 20 \cdot 7 + 20 \cdot 4$

Apply

16. The Distributive Property states that $9(108) = 9 \cdot (100 + 8) = 9 \cdot 100 + 9 \cdot 8$. This facilitates mental math since it is easy to find $900 + 72$. Use the property to mentally determine how many wheel covers are needed for 212 cars.

Classification of Numbers

Construct Meaning

The system of scientific classification places the Caribbean reef shark in the same kingdom, phylum, and class as the great white shark. However, the two types of sharks are in separate scientific orders. Scientists classify creatures to assist with research and study.

Numbers are classified to improve our understanding of mathematics as well as our ability to calculate. They can be grouped into **sets**, which are finite or infinite collections of elements.

Counting numbers, also called natural numbers, are whole numbers beginning with 1 and continuing infinitely. The set of counting numbers may be shown as $\{1, 2, 3, 4, \ldots\}$.

CARIBBEAN REEF SHARK

Whole numbers include the counting numbers and 0. $\{0, 1, 2, 3, 4, \ldots\}$

Integers are whole numbers and their opposites and 0. $\{\ldots -4, -3, -2, -1, 0, 1, 2, 3, 4, \ldots\}$

A **rational number** is a real number that can be expressed as an exact ratio of two integers other than 0, such as $\frac{1}{3}$. Rational numbers include integers, fractions, and terminating and repeating decimals. $\{-4, -3, -2.5, -1, -\frac{3}{4}, 0, \frac{2}{3}, 1, 1.6, 2, 3, 4\}$ is a set of rational numbers.

> A **terminating decimal** is a decimal that ends.
> $\frac{1}{8} = 0.125$

> A **repeating decimal** is a decimal that repeats a pattern of digits.
> $\frac{1}{3} = 0.3333\ldots = 0.\overline{3}$

An **irrational number** is a real number that cannot be expressed as a terminating or repeating decimal. $\{\sqrt{2}, \sqrt{3}, \sqrt{5}\}$ is a set of irrational numbers.

The set of **real numbers** includes all rational and irrational numbers. $\{-2, -1, -0.2, 0, \frac{1}{7}, 1, \sqrt{2}\}$ is a set of real numbers.

Check Understanding

a. The graphic shows the relationship between the sets of numbers defined above. Irrational numbers, although not shown on the graphic, are a subset (portion) of only one set of numbers. Name it.

b. The square root of each whole number between 1 and 17 is an irrational number, with three exceptions. What are the three whole numbers?

c. The formula for finding the area of a circle is $A = \pi r^2$. The solution for the area of a circle uses the $\approx$ (approximately equal to) sign because π is an irrational number. Use 3.14 for π to find the area of the circle.

r = 3 in.

Practice

Identify the type of numbers in each set. Write *rational, irrational,* and/or *integers*.

1. $\{0.\overline{3}, 7, 10.25, \sqrt{25}\}$
2. $\{-5, -1, 0, \frac{1}{3}, 8\}$
3. $\{-100, 0, 100\}$
4. $\{\pi, \sqrt{13}, \sqrt{17}\}$

Write *true* or *false*.

5. Only one digit separates the set of whole numbers from the set of counting numbers.

6. A rational number cannot be written as a fraction.

7. An irrational number cannot be written as a fraction.

8. The number 0 is an element of the set of all integers, rational numbers, and real numbers.

9. Decimals and fractions are elements of the set of integers.

10. If $x^2 = 2$, then x is an irrational number.

11. The statement $r = \frac{p}{q}$ where p and q are integers other than 0, demonstrates the meaning of the rational number r.

12. The elements in the set $\{-0.65, 0, 0.65\}$ are rational numbers and integers.

Matters of Math

The irrational number *pi* is represented by the Greek letter π. The value of π is often rounded to 3.14 for calculating purposes. In A.D. 150, Ptolemy determined the value of π as 3.1416. Today, computers have calculated π to more than 6 billion places.

Apply

13. Which of the following are infinite sets: the set of real numbers, the set of rational numbers, the set of irrational numbers, the set of integers, the set of whole numbers, and/or the set of counting numbers?

14. Is the set of rational numbers from –2 to 2 a finite set? Explain.

15. Is the set of integers from –95 to 95 a finite set? Explain.

16. The formula for finding the circumference of a circle is $C = 2\pi r$. Determine C for the circle shown. Is circumference an exact measurement or an approximation? Explain.

$r = 2.3$ cm

17. Draw and label a number line showing the integers from –3 to 3. Mark and label two additional rational numbers and two irrational numbers.

Estimation and Mental Math

Construct Meaning

The environmental studies class at Calvary Christian School focuses on wise stewardship of God's creation. The students related the worldwide loss of forests to the information on the chart.

Top Paper Consumers	
Country	Tons per year
United States	76,277,468
Japan	28,631,362
Germany	16,366,262

Clark wrote a short summary of their investigation titled "Wise Consumers and Finite Resources." He rounded the figures from the chart to the nearest million and added to find the approximate amount of paper used by the three countries in one year.

To round a whole number or decimal:
1. Consider the digit to the right of the place value digit.
2. If the digit is greater than or equal to 5, add 1 to the place value digit.
3. If the digit is less than 5, the place value digit is not changed.

Round to the nearest million

76,277,468 $\longrightarrow$ 76,000,000
28,631,362 $\longrightarrow$ 29,000,000
16,366,262 $\longrightarrow$ 16,000,000
The total is approximately   121,000,000 tons

Rounding may be used to:
- Estimate an approximate answer.
- Facilitate mental computation.

Round 121,275,090 to the nearest hundred.
Consider the place value digit and the digit to its right.
121,275,090 rounded to the nearest hundred = ?

Ecology Connection
The average US resident annually uses about five times his or her weight in paper.

Round each to the nearest whole number.
674.48 $\longrightarrow$ 674

674.71 $\longrightarrow$ 675

Round 674.71 to the nearest tenth.
674.71 $\longrightarrow$ 674.$\square$

Round each decimal to the nearest whole number and use mental math.

$9.3 \times 6.8 \approx 9 \times \square = \square$

$99.7 \div 25.1 \approx \square \div \square = \square$

$34.6 + 59.9 \approx \square + \square = \square$

$224.8 - 23.8 \approx \square - \square = \square$

In each problem here, rounding produces **compatible numbers**, *which are numbers that facilitate mental math.*

Ecology Connection
The production of one ton of new paper requires 17 trees and 7,000 more gallons of water than a ton of 100% recycled paper.

Compatible numbers also facilitate mental math with whole numbers. To estimate dividing $190 among 6 people, substitute $180, the closest multiple of 10 and 6. $180 \div 6 = $30

You may use mathematical properties to find compatible numbers for mental math.

Commutative Property of Addition: $a + b + c = a + c + b$
$14 + 89 + 36 = (14 + 36) + 89 = 50 + 89 = \square$
Associative Property of Multiplication: $a \cdot (b \cdot c) = (a \cdot b) \cdot c$
$7 \cdot (9 \cdot 2) = (7 \cdot 9) \cdot 2 = 63 \cdot 2 = \square$
Distributive Property: $a(b + c) = ab + ac$
$8(14) = 8(10) + 8(4) = 80 + 32 = \square$

Check Understanding

a. How can you use estimation to improve your test-taking skills?

b. You have only ten dollars to spend and have selected items that cost $3.78, $2.30, and $4.10. What will occur at the checkout counter if you have used $3.75, $2.25, and $4.00 as compatible numbers for mental math?

Practice

Round each amount.

1. Thirty-six dimes to the nearest dollar
2. 7.284 to the nearest hundredth
3. 422 to the nearest ten
4. 22.6 to the nearest whole number
5. 33.1479 to the nearest thousandth
6. 18,500,000 to the nearest million

Show how the property may be used to find compatible numbers for mental math. Solve.

7. The Distributive Property for 9(52)
8. The Commutative Property of Multiplication for $25 \times 6 \times 8 \times 4$
9. The Commutative Property of Addition for $75 + 119 + 25$
10. The Associative Property of Multiplication for $25 \cdot (4 \cdot 7)$

Apply

11. The students in the environmental studies class hope to decrease paper consumption by raising $223.00 to purchase small dry erase boards for student use. They will sell first-aid kits for seven dollars each. Use compatible numbers and mental math to estimate the number of kits that must be sold.

12. In the spring of 2002, the market value of recyclable white ledger paper was $127 per ton. The paper must be in 1,000-pound bales. Mentally determine the market value of 20 bales of paper for recycling.

13. It is suggested that a business supplies one paper-recycling bin for every fifteen employees. Use the Distributive Property and mental math to determine the approximate number of employees at a forest conservation organization if its office has 25 recycle containers.

Inverse Operations

Construct Meaning

A Christian radio station gave a compact disc to each of the first dozen callers and divided the remaining CDs evenly among the three afternoon volunteers. If each volunteer received four CDs, how many CDs were distributed?

$(\square - 12) \div 3 = 4$

$(\square - 12) \div 3 = 4$

STEP 1 $(4 \times 3) + 12 = 12 + 12 = \boxed{24}$ CDs

STEP 2

STEP 1	Begin with the answer. Perform the inverse of the final operation.
STEP 2	Perform the inverse of the previous operation.

To find the missing number, work backward from the answer by "undoing" each operation in reverse order. An **inverse operation** is the opposite of a mathematical operation. Addition and subtraction are inverse operations. What is the inverse of multiplication?

> Consider putting on your sock, putting on your shoe, and tying your shoe. The inverse is not only to "undo" what you did, but to perform it in reverse order: untie your shoe, take off your shoe, and take off your sock.

The Stewart Donut Company baked twice as many batches of donuts during the second week of May as it had baked the first week. Mr. Stewart ran another shift on Saturday of the second week to fill additional orders. That shift baked 200 batches, which made the total for the second week 1400 batches. How many batches were baked the first week?

$$\square \times 2 + 200 = 1400$$

What is the first inverse operation needed to find the missing number? What is done next?

Check Understanding

Use an inverse operation to find the missing number.

a. $\square \div 6 = 30$ **b.** $\square + 9 = 28$ **c.** $\square \times 5 = 95$ **d.** $\square + 72 = 92$

Practice

Use inverse operations to find the missing number.

1. $\square - 16 = 52$
2. $\square \times 7 = 42$
3. $\square \div 25 = 25$
4. $\square - 6 = 11$

5. $\square \times 2 \div 6 = 12$
6. $(\square - 5) \times 5 = 15$
7. $(\square + 1) \div 10 = 2$

8. $\square - 23 - 14 = 17$
9. $\square \times 23 \times 4 = 828$
10. $\square \times 7 + 3 = 45$

Begin with an empty box to represent the missing number. Write a number sentence and work backward using inverse operations to find the missing number.

11. A number divided by fifteen and increased by 10 is 12. What is the number?

12. Two less than 25 times a number is 123. What is the number?

Apply

Write a number sentence to solve each problem.

13. Jerod climbed twice as high as his brother Josh and then descended 6 feet. If Jerod is now 32 feet above his starting point, how high is Josh?

14. Rachel spent $50 on climbing gear. She said that it was half of $5 more than Amy spent on similar equipment. How much did Amy spend?

15. The seventh grade classes at Mountainview Christian Academy brought in canned goods for a food drive. Mr. Booker's class contributed 59 pounds and Mrs. Rami's class brought 93 pounds. If the average amount collected by each of the three classes was 83 pounds, how many pounds of canned goods did Miss Samson's class contribute?

Challenge

16. Nariko's father told her that for every dollar she saved after the first $25, he would double each of the extra dollars she earned. If she wants to attend a rock-climbing camp that costs $135, how much does she need to save?

1.9 | *Problem Solving*

Construct Meaning

Mr. Corcoran raced out of his business meeting to catch a taxi to the airport. The taxi fare was based on $0.95 for the first mile and $0.80 for each additional mile. What was the distance to the airport if the total fare was $10.55?

Solving word problems with confidence requires a variety of learned skills. If you systematically use the Problem-Solving Guide and apply appropriate strategies, you will be prepared to tackle many types of problems.

Problem-Solving Guide

1. Read and analyze.

What information is given, what am I expected to infer, and what am I asked to find?

For the problem above, the needed information includes the rate charged for mile one ($0.95), the rate for the additional miles ($0.80), and the total fare ($10.55). The inference is that more than one step is needed to find the total mileage.

2. Select a strategy.

What method will help solve the problem?

One possible strategy is to begin with the total fare and work backward.

> **Possible Strategies**
> - Use estimation.
> - Write an equation.
> - Draw a diagram.
> - Find a pattern.
> - Work backward.
> - Try and check.
> - Solve a simpler problem.

3. Apply the selected strategy using the appropriate operations.

How are the numbers and operations used with the strategy?

Total cab fare	$10.55
Fare for mile 1	− 0.95
Fare for additional miles	$ 9.60

The fare of $9.60 was based on $0.80/mile.
$9.60 ÷ $0.80 = 12 miles
1 mile + 12 miles = 13 miles total distance

4. Check for reasonableness.

How can math reasoning be used to check the answer?

Use mental math.
$0.80 per mile × 10 miles = $8.00, and the actual fare must be a greater amount to account for the additional miles and the extra charge for mile 1.

Water taxi in Maldives

Career Connection ...
Excellent problem-solving skills might lead you to an interesting career in Operations Research and Statistics. Consultants in this field solve problems for corporations.

Check Understanding

a. Another possible strategy to solve the taxi fare/distance problem is *write an equation*. Use $10.55 = ($0.95 \times 1) + ($0.80 \times n)$ where n = the number of miles after mile 1. Solve and compare your answer to the solution found using the *work backward* strategy.

b. Select an appropriate strategy and solve: A rectangle with a width of 3" has the same area as a square with a side length of 6". What is the perimeter of the rectangle?

Apply

Solve using the steps of the Problem-Solving Guide and an appropriate strategy.

1. Determine the number of seconds in twenty-four hours.

2. The sum of the squares of two consecutive whole numbers is 100 plus thirteen-hundredths of 100. Name the two numbers.

3. What kind of numbers would have sums such as 9 + 4 = 1, 11 + 6 = 5, 12 + 8 = 8, and 10 + 7 = 5? (Hint: These numbers are an important part of your life every day.)

4. One batch of Tutti-Frutti ice cream is made with: 120 more peaches than cherries; 20 more blueberries than walnuts; three times as many cherries as blueberries; eight times as many walnuts as bananas. There are ten bananas in one batch. How many of each ingredient does one batch contain?

5. On Monday, the first day of church camp, the counselor told two campers that there would be banana splits on the last night of camp. The next day, the two campers each told two others about the treat, and the following day, each of those campers told two people. Express as an exponent the number of campers that will have heard the plan by Saturday night assuming that it is repeated at this rate.

6. Find $\sqrt{33}$ to the nearest tenth.

7. In a game played with four number cubes, Sarah rolled a 2, 3, 4, and 5. She receives points equal to the value of the expression she writes using each number only once. She may use exponents and any operation sign. Write the expression that gives the greatest amount of points with the four numbers.

Construct Meaning

How long would it take for a restaurant to serve an infinite number of hamburgers to an infinite number customers? Could the infinite set of customers be greater than the infinite set of hamburgers?

Infinity implies the concept of limitless quantity rather than a specific number. Comparing finite sets is easily done using one-to-one correspondence.

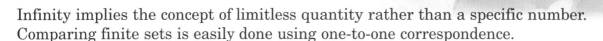

The set of negative integers greater than –5 {–4, –3, –2, –1}
The set of positive integers less than 5   { 4,   3,   2,   1}

The sets are the same size as demonstrated by the one-to-one correspondence.

Which is greater, the set of all positive integers or the set of all odd positive integers? Use one-to-one correspondence to compare the infinite sets.

The set of positive integers   {1, 2, 3, 4, 5, 6, . . .}
The set of odd positive integers   {1, 3, 5, 7, 9, 11 . . .}

The one-to-one correspondence continues infinitely.

The field of transfinite arithmetic compares infinite amounts and has shown that not all infinite sets are the same size. In daily mathematics, however, our task is to develop a clear idea of the difference between infinite and finite quantities while strengthening accurate concepts of very great finite numbers.

Given enough time, which task is possible, to calculate all the digits of *pi*, which is an irrational number, or to write the number for one million to the millionth power in standard form?

Which is finite, a pair of parallel lines or the number of points on a line six inches long?

Can you think of a way to determine the approximate amount of time it would take you to write a googol?

> **A googol is the digit 1 written with one hundred zeros.**

Just for Fun

Mr. Haverhill had more fashion sense than number sense. When he opened Haverhill's Haberdashery, he told his buyer to order hats from the wholesaler in the following manner to keep costs down: Order one hat on January 1, two hats on January 2, four hats on January 3, eight hats on January 4, continuing the pattern until told otherwise. His buyer, Matt Multiple, objected, but Mr. Haverhill insisted on his own idea. How many hats will be delivered on January 21? (Use a calculator.)

Chapter 1 Study Guide

0.4501	0.3499	0.3600
0.3500	0.3386	0.3503

1. Select three numbers from the box that are greater than 0.3501. *Lesson 1.1*

2. Order the numbers from greatest to least. *Lesson 1.2*

     10,010.865   10,001.865   1999.999   10,101.865   10,010.855

3. Which is greater, 8^3 or 7^4? Write the difference. *Lesson 1.2*

4. Find the value of x if $3^x = 81$. *Lesson 1.2*

5. Which two perfect squares would be used to estimate $\sqrt{108}$? Show your work for finding $\sqrt{108}$ rounded to the nearest tenth. *Lesson 1.3*

6. List the numbers from 0 to 150 that are perfect squares. *Lesson 1.3*

7. Write 8.49×10^3 in standard notation. *Lesson 1.4*

8. Write 2,800,000 in scientific notation. *Lesson 1.4*

9. Use the order of operations to solve $275 - 5^2 \cdot 10 + 5$. *Lesson 1.5*

10. Insert parentheses to make the equation true. $30 - 15 \cdot 2 + 8 = 38$ *Lesson 1.5*

11. Copy and complete the equation using the Distributive Property. *Lesson 1.5*

    $9(211) = 9 \bigcirc (200 \bigcirc 11) = 9(\square) + 9(\square) = \square + \square = \square$

12. The statement $ab = ba$ demonstrates the $\boxed{}$ Property of $\boxed{}$. *Lesson 1.5*

13. Define the terms *rational number* and *irrational number* and write a set with at least four elements to demonstrate each type of number. *Lesson 1.6*

14. Round to the nearest ten and use mental math to solve $318 \div 44$. *Lesson 1.7*

IT'S A LITTLE ODD...

15. Which property is demonstrated by $x \cdot (y \cdot z) = (x \cdot y) \cdot z$? *Lesson 1.7*

16. Use the inverse operation to find the missing number if $\square \div 13 = 49$. *Lesson 1.8*

17. Use a pattern to find the sum of the first 40 consecutive odd numbers. (Hint: Find the sum of the first two odd numbers, the first three odd numbers, etc.) *Lesson 1.9*

Never Ending Numbers

Write the letter of the term that matches the definition.
1. A number used as a repeated factor
2. The opposite mathematical operation
3. A number which when multiplied by itself results in the given number
4. Whole numbers and their opposites and zero
5. The usual way to express numbers using digits
6. The set of numbers from zero to infinity
7. A base number and an exponent
8. A real number that can be expressed as an exact ratio of two integers other than zero

> a. Integers
> b. Whole numbers
> c. Inverse operation
> d. Exponential notation
> e. Base
> f. Standard notation
> g. Rational number
> h. Square root

9. Write the numbers from least to greatest.

$$15.\overline{6} \qquad 15.6 \qquad 15.59 \qquad 15.509$$

10. Find two perfect squares that have a sum of 100.

Evaluate.

11. 8^3 12. $3^2 \times 2^4$ 13. 7^0 14. Ten to the fifth power

Solve for x.

15. $5^x = 125$ 16. $x^4 = 16$ 17. $x = \sqrt{144}$ 18. $\sqrt{x} = 13$

19. What is the approximate square root of 118? Round to the nearest tenth.

20. Write 1.54×10^4 in standard form.
21. Write 3,600,000 in scientific notation.

22. Use a scientific calculator to find the product of 5.02×10^7 and 3.6×10^5.

> Evaluate each expression.
> 23. $(9 + 1) \div 5 + 2$
> 24. $7 \times \frac{19+5}{6}$
> 25. $6 + 3 \times 7 - 7$
> 26. $100 - 5^2 \times 2$

Statue at the Lincoln Memorial

Begin with an empty box to represent the missing number. Write a number sentence and work backward by using inverse operations to find the missing number.

27. A number divided by 25 and increased by 2 is seven. What is the missing number?

28. Six less than nine times a number is 174. What is the missing number?

Solve.

29. Mrs. Gordon's class visited the Lincoln Home National Historic Site in Springfield, Illinois. Each of the 24 students was required to pay $12 to participate. If the bus company charged $125 for transporting the students, supplies for the picnic lunch cost $42.57, and the total bill for dinner on the way home was $113.07, did the price the students paid cover the cost of the trip? Show how you determined your answer.

30. Two million dollars was set aside in 1911 for the construction of the Lincoln Memorial in Washington, D.C., although it was not completed until 1922. Compare that to the Franklin Delano Roosevelt Memorial completed in 1997 at a cost of $48,500,000. About how many times more did the Roosevelt Memorial cost? Use mental math.

31. The height from the road in front of the Thomas Jefferson Memorial to the outside top of the dome is 129 feet. The increase in vertical height from the road to the floor of the memorial is 33 feet. If the distance from the floor to the inside of the top of the dome is 92 feet, how thick is the dome?

Lincoln Memorial

32. The grounds of the Thomas Jefferson Memorial cover 10,117 square meters. Estimate the length of each side of a square having that area.

33. It took Drew and Paula four hours to drive to the Lincoln Boyhood National Monument in Lincoln City, Indiana, from their home 180 miles away. Use the formula *distance = rate × time* to determine their average rate for the trip.

Thomas Jefferson Memorial

THINK

eas

CC

anguage

ematics

Chapter Theme:
Cryptography

ENCC

Chapter

Number Theory

Divisibility Rules

Construct Meaning

The trick to deciphering a secret code is discovering the rules by which the code is written. The study of the techniques of secret writing is called **cryptography**. The ability to understand division is also found in discovering the rules which govern it.

Galilee Middle School has 1236 students. They will be participating in an activity that requires groups of 4 students. Is it possible to make groups of exactly 4 students each?

First, discover a rule for divisibility by 4.

If two numbers are each divisible by another number, is their sum divisible by that number?

24 and 36 are both divisible by 4. Is their sum of 60 divisible by 4?
Use base ten blocks to make groups of 4 for the numbers 24 and 36.

24 in groups of 4   36 in groups of 4

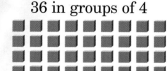

Since each of the numbers is divisible by 4, their sum must also be divisible by 4.

Use this fact to rewrite a number as a sum of a multiple of 100 and another number.

716 can be rewritten as 700 + 16.   *think* 700, a multiple of 100, is divisible by 4.
16 is divisible by 4.
The sum of 700 and 16 must be divisible by 4.

The rule for divisibility by 4 is:

> If the number formed by the last two digits is divisible by 4, the number is divisible by 4.

Is 1236 divisible by 4?
Look at the last two digits of the number.
Is 36 divisible by 4?
Therefore, 1236 is divisible by 4.

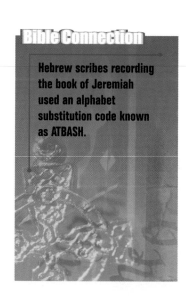

Bible Connection

Hebrew scribes recording the book of Jeremiah used an alphabet substitution code known as ATBASH.

RULES OF DIVISIBILITY

If the number is divisible by:

2	The digit in the ones place will be an even number.
3	The sum of the digits will be divisible by 3.
4	The last two digits of the number are divisible by 4.
5	The digit in the ones place will be a 5 or a 0.
6	The number is divisible both by 2 and by 3.
9	The sum of the digits will be divisible by 9.
10	The digit in the ones place will be 0.

26

Check Understanding
Write *yes* if the black number is divisible by the green number. Write *no* if it is not divisible. Use the rules of divisibility.

a. 572,372   **4**

b. 148,205   **3**

c. 821,062   **4**

d. 152,748   **6**

Practice
Write each number (*2, 3, 4, 5, 6, 9, 10*) by which the given number is divisible.

1. 6320

2. 175,348

3. 72,615

4. 294,516

5. 5,249,130

6. 2000

Write *yes* if the black number is divisible by the green number. Write *no* if it is not divisible.

7. 388   **4**

8. 96,155   **5**

9. 777   **6**

10. 6939   **3**

11. 19,997,580   **4**

12. 460   **9**

13. Explain how you arrived at the answer to problem 11 without dividing.

14. What is the difference between a Squiggle and a Non-Squiggle?
(Hint: Think about numbers that divide evenly into each group.)

These are Squiggles:

These are Non-Squiggles:

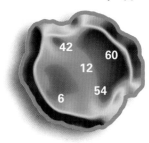

15. Ed's Discount Delicious Delicacies donated 1350 wrapped candies to the school fund raiser. The students want to sell small treat bags with a minimum of five and a maximum of ten candies. Name all the ways the candies can be grouped for the treat bags if each bag contains the same number of candies.

Review
Find each square root.

1. $\sqrt{16}$

2. $\sqrt{9}$

3. $\sqrt{100}$

4. $\sqrt{64}$

Write in scientific notation.

5. 300

6. 420

7. 6200

8. 54,600

Primes, Composites, and Factors

Construct Meaning

A **composite number** is a whole number that has more than two factors. A **prime number** has only two factors, 1 and the number itself.

The number 1 is neither prime nor composite.

To find the factors of a number, divide it by 1, 2, 3, 4, 5, and so forth. To determine when to stop checking for factors:

- Stop checking when there is a duplicate pair of factors or a pair of factors that are the same number.

Find the factors for 15.
1×15 3×5 5×3

         duplicate pair of factors

Find the factors for 25.
1×25 5×5

         same number

- Determine between which two numbers the square root of the number lies. Stop checking once the smaller of the two numbers has been checked.

Find all the factors of 80.

$\sqrt{80}$ is between 8 and 9. We need to check all the numbers from 1 to 8.
Factors of 80:

$$1 \times 80$$
$$2 \times 40$$
$$4 \times 20$$
$$5 \times 16$$
$$8 \times 10$$

80 has 10 factors: 1, 2, 4, 5, 8, 10, 16, 20, 40, and 80.
80 is a composite number.

When checking to see if a number is prime, check the prime numbers up to the square root of the number.

Is 53 a prime number? $\sqrt{53}$ is between 7 and 8. Check by dividing 53 by prime numbers ≤ 7.

53 is not divisible by 2.
53 is not divisible by 3.
53 is not divisible by 5.
53 is not divisible by 7.

53 is a prime number.

Check Understanding

Write *composite*, *prime*, or *neither*. If the number is composite, write the greatest number to check when finding all of the factors.

- **a.** 83
- **b.** 26
- **c.** 1

- **d.** 71
- **e.** 87
- **f.** 59

History Connection

Marian Rejewski, a cryptoanalyst, used mathematics to solve the German Enigma Cipher Machine during WWII and helped save many lives.

Practice

Write the factors for each number.

1. 51   **2.** 119   **3.** 171   **4.** 357   **5.** 123

Complete the chart.

n	____ $\leq \sqrt{n} \leq$ ____		Greatest number to check to find all factors
6. 32			
7. 75			
8. 50			
9. 98			
10. 48			

Write the factors for each number and tell how many factors the number has.

11. 88

12. 120

13. 132

14. 144

15. 180

Use your completed Primes to 100 blackline to answer.

16. What is the greatest prime number less than 100?

17. What are the first three prime numbers greater than 100?

18. 3 and 5 are called twin primes because they are consecutive prime numbers that differ by two. Find five more pairs of twin primes on your number path.

19. Find a string of consecutive composite numbers that is longer than five.

20. Find three numbers less than 100 that are the product of three prime numbers.

21. The number 360 has 24 factors. Try to find them all.

Apply

22. Show that every even number greater than 6 and less than 30 is the sum of two odd prime numbers. Do you think the pattern continues beyond 28?

Review

1. Write the number two thousand and three hundred eight thousandths in standard notation.

2. Write the product using exponents. $2 \times 2 \times 2 \times 3 \times 3 \times 5 \times 5 \times 5$

3. Simplify $3 + 4(2 + 5)$.

4. Use the Commutative Property of Addition to rewrite the expression $2(5 + 7)$.

Prime Factorization

Construct Meaning

The **prime factorization** of a number is a way to express that number as the product of only prime numbers. Any number can be factored into prime numbers using a factor tree or by repeated division.

FACTOR TREE METHOD

Start with any pair of factors to make a factor tree for 84.

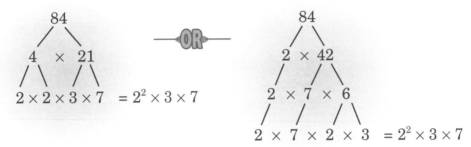

Arrange the factors in order from least to greatest and use exponents to simplify.

REPEATED DIVISION METHOD

For repeated division, start by dividing by the smallest prime number by which the number is divisible. Keep dividing by that prime number until it will no longer divide the quotient evenly. Then try the next largest prime number until the quotient is a prime number.

$$\begin{array}{r} 7 \\ 3\,\overline{)21} \\ 2\,\overline{)42} \\ 2\,\overline{)84} \end{array}$$

$$84 = 2^2 \times 3 \times 7$$

Check Understanding

a. Find the prime factorization of 44 using a factor tree.

b. Find the prime factorization of 28 using repeated division.

Use the method you prefer.

c. Find the prime factorization of 50.

d. Find the prime factorization of 27.

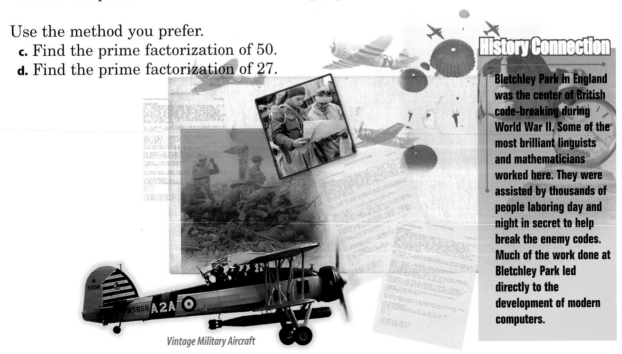

Vintage Military Aircraft

History Connection

Bletchley Park in England was the center of British code-breaking during World War II. Some of the most brilliant linguists and mathematicians worked here. They were assisted by thousands of people laboring day and night in secret to help break the enemy codes. Much of the work done at Bletchley Park led directly to the development of modern computers.

Practice

1. Break the code. Write the number each color represents.

75 =    36 = ▮▮▮▮   42 = ▮▮▮

2. Use the code to determine the number represented.

▮▮▮

Copy and complete the following factor trees and write the prime factorization in exponential form.

3. 92
／＼
□ × 2

4. 240
／＼
10 × □

5. 108
／＼
2 × □

Determine the prime factorization. Write it in exponential form.

6. 72   **7.** 98   **8.** 102   **9.** 112   **10.** 120

Apply

These are lemmics.	These are not lemmics.
28 100	8 32
52	14
36 84	18 48

11. What is a lemmic? (Hint: Think about the prime factors of each number.)

12. Is 76 a lemmic? Why or why not?

13. Write your own numerical definition of a nonsense word like lemmic. Give five examples of numbers that fit your definition and five that do not. Have two other students determine the definition by studying your examples.

Review

1. Simplify $\sqrt{121}$.

2. Write 1,203,000 in scientific notation.

3. Write = or ≠. $2 + (3 \times 4) \bigcirc 2 + 3 \times 2 + 4$

4. Round 1.28499 to the nearest hundredth.

Find all the factors of each number.

5. 100   **6.** 78

7. 96   **8.** 114

SHIP'S TELEGRAPH

Greatest Common Factor

Construct Meaning

A local discount store donated 132 bars of soap and ten dozen tubes of toothpaste to Mrs. Thomas's homeroom class for a missions project. The students want to send these items to churches overseas to distribute to needy families. If the students package an equal amount of soap and an equal amount of toothpaste in each box they ship, how many churches can they send these gifts to?

> Solve this problem by finding the greatest common factor. The **greatest common factor (GCF)** is the largest common factor of two or more numbers.

Three methods can be used to find the greatest common factor.

1. List the factors of each number.

> The maximum number of boxes they can ship is 12.

132 = 1, 2, 3, 4, 6, 11, ⑫, 22, 33, 44, 66, 132
120 = 1, 2, 3, 4, 5, 6, 8, 10, ⑫ 15, 20, 30, 40, 60, 120
The greatest common factor is 12.

2. List all the factors of one of the numbers.

Find the GCF of 18 and 45.

Start with the greatest factor, 18, and determine if 45 is evenly divisible by 18. No.

18 = 1, 2, 3, 6, 9, 18

Determine if 45 is evenly divisible by the next smallest factor, 9. Yes.

Therefore, the GCF of 18 and 45 is ⑨.

3. Write each number in prime factorization form.
Find the GCF of 20 and 30.

20 = ②× 2 ×⑤   Circle the common prime factors.
30 = ②× 3 ×⑤   Both numbers have 2 and 5 as prime factors.

2 × 5 = ⑩   Multiply the common prime factors to find the GCF.

Check Understanding

Find the greatest common factor for each pair of numbers.
a. 12 and 15   **b.** 24 and 30   **c.** 18 and 35

d. Are any of the pairs of numbers in a.–c. relatively prime?
    (Hint: **Relative primes** are two numbers having no common factors other than 1.)

Practice

Find the greatest common factor for each pair of numbers.

1. 28 and 36   **2.** 54 and 36   **3.** 42 and 24

4. 120 and 64   **5.** 40 and 150   **6.** 16 and 48

7. Explain how the GCF of 64 and 120 will help you simplify $\frac{64}{120}$.

8. Two numbers have a GCF of 6. One number is 24. The other number is less than 30. What could the other number be?

9. Write two numbers less than 20 that are relatively prime.

Apply

10. The Computer Store gave away 130 T-shirts and 78 computer programs to Grace High School to divide evenly among their classrooms. What is the greatest number of classrooms that could be at Grace Middle School?

11. Coach Parks has 207 candies and 161 cookies to share with the soccer team. Each team member will get the same number of candies and the same number of cookies. What is the maximum number of members on the soccer team? How many cookies and how many candies will each member get?

12. A seventh-grade class has found a jar of dimes and nickels. There are 301 dimes and 215 nickels in the jar. The coins can be divided equally among the class members. What is the maximum number of students in the class?

13. Each student in Beginning Orchestra tried each type of instrument. The try-out period was the same length for each student, but different for each type of instrument. By the time everyone had tried each type, a total of 217 minutes had been logged for percussion instruments, 93 minutes for strings, and 155 minutes for horns. How many students are in the class? What is the length of the try-out period for each of the three types of instruments?

14. For a picnic, Mrs. Pierce bought 48 hamburgers and 120 cups of lemonade so that each person could receive the same number of hamburgers and the same amount of lemonade with none left over. What is the greatest number of people for which Mrs. Pierce planned?

15. Gavin has 99 blue marbles and 70 red marbles. Is there any way that he could divide them into bags containing the same number of red marbles and the same number of blue marbles? Explain your answer.

Least Common Multiple

Construct Meaning

At Nelson Manufacturing there are two machines that work on the Whirlygigs the company produces. Machine A takes twelve minutes to complete its task, then it beeps and begins to work on the next Whirlygig. Machine B takes fifteen minutes to complete its task, then it buzzes and begins to work on the next Whirlygig. Machine A just beeped and Machine B just buzzed. How long will it be before they beep and buzz at the same time again?

One way to solve this problem is to list the multiples of each time interval. A **multiple** of a number is the product of a given number and any whole number.

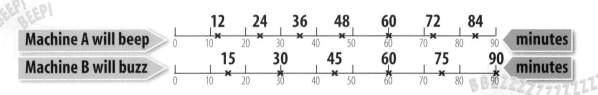

Compare the two lists of time intervals. What is the smallest number that is common to both lists? It will be 60 minutes, or 1 hour, before they beep and buzz at the same time.

The smallest common multiple of two or more numbers is called the **least common multiple (LCM)**. The LCM of 12 and 15 is 60.

Another way to find the least common multiple is to determine the prime factorization of each number. The LCM is the product of each prime number raised to its highest power.

$$12 = 2 \times 2 \times 3 = 2^2 \times 3$$
$$15 = 3 \times 5$$
$$\text{LCM} = 2^2 \times 3 \times 5 = 60$$

Check Understanding

a. List the first six multiples of 11, not including 11.

b. Compare using prime factors to determine the greatest common factor with finding the least common multiple with prime factors.

c. Find the greatest common factor and the least common multiple of 15 and 9.

Practice

1. Find the least common multiple of 18 and 8 using the list method.

2. Find the least common multiple of 14 and 8 using prime factorization.

Find the least common multiple of each number pair.

3. 16 and 12   **4.** 4 and 7   **5.** 15 and 18   **6.** 6 and 8

7. Velvet has been absent from math class for two days. She does not understand the difference between factors and multiples. Write her a note explaining the difference.

8. Find the LCM of 15 and 12. Then list the next three common multiples of 15 and 12.

9. The LCM of a number and 18 is 90. Find at least two possible values for that number.

10. Two factors of a number are 6 and 15. What is the smallest number it could be?

11. Explain how knowing the LCM of 6 and 8 would help in determining the sum of $\frac{3}{8}$ and $\frac{5}{6}$.

Apply

12. Mrs. Trufler has lunch duty every 12 days. Mrs. Sigley has lunch duty every 10 days. Both of them have lunch duty today. How many days will it be until they have lunch duty together again?

13. One string of Christmas tree lights blinks on every 6 seconds. Another string blinks on every 4 seconds. Both of the strings of lights just blinked on. When will they blink together again? How many times in one hour will both of the strings of lights blink on at the same time?

14. Yummy Smack Candies come in two different package sizes.

8 oz $0.89   12 oz $1.34

a. What is the LCM of the package weights?
b. How many 8-ounce packages would you need to buy to have the equivalent of the least common multiple?
c. How many 12-ounce packages would you need to buy to have the equivalent of the least common multiple?
d. Which package is the better deal?

15. Sue is designing a science fair project that uses rotating gears. Gear A has 12 teeth. Gear B has 16 teeth. Gear C needs to rotate once while both gears A and B turn a <u>whole number</u> of times. What is the least number of teeth that Gear C could have?

Problem Solving

Construct Meaning

To provide variety, the school cafeteria serves 8 main dishes, 6 salads, and 5 desserts on a rotating schedule. Today lasagna was served with carrot raisin salad and brownies. How many days will it be before this combination is served again?

Make a list of the days on which lasagna is served, carrot raisin salad is served, and brownies are served.

Lasagna:	8, 16, 24, 32, 40, 48, 56, 64, 72, 80, 88, 96, 104, 112, 120, 128
Carrot Raisin Salad:	6, 12, 18, 24, 30, 36, 42, 48, 54, 60, 66, 72, 78, 84, 90, 96, 102, 108, 114, 120, 126
Brownies:	5, 10, 15, 20, 25, 30, 35, 40, 45, 50, 55, 60, 65, 70, 75, 80, 85, 90, 95, 100, 105, 110, 115, 120

Since the least common multiple in all three lists is 120, this combination will be served again in 120 days (or 24 school weeks).

When will the lasagna and the brownies be served again on the same day?

Look at the lists for the lasagna and the brownies. The first number in common is 40. Lasagna and brownies will be served together again in 40 school days (or 8 school weeks).

When will the carrot raisin salad and brownies be served again on the same day? How many school weeks is that?

Apply

1. The ancient Greek mathematicians classified numbers into three categories: perfect, abundant, and deficient. To determine how to classify each number, they found the sum of all the proper factors of the number. **Proper factors** are factors that are less than the number. The chart below shows how to classify numbers.

Deficient	sum of proper factors < number
Perfect	sum of proper factors = number
Abundant	sum of proper factors > number

Determine the classification of each number.

a. 6   b. 15
c. 20   d. 24
e. 28   f. 32

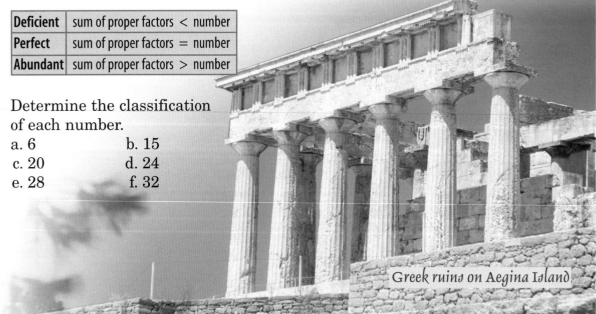

Greek ruins on Aegina Island

2. Mrs. Green wonders why there are so few numbers that have an odd number of factors. Use the *Factors Graph* on the blackline provided by your teacher to make a list of these numbers. What do the numbers with an odd number of factors have in common?

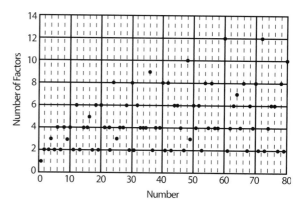

3. The bus to downtown arrives every 20 minutes at Sam's bus stop. The bus to the mall arrives every 24 minutes. Both buses arrive at Sam's bus stop at 6 A.M. The buses run from 6 A.M. to 9 P.M. each day. At what other times during the day will both buses arrive at the same time at Sam's bus stop?

4. Mr. Jones is planning to tile the floor of his den. The room measures 100 inches by 96 inches. What is the largest square tile size that he can use without cutting any tiles?

5. The class store has 54 packages of paper and 12 dozen pencils left at the end of the year. The class decides to distribute them so that each student in the class receives an equal amount of paper and an equal number of pencils. What is the largest number of students that could be in the seventh grade class if an equal distribution is possible?

6. Hot dogs are sold in packages of 10. Hot-dog buns are sold with 8 in a package. What is the least number of each that must be bought in order to have an equal number of hot dogs and hot-dog buns? How many packages of each should be purchased?

7. Mrs. Nossaman is hosting a luncheon. She has 48 cheese sticks and 100 crackers. If she divides them evenly between the serving platters, what is the greatest number of platters she can use and have nothing left over? How many cheese sticks and how many crackers should she put on each platter?

8. Mrs. Helpful is baking cookies for school lunches today. She just put in a tray of chocolate-chip cookies and a tray of peanut-butter cookies. Chocolate-chip cookies bake for 10 minutes and peanut-butter cookies bake for 8 minutes. In how many minutes will she again put a tray of chocolate-chip cookies and a tray of peanut-butter cookies into the oven at the same time?

Construct Meaning

The post office uses bar codes for zip codes to speed the delivery of mail. The last two digits of the eleven-digit zip code are the last two digits of the street address or box number. To ensure that the bar code is read correctly, an extra digit, called a check digit, is added to the end. A **check digit** is a number that is added to the sum of all the zip code digits to make the sum divisible by ten. When a machine reads the bar code and the sum is not divisible by ten, it recognizes the zip code as incorrect.

Find the check digit for the zip code 14358-5955-72.
The sum of the digits is $1 + 4 + 3 + 5 + 8 + 5 + 9 + 5 + 5 + 7 + 2 = 54$
The check digit is 6 to make the sum 60, which is divisible by 10.

Find the check digit for the zip code 13579-2468-64.
$1 + 3 + 5 + 7 + 9 + 2 + 4 + 6 + 8 + 6 + 4 = 55$
The check digit is 5.

The bar code for the zip code is coded with 1s and 0s. The 1s are represented by a long line and the 0s by a short line. The post office uses a group of five lines of 1s and 0s to represent each number of the zip code.

#	Binary Code	Bar Code	#	Binary Code	Bar Code
1	00011	ıııll	6	01100	ılılıı
2	00101	ılııl	7	10001	lıııl
3	00110	ıllıı	8	10010	lıılı
4	01001	ılııl	9	10100	lılıı
5	01010	ılılı	0	11000	llııı

Translating the Bar Code
- Note the long lines at the beginning and the end of the bar code that indicate where to begin and end reading. These are not part of the number code.
- Divide the rest of the bar code into groups of five lines.
- Use the code above to determine each of the numbers in the zip code.
- You will notice an extra number at the end of the zip code. This is the check digit.

What zip code is represented?

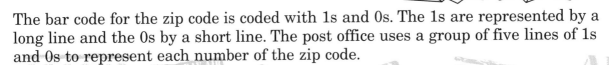

begin — end
9 1 0 1 7 - 9 8 7 2 - 8 7 1 ← check digit
zip code

Is the sum of the zip code digits and the check digit equal to a number divisible by ten?

Write the bar code for zip code 50021-3228-88.

Check Understanding

a. Determine the zip code represented by llıılılllıııılılııllllıııllıılılıııılılılılılıllıııılllıllıll. Use the check digit to "check" your answer.

b. Write the bar code for zip code 40160-7933-37. Remember the check digit.

Chapter 2 Study Guide

By which numbers (*2, 3, 4, 5, 6, 9, 10*) is the given
number divisible? *Lesson 2.1*

1. 78,324
2. 59,670
3. 412 + 1084

Solve. *Lesson 2.2*

4. Find all the factors of 112.
5. To determine if 131 is prime, you need to check by
   dividing by what numbers?
6. List the factors of 60.

Write the prime factorization in exponential form. *Lesson 2.3*

7. 120
8. 38

Find the GCF. *Lesson 2.4*

9. 12 and 28
10. 64 and 48

Find the LCM. *Lesson 2.5*

11. 12 and 28
12. 15 and 24

Solve.

13. Are 15 and 32 relatively prime? *Lesson 2.5*
14. List the first eight multiples of 60, including 60. *Lesson 2.5*
15. What is the largest size of square tile that can be used to tile an
    area 42 inches by 72 inches if only whole tiles are used?
    Lesson 2.6
16. Frieda has practice for a Thanksgiving program every third day
    in November. John has basketball practice every fourth day.
    Frieda's first practice was November 3 and John's first practice
    was November 4. What is the first date that they both practice
    on the same day? How many times in November will they
    both practice on the same day? *Lesson 2.6*

BULK RATE
POSTAGE
PAID

Keep a Secret

Write the letter of the words that match each numbered item.

1. A number divisible by numbers other than 1 and itself
2. Always greater than or equal to the number
3. Product of a number and any whole number
4. One
5. The sum of the digits is divisible by three.
6. Two numbers whose GCF is 1
7. Always less than or equal to the numbers
8. The last two digits form a number divisible by four.
9. A number that is divisible only by 1 and itself

a. **Prime number**
b. **Relatively prime**
c. **Greatest common factor**
d. **Composite number**
e. **Least common multiple**
f. **A number divisible by four**
g. **A number divisible by three**
h. **Multiple**
i. **Neither prime nor composite**

Write each number (*2, 3, 4, 5, 6, 9, 10*) by which the given number is divisible.
10. 763,905,240
11. 1017

Write *prime*, *composite*, or *neither* for each number. For composite numbers, determine the largest number necessary to check when finding all the factors.
12. 117
13. 133
14. 1
15. 87
16. 89

Write the nearest whole numbers between which the square root lies.
17. $\sqrt{69}$
18. $\sqrt{113}$

Find all the factors for each number.
19. 130
20. 96

Write four multiples of each number.
21. 13
22. 24

Write the prime factorization in exponential form.
23. 56
24. 120

Find the GCF of each number.
25. 27 and 42
26. 60 and 72

JAMAICAN CARVINGS

Write *yes* or *no* to tell if each number is relatively prime.

27. 56 and 33

28. 68 and 42

29. Joel is thinking of two numbers, each less than 20, that are relatively prime. One number is 12. Find at least three possibilities for the other number.

Find the LCM of each pair of numbers.

30. 24 and 30

31. 15 and 20

32. The Idle family ran the sprinklers, fed the fish, and watered their plants the day they left on a month-long vacation. Ned the neighbor kid came to feed the Idle family's fish on October second, two days after the Idles went on vacation. Two days after Ned fed the fish, Miss Agua watered the lawn, and three days after Miss Agua's visit, Mr. Stamen came over to water the plants. If Ned, Miss Agua, and Mr. Stamen maintain the same time schedule, what day of the month will they all be at the Idle's house?

33. What is the largest size square tile that can be used to cover an area 56 inches by 72 inches using whole tiles?

A talebearer reveals secrets,
But he who is of a faithful spirit conceals a matter.
Proverbs 11:13

Chapter Theme:
Inventions

3 Chapter

Fractions and Decimals

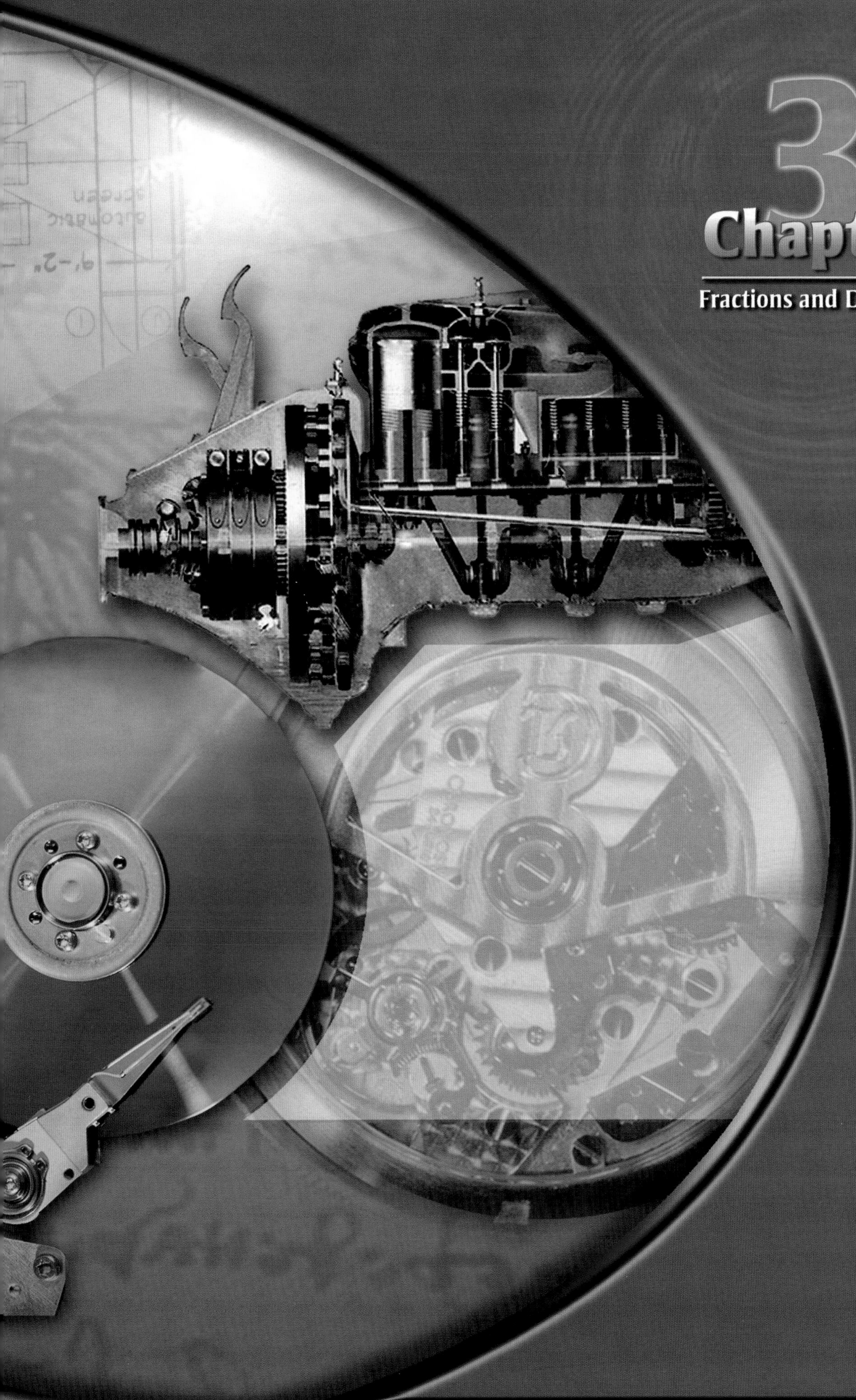

3.1 Compare and Order Fractions

Construct Meaning

Millions of inventions have been patented since 1790. Games, appliances, medicines, and tools are examples of patented items. Mechanics have found that the ratchet wrench, patented in 1913, has made their jobs easier.

The sockets for a ratchet wrench are made in fractional sizes. Order the fractions of three sockets measuring $\frac{11''}{32}$, $\frac{7''}{16}$, and $\frac{1''}{4}$ from least to greatest.

- Find the **least common denominator** (LCD). The LCD is the least common multiple of two or more denominators. Find the least common multiple (LCM) of 32, 16, and 4.

$$4: 4, 8, 12, 16, 20, 24, 28, \textcircled{32}$$
$$16: 16, \textcircled{32}$$
$$32: \textcircled{32}$$

> **Equivalent fractions** name the same number.
> $$\frac{2}{3} = \frac{8}{12}$$

- Write equivalent fractions for $\frac{11}{32}$, $\frac{7}{16}$, and $\frac{1}{4}$ by multiplying the numerator and denominator by the same number.

numerator →
denominator →
$$\frac{11 \times 1}{32 \times 1} = \boxed{\frac{11}{32}} \qquad \frac{7 \times 2}{16 \times 2} = \boxed{\frac{14}{32}} \qquad \frac{1 \times 8}{4 \times 8} = \boxed{\frac{8}{32}}$$

The fraction sizes of the sockets are ordered as $\frac{1}{4} < \frac{11}{32} < \frac{7}{16}$.

Compare $\frac{18}{4}$ and $4\frac{2}{7}$.
Change the improper fraction to a mixed number.

think $18 \div 4 = 4\frac{2}{4} = 4\frac{1}{2}$

Compare $4\frac{1}{2}$ to $4\frac{2}{7}$.
The whole numbers are the same, so compare the fractions.

$$4\,\boxed{\frac{1}{2}} \qquad 4\,\boxed{\frac{2}{7}}$$

Find the LCD of 2 and 7 and use equivalent fractions.

$$\frac{1 \times 7}{2 \times 7} = \boxed{\frac{7}{14}} \qquad \frac{2 \times 2}{7 \times 2} = \boxed{\frac{4}{14}}$$

$$4\frac{1}{2} = 4\frac{7}{14} \qquad 4\frac{2}{7} = 4\frac{4}{14}$$

Since $4\frac{1}{2} > 4\frac{2}{7}$, $\frac{18}{4}$ is greater than $4\frac{2}{7}$.

Explain how to use mental math to order $7\frac{1}{3}$, $7\frac{1}{2}$, $7\frac{1}{4}$, and $7\frac{1}{5}$.

Check Understanding

a. Compare the size of a slice in one pizza that is divided into ten equal slices with the size of a slice of another same-size pizza that is divided into twelve equal slices.

b. If you have $\frac{9}{10}$ and $\frac{9}{12}$, which amount is less? Explain.

Order from least to greatest.   Write >, < or =.

  c. $\frac{2}{7}$ $\frac{1}{4}$ $\frac{3}{8}$ **d.** $\frac{12}{5}$ ◯ $2\frac{3}{7}$

e. Refer to the model of equivalent fractions on page 44. What is the multiplicative relationship between two-thirds and eight-twelfths? How does this affect the number of equal parts in the whole and the size of each part?

Practice

1. Sally used the $\frac{9}{32}''$, $\frac{3}{16}''$, $\frac{3}{8}''$, and $\frac{1}{4}''$ sockets to repair her bicycle. What was the largest socket she used?

2. List three fractions between $\frac{1}{2}$ and $\frac{7}{8}$.

3. List three fractions between $\frac{1}{8}$ and $\frac{3}{4}$.

4. Which musical note is held longer, an eighth note (♪) or a quarter note (♩)?

Apply

5. Brad spent $\frac{3}{4}$ of an hour rollerblading and Joel spent $\frac{2}{3}$ of an hour. Who spent a longer time rollerblading?

6. Mrs. Thompson's dog had three puppies that weighed $3\frac{2}{3}$, $3\frac{3}{5}$, and $3\frac{3}{4}$ pounds. List the weights from least to greatest.

7. Suzy tried a $\frac{1}{2}''$ socket and found it was slightly small for the job. Which socket would she most likely try next, the $\frac{5}{8}''$ socket, the $\frac{11}{16}''$ socket, or the $\frac{9}{16}''$ socket?

8. Draw a number line to show why $\frac{3}{4}$ is less than $\frac{10}{12}$.

9. Miss Bowen needs $7\frac{5}{8}$ yards of fabric having a geometric design. The store has two bolts of fabric, one with $7\frac{3}{4}$ yards and one with $7\frac{1}{2}$ yards. Which amount should she purchase?

THE INVENTION STUDIO

In 1979, two brothers from Minneapolis found an old skate with a single line of wheels. They designed a better inline skate that they used to cross-train for ice hockey. Scott and Brennan Olson went on to sell inline skates and founded Rollerblade, Inc., in 1980.

Add Fractions and Mixed Numbers

da Vinci's helicopter design

Construct Meaning

Leonardo da Vinci was not only a painter but an inventor of intriguing designs. His helicopter illustration helped to inspire the idea of flight.

One of the first flights carrying people was attempted in 1783. Two people, Rozier and d'Arlandes, rode in a Montgolfier balloon made of cotton and paper.

If a Montgolfier balloon flew $\frac{1}{4}$ mile during one flight and $\frac{3}{8}$ mile during another flight, what was the total number of miles flown?

$$\frac{1}{4}$$
$$+ \frac{3}{8}$$
$$\frac{5}{8}$$

think

$$\frac{1 \times 2}{4 \times 2} + \frac{3}{8}$$

$$\frac{2}{8} + \frac{3}{8} = \frac{5}{8}$$

The balloon flew $\frac{5}{8}$ mile.

Solve $2\frac{2}{5} + \frac{4}{5}$.

$$2\frac{2}{5} + \frac{4}{5} = 2\frac{6}{5} = 2 + 1\frac{1}{5} = 3\frac{1}{5}$$

Add the fractions.   Rename the improper fraction as a mixed number.

> An improper fraction is a fraction that has a numerator equal to or greater than its denominator.

OR Change the mixed number $2\frac{2}{5}$ into an improper fraction. $2\frac{2}{5} = \frac{12}{5}$

Then add and simplify. $\frac{12}{5} + \frac{4}{5} = \frac{16}{5} = 3\frac{1}{5}$

Solve $4\frac{1}{3} + 4\frac{5}{6}$.

Rename to get like denominators. $4\frac{1}{3} = 4 + \frac{1 \times 2}{3 \times 2} = 4\frac{2}{6}$

Add the fractions, then add the whole numbers.

$$\begin{array}{r} 4\frac{2}{6} \\ + 4\frac{5}{6} \\ \hline 8\frac{7}{6} \end{array}$$

Express in simplest form. $8\frac{7}{6} = 9\frac{1}{6}$

Check Understanding

a. Explain one method to add mixed numbers.

b. $\frac{2}{3} + \frac{3}{4}$ **c.** $3\frac{4}{7} + \frac{3}{5}$ **d.** $11\frac{2}{3} + 7\frac{2}{9}$ **e.** $\frac{12}{7} + 2\frac{1}{2}$

Practice

Find the sum. Write the sum in simplest form.

1. $\frac{3}{8} + \frac{5}{8}$ **2.** $\frac{7}{9} + \frac{2}{3}$ **3.** $5\frac{1}{4} + 3\frac{1}{2}$ **4.** $6\frac{5}{12} + \frac{7}{8}$ **5.** $12\frac{5}{7} + 14\frac{2}{3}$

Find the unknown term.

6. $y = \frac{2}{3} + \frac{1}{4}$ **7.** $\frac{3}{4} = x + \frac{1}{4}$ **8.** $\frac{5}{6} = \frac{1}{2} + a$ **9.** $1\frac{1}{5} + \frac{3}{10} = n$

Apply

10. The table shows the amount of fabric each crew at Fabulous Fabrics produced beyond the target production of 40 yards per day. At the end of Day 5, which crew had the greatest total increase in fabric production? Compare the amounts.

THE
INVENTION
STUDIO

	Day 1	Day 2	Day 3	Day 4	Day 5
Crew 1	$+\frac{1}{8}$ yd	$+\frac{1}{4}$ yd	$+1\frac{1}{2}$ yd	$+\frac{3}{4}$ yd	$+\frac{1}{2}$ yd
Crew 2	$+\frac{1}{2}$ yd	$+\frac{1}{4}$ yd	$+\frac{1}{8}$ yd	$+1$ yd	$+\frac{3}{4}$ yd

The Montgolfier balloon

11. Henry's Hot Air Balloon Company offers an educational program in the community. A circle graph on the publicity ad shows the following fractions to represent the places where the program is presented: $\frac{3}{8}$ at schools, $\frac{1}{3}$ at community centers, $\frac{1}{4}$ at resorts, and $\frac{1}{6}$ at service organizations. How do you know the information on the circle graph is inaccurate?

12. Explain how you would draw or build a model to show a younger child how to find the sum of $\frac{13}{6}$ and $1\frac{1}{3}$.

13. In the Great Reno Balloon Race, balloonists race to a target area and toss a marker onto a target. If Balloon 1 reaches the target area in $\frac{5}{8}$ of an hour, Balloon 2 in $\frac{3}{4}$ of an hour, Balloon 3 in $\frac{7}{12}$ of an hour, and Balloon 4 in $\frac{5}{6}$ of an hour, which balloon reaches the target area first?

Review

Write *composite* or *prime* for each number.

1. 7   **2.** 64   **3.** 59   **4.** 33   **5.** 128

Find all the factors for each number.

6. 82

7. 105

8. 36

Write the prime factorization in exponential form.

9. 45

10. 60

Subtract Fractions and Mixed Numbers

Construct Meaning

In 1797 a man named André Jacques Garnerin made the first parachute jump from a balloon at an altitude of 700 meters. The first emergency free fall parachute jump from an airplane took place in 1922 in Ohio.

Skydiver 1 jumped from a plane at an altitude of 5000 feet and free-fell for $\frac{2}{6}$ of a minute. Skydiver 2 jumped from another plane at 7500 feet and free-fell for $\frac{7}{12}$ of a minute. Find the difference in the free fall times of the two skydivers.

$$\frac{7}{12} - \frac{2}{6} = \frac{7}{12} - \frac{4}{12} = \frac{3}{12} = \frac{1}{4}$$

The difference is $\frac{1}{4}$ minute.

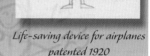

Life-saving device for airplanes patented 1920

Solve $3\frac{2}{3} - 2\frac{4}{9}$.

$\frac{2 \times 3 = 6}{3 \times 3 = 9}$	Rename using the LCD.
$\frac{6}{9} - \frac{4}{9} = \frac{2}{9}$	Subtract the fractions.
$3 - 2 = 1$	Subtract the whole numbers.
$1\frac{2}{9}$	Write the combined answer in simplest form.

Solve $8\frac{2}{3} - 5\frac{3}{4}$.

$\frac{2 \times 4 = 8}{3 \times 4 = 12}$ $\frac{3 \times 3 = 9}{4 \times 3 = 12}$	Rename the fractions.
$8\frac{8}{12} - 5\frac{9}{12}$	
$7\frac{20}{12} - 5\frac{9}{12}$	Rename the mixed numbers in order to subtract.
$2\frac{11}{12}$	Subtract.

A cropduster covered $\frac{3}{4}$ acre of a cornfield before a storm prevented him from covering the remaining $\frac{1}{8}$ acre of the field. What is the total area of the field in acres?

An addition equation or a subtraction equation may be used.

Method A		Method B
Let a = area of the field.	Choose a variable. Write an equation. Rename using the LCD.	Let a = area of the field.
$a = \frac{3}{4} + \frac{1}{8}$		$a - \frac{1}{8} = \frac{3}{4}$
$a = \frac{6}{8} + \frac{1}{8}$		$a - \frac{1}{8} = \frac{6}{8}$
$a = \frac{7}{8}$ acre	$\frac{3}{4} = \frac{3 \times 2}{4 \times 2} = \frac{6}{8}$	Use inverse operations.
		$a - \frac{1}{8} + \frac{1}{8} = \frac{6}{8} + \frac{1}{8}$
		$a = \frac{6}{8} + \frac{1}{8}$
		$a = \frac{7}{8}$ acre

Check Understanding

a. How is the strategy of *write an equation* helpful?

b. $\frac{3}{5} - \frac{1}{10}$ **c.** $5\frac{3}{4} - 2\frac{1}{3}$ **d.** $7\frac{2}{9} - \frac{5}{6}$ **e.** $\frac{7}{15} - \frac{5}{12}$

Practice

Find the difference. Write your answer in simplest form.

1. $\frac{5}{6} - \frac{5}{18}$ **2.** $4\frac{8}{9} - 4\frac{2}{3}$ **3.** $\frac{17}{24} - \frac{5}{12}$ **4.** $9\frac{3}{7} - 6\frac{11}{14}$

Find the unknown term. Write your answer in simplest form.

5. $b - \frac{1}{2} = \frac{3}{4}$ **6.** $x = \frac{4}{7} + \frac{2}{3}$ **7.** $n - \frac{5}{8} = \frac{1}{12}$ **8.** $y = \frac{4}{9} + \frac{7}{18}$

Apply

Refer to the circle graph for problems 9 through 11.

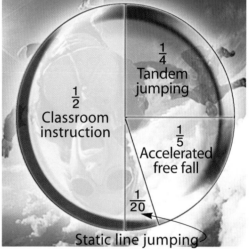

9. What is the fractional difference between the amount of time the instructor spends teaching static line jumping and the time spent on tandem jumping with the students?

10. What is the sum of the time spent on accelerated free fall and the time spent in the classroom?

11. Suppose the instructor begins to spend more time in the classroom and less time doing tandem jumping. If the classroom instruction becomes $\frac{3}{5}$ of the total, what fraction will now represent the instructor's time spent tandem jumping?

12. In the girls long jump event at the state track meet, the winner jumped 19' $1\frac{1}{2}$" and the girl who took second place jumped 18' $11\frac{1}{4}$". The first and second place marks differ by what number of inches?

13. Mr. Kayhill had a bag of 3-inch nails in his shop. He purchased an additional $1\frac{1}{2}$ pounds of 3-inch nails to make a total of $2\frac{2}{7}$ pounds. How many pounds of nails were in the original bag? Write an equation and solve.

14. Pauline used $\frac{3}{4}$ pound of beef for a stew and had $\frac{3}{16}$ pound of beef remaining. Write an equation that shows the amount of meat she had originally. Solve.

THE INVENTION STUDIO

In 1978, the US Patent Office issued a patent for object-dispensing wearing apparel to Californian Frank R. Nemirofsky. One version of the invention is a T-shirt illustrated with a gumball machine. An inner pocket contains gumballs that are dispensed one-at-a-time from an appropriately placed slit in the shirt.

Review

1. $\frac{3}{14} + \frac{2}{7}$ **2.** $6\frac{5}{8} + 4\frac{5}{16}$ **3.** $9\frac{2}{3} + \frac{4}{5}$ **4.** $\frac{2}{3} + \frac{5}{9}$

Multiply Fractions and Mixed Numbers

Construct Meaning

The high-wheel bicycle built in 1870 was the first bicycle made of metal. The cost was an average worker's six-month salary. To determine the correct size, one would select a bicycle with a front wheel as large as a leg's length would allow.

Mr. Charboneau purchased a bicycle with a front wheel that is 54 inches in diameter. The back wheel is $\frac{1}{3}$ the size of the front. What is the diameter of the back wheel?

$$54'' \cdot \frac{1}{3} = \frac{54}{1} \times \frac{1}{3} = \frac{54}{3} = 18''$$

To find the product of two fractions, multiply the numerators, then multiply the denominators. Write the product in simplest form.

$$\frac{3}{8} \cdot \frac{2}{3} = \frac{6}{24} = \frac{1}{4}$$

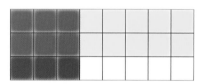

Three-eighths was shaded blue and two-thirds was shaded yellow. The section where the two colors overlap and become green represents the product.

Use common factors to simplify multiplication.

$\frac{3}{8} \cdot \frac{2}{3}$ Find a common factor of the numerator of one fraction and the denominator of the other fraction.

$\overset{1}{\underset{4}{\frac{3}{8}}} \cdot \overset{}{\underset{1}{\frac{2}{3}}}$ Divide by the factor, cross out, and write the quotients.

$\frac{1}{4} \cdot \frac{1}{1} = \frac{1}{4}$ Multiply the renamed fractions.

Find $12 \cdot 5\frac{1}{4}$.

| Rename the mixed number as an improper fraction. | OR | Use the Distributive Property to find the answer mentally. |

$$
\begin{aligned}
12 \cdot 5\tfrac{1}{4} &= 12 \cdot \tfrac{21}{4} \\
&= \overset{3}{\tfrac{12}{1}} \cdot \tfrac{21}{4}_{1} \quad \text{Simplify with common factors.} \\
&= \tfrac{3}{1} \cdot \tfrac{21}{1} \quad \text{Multiply the renamed fractions.} \\
&= 63
\end{aligned}
$$

$$
\begin{aligned}
12 \cdot 5\tfrac{1}{4} &= 12(5 + \tfrac{1}{4}) \\
&= (12 \cdot 5) + (12 \cdot \tfrac{1}{4}) \\
&= 60 + \tfrac{12}{4} \\
&= 60 + 3 \\
&= 63
\end{aligned}
$$

Find $3\frac{3}{5} \cdot 4\frac{1}{2}$.

$\frac{18}{5} \cdot \frac{9}{2}$ Rename each mixed number as an improper fraction.

$\overset{9}{\frac{18}{5}} \cdot \frac{9}{2}_{1}$ Use common factors to simplify.

$\frac{81}{5} = 16\frac{1}{5}$ Multiply the renamed fractions and express in simplest form.

Check Understanding

a. When two proper fractions are multiplied, is the product less than or greater than the factors? How will this help you check the reasonableness of your answer?

b. Use the Distributive Property to mentally compute $8 \cdot 4\frac{1}{2}$.

Practice

1. $\frac{2}{3} \cdot \frac{5}{6}$

2. $5 \cdot \frac{7}{8}$

3. $\frac{9}{10} \cdot \frac{4}{7}$

4. $\frac{3}{4} \cdot \frac{4}{9}$

5. $\frac{2}{15} \cdot \frac{3}{4}$

6. $10 \cdot \frac{2}{5}$

7. $9 \cdot \frac{1}{3}$

8. $5 \cdot 1\frac{2}{3}$

9. $8 \cdot 10\frac{1}{4}$

10. $4\frac{1}{3} \cdot 2\frac{1}{3}$

11. $3\frac{3}{4} \cdot 4\frac{2}{5}$

12. $5\frac{1}{3} \cdot 1\frac{7}{8}$

Use $A = l \cdot w$ to find the area of each rectangle.

13. 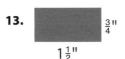 $\frac{3}{4}''$ $1\frac{1}{2}''$

14.  $\frac{2}{5}''$ $\frac{4}{5}''$

15.  $2\frac{1}{5}''$ $3''$

Apply

16. An 1865 two-wheeled riding machine called the *Boneshaker* could be made with a front tire with a 48-inch diameter. If the back tire was $\frac{9}{16}$ of the size of the front tire, what was the diameter of the back tire?

17. Each stone used to build a fence measured $7\frac{1}{2}$ inches in length. If the fence had three equal sides, each being 30 stones long, how many feet of fence were built?

18. A window in the Carlson's house is being replaced with a larger window. The original window measured 3 feet by 3 feet. Each side of the window will be enlarged by $2\frac{1}{2}$ feet. What will be the area of the new window?

19. The rectangular mirror on the bathroom wall is surrounded by $2\frac{1}{2}$-inch tiles. The longer side has 15 tiles while the shorter side has 10 tiles. How many inches make up the outer perimeter of the tiles around the mirror?

Construct Meaning

The original Ferris wheel was invented by George Ferris in 1893 for the World's Fair in Chicago. The wheel section had a circumference of 825 feet and 36 wooden cars, each of which held up to 60 riders. Each car was 9 feet tall, 13 feet wide, and 27 feet long.

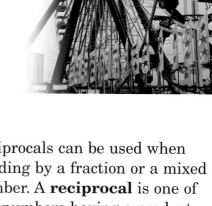

If the 9-foot-tall wooden car had nails every $\frac{3}{4}$ of a foot, how many nails were found in the 9-foot span?

$9 \div \frac{3}{4}$ means how many $\frac{3}{4}$ are in 9?

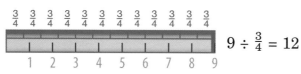

$9 \div \frac{3}{4} = 12$

There are 12 nails in the 9-foot span.

Solve $9 \div \frac{3}{4}$.

$9 \cdot \frac{4}{3}$ Multiply the dividend by the reciprocal of the divisor.

$\frac{9}{1} \cdot \frac{4}{3}_1^3$ Cross-cancel.

$\frac{3}{1} \cdot \frac{4}{1}$ Multiply the renamed fractions.

$\frac{12}{1} = 12$ Simplify.

Solve $\frac{8}{9} \div \frac{2}{3}$.

$\frac{8}{9} \cdot \frac{3}{2}$ Multiply the dividend by the reciprocal of the divisor.

$\frac{8}{9}_3^4 \cdot \frac{3}{2}_1^1$ Cross-cancel.

$\frac{4}{3} \cdot \frac{1}{1}$ Multiply the renamed fractions.

$\frac{4}{3} = 1\frac{1}{3}$ Simplify.

Solve $82\frac{1}{2} \div 4\frac{3}{8}$.

$\frac{165}{2} \div \frac{35}{8}$ Write the mixed numbers as improper fractions.

$\frac{165}{2} \cdot \frac{8}{35}$ Multiply the dividend by the reciprocal of the divisor.

$\frac{165}{2}_1^{33} \cdot \frac{8}{35}_7^4$ Cross-cancel.

$\frac{33}{1} \cdot \frac{4}{7} = \frac{132}{7} = 18\frac{6}{7}$ Multiply the renamed fractions and simplify.

Reciprocals can be used when dividing by a fraction or a mixed number. A **reciprocal** is one of two numbers having a product of 1. $\frac{3}{4}$ and $\frac{4}{3}$ are reciprocals.

$$\frac{a}{b} \cdot \frac{b}{a} = 1$$

A **complex fraction** has a fraction in the numerator and/or the denominator.

$\frac{\frac{8}{9}}{\frac{2}{3}}$ is a complex fraction and can be solved by writing it in a more familiar format of $\frac{8}{9} \div \frac{2}{3}$.

$$\frac{\frac{a}{b}}{\frac{c}{d}} = \frac{a}{b} \div \frac{c}{d}$$

Check Understanding

a. Draw a diagram to show $5 \div \frac{2}{3}$. Why is the quotient always greater than the original whole number when a whole number (besides zero) is divided by a proper fraction?

Divide. Check your answer by multiplying the divisor by the quotient.

b. $\frac{3}{4} \div \frac{1}{8}$ **c.** $50 \div 4\frac{2}{5}$ **d.** $\dfrac{3\frac{1}{2}}{\frac{1}{4}}$ **e.** $\dfrac{6}{\frac{3}{4}}$

Practice

1. $4 \div \frac{1}{2}$ **2.** $\dfrac{8}{\frac{2}{3}}$ **3.** $10 \div 2\frac{1}{2}$ **4.** $12 \div 3\frac{3}{4}$

5. $\frac{8}{9} \div \frac{2}{9}$ **6.** $\dfrac{\frac{3}{4}}{\frac{1}{4}}$ **7.** $\frac{5}{12} \div \frac{1}{6}$ **8.** $\frac{4}{5} \div \frac{1}{2}$

9. $2\frac{1}{2} \div 1\frac{1}{4}$ **10.** $6\frac{3}{8} \div 2\frac{3}{7}$ **11.** $5\frac{3}{5} \div 6\frac{2}{9}$ **12.** $12\frac{5}{6} \div 3\frac{1}{3}$

Apply

The area and measure of a side are given for the floor of a pantry and the floor of a closet. Write an equation and solve for the missing side. Remember $A = l \cdot w$.

13.

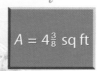

$3\frac{1}{4}'$

$A = 7\frac{5}{16}$ sq ft w

pantry

14.

l

$A = 4\frac{3}{8}$ sq ft $1\frac{3}{4}'$

closet

15. After Austin's grandfather painted one-fourth of the deck last year, Austin agreed to complete the job this summer. It took Austin 6 days to finish the job. If he painted the same fractional amount each day, what amount of the deck did he complete daily?

16. If a ride on a Ferris wheel lasts $3\frac{1}{4}$ minutes, how many rides can be given in 1 hour and 5 minutes?

17. It takes Jerry $\frac{2}{3}$ minute to do a safety check on each Ferris wheel car. How many cars can he check in $5\frac{1}{3}$ minutes?

18. The kiddie Ferris wheel ride only lasts for $1\frac{1}{2}$ minutes. How many rides can be given in $\frac{5}{8}$ of an hour?

THE INVENTION STUDIO

Combination Toy Dog and Vacuum Cleaner patented in 1973

Review

Find the LCM.

1. 8 and 32 **2.** 4 and 6 **3.** 10 and 5 **4.** 9 and 7 **5.** 21 and 18

Problem Solving

Construct Meaning

Australian aborigines invented the boomerang thousands of years ago. They were originally used for hunting and warfare. There are two types of boomerangs, returning and non-returning.

Three people threw a returning boomerang various distances and measured using different units, such as $32\frac{8}{10}$ feet, 15 meters, and $\frac{1}{25}$ of a kilometer. Order the distances from greatest to least.

Problem-Solving Guide

1. Read and analyze.
2. Select a strategy.
3. Apply strategy and appropriate operations.
4. Check for reasonableness.

Possible Strategies

- Write an equation.
- Choose an operation.
- Draw a diagram.
- Use a formula.
- Identify the sub-goals.
- Find a pattern.
- Try and check.

Identify the sub-goals is one possible strategy to solve the problem.

think The given measurements are in different units and need to be converted to one type of unit to compare the distances.

Start by converting all the measurements into meters.

$32\frac{8}{10}$ feet $\div 3\frac{7}{25}$ feet per meter

Given
| 1 meter $= 3\frac{7}{25}$ feet |
| 1000 meters $= 1$ kilometer |

$\frac{\overset{164}{\cancel{328}}}{10} \cdot \frac{25}{\underset{41}{\cancel{82}}} = \frac{4100}{410} =$ **10 meters**

$\frac{1}{25}$ kilometer $\cdot \frac{1000 \text{ meters}}{1 \text{ kilometer}} = \frac{1}{25} \cdot \frac{1000}{1} = \frac{1000}{25} =$ **40 meters**

15 meters does not need to be converted.

$\frac{1}{25}$ kilometer > 15 meters $> 32\frac{8}{10}$ feet

Apply

1. Jerry and Grace are picking strawberries. Every half-hour they weigh and record the total amount they each have picked. If they continue at this rate, what time will it be when they have picked the same number of pounds?

Time	Jerry	Grace
8:00	$5\frac{1}{2}$ lb	$11\frac{1}{2}$ lb
8:30	$11\frac{1}{2}$ lb	$16\frac{1}{2}$ lb
9:00	$17\frac{1}{2}$ lb	$21\frac{1}{2}$ lb
9:30	$23\frac{1}{2}$ lb	$26\frac{1}{2}$ lb

2. Mr. Howe drove 50 miles per hour for $3\frac{2}{3}$ hours due to construction work on the freeway. When the construction ended, he drove 75 miles per hour for $1\frac{1}{2}$ more hours. If *distance = rate × time*, how far did Mr. Howe travel? Round your answer to the nearest mile.

3. Mr. Jessup used $4\frac{1}{2}$ pounds of hamburger for one batch of hamburger patties and $3\frac{2}{3}$ pounds for another batch. There were $2\frac{1}{2}$ pounds remaining. Find the total amount of hamburger.

4. A circular birthday cake was cut four times, resulting in equal parts. What fractional size are the slices? If $\frac{3}{4}$ of the cake is eaten, how many pieces remain?

5. A resort normally rents snowboards for $24 a day. During early season, the daily rental rate is one-third less than the regular price. During late season, the snowboard rental rate is one-fourth less than the regular rate. Compare the cost of a three-day snowboard rental during early season with the cost of a three-day rental in late season.

6. When the value of Zachery's nickels is $\frac{1}{6}$ the value of his dimes, he will have how many times as many dimes as nickels?

7. The canned food shelf at Grocery Mart will hold 1504 cans. Three-eighths of the cans may be canned tomatoes. On Monday, 200 16-ounce cans of tomatoes and an unknown number of 8-ounce cans of tomatoes were on the shelf. If the space for tomatoes was $\frac{3}{4}$ full, how many 8-ounce cans were on the shelf?

8. Celine sold her scuba gear to Howard for $\frac{5}{8}$ of the price she had paid. He sold it to Amud for $\frac{7}{9}$ the price he paid, and Amud sold it to Sonja for $\frac{1}{2}$ the price he paid. How much did Sonja pay? Celine had paid $2400. Round your answer to the nearest cent.

9. The packaging of an item was $\frac{1}{16}$ of its total weight of 46 pounds. What was the weight of the item rounded to the nearest pound?

THE INVENTION STUDIO

The snowboard was invented in 1963 by an eighth grader named Tom Sims. He first called it the "ski board."

3.7 Convert Fractions and Decimals

Construct Meaning

Germany's Karl Benz invented a gasoline-powered automobile in 1886. It was a three-wheeler with the engine in the rear of the vehicle. This automobile could travel at a top speed of 15 kilometers per hour, which is about 9 miles per hour, with its $\frac{9}{10}$ horsepower engine.

$\frac{9}{10}$ has a power of 10 in the denominator and can be read as nine-tenths, which is equivalent to 0.9.

$\frac{1}{10}$ = one-tenth = 0.1

$\frac{1}{100}$ = one-hundredth = 0.01

$\frac{1}{1000}$ = one-thousandth = 0.001

Converting a fraction to a decimal is simple when the denominator is a power of 10.

$\frac{8}{100} = 0.08 \qquad \frac{12}{1000} = 0.012 \qquad \frac{450}{1000} = 0.450$

To convert a fraction to a decimal when the denominator is not a power of 10, divide the numerator by the denominator. You will obtain a terminating or repeating decimal.

USING A CALCULATOR

$\frac{3}{8} = 0.375$

A terminating decimal results when the numerator of a fraction is divided by the denominator and a remainder of zero can be obtained.

$\frac{5}{11} = 0.\overline{45}$

A bar is placed only over the digits that repeat.

A repeating decimal is a decimal that repeats a pattern of digits. It results when the numerator of a fraction is divided by the denominator and a remainder of zero cannot be obtained.

Place value is important when converting a decimal to a fraction.

0.3 is read as "three-tenths."
Use 10 as the denominator.

$\frac{3}{10}$ ←— three ←— tenths

0.007 is read as "seven-thousandths."
Use 1000 as the denominator.

$\frac{7}{1000}$ ←— seven ←— thousandths

Decimals can be written as fractions or mixed numbers in simplest form.

$0.32 = \frac{32}{100} = \frac{32 \div 4}{100 \div 4} = \frac{8}{25} \qquad\qquad 1.8 = 1\frac{8}{10} = 1 + \frac{8 \div 2}{10 \div 2} = 1\frac{4}{5}$

Check Understanding

a. Write two decimals that represent the same fraction.

b. Under what circumstances might a decimal be used instead of a fraction?

Practice

Convert each fraction to a decimal. Write a bar over the repeating digits of each repeating decimal.

1. $\frac{2}{3}$ **2.** $\frac{30}{100}$ **3.** $\frac{2}{11}$ **4.** $\frac{375}{1000}$

5. $\frac{49}{50}$ **6.** $\frac{5}{6}$ **7.** $\frac{10}{100}$ **8.** $\frac{1}{8}$

Convert each decimal to a fraction in simplest form.

9. 0.4   **10.** 0.95   **11.** 0.875   **12.** 0.01

13. 0.625   **14.** 1.2   **15.** 0.3   **16.** 41.85

The idea for a trampoline was conceived in 1926 by eleven-year-old Iowan George Nissen while he was visiting the circus.

1913 Model T Ford Pie Wagon

Apply

17. The Old-Fashioned Pie Catering Service hosts parties for private homes and businesses. After three parties, the following amounts of pies remained: $1.\overline{6}$, $0.\overline{2}$, and 2.125. Change each decimal into a fraction. Why is it easier to see how much pie is left over when the numbers are in fractional form?

18. The 1901 Panhard et Levassor B2 automobile had an engine length of $31\frac{93}{100}$ centimeters, width of $18\frac{3}{4}$ centimeters, and height of $24\frac{4}{5}$ centimeters. Convert each mixed number to a decimal.

19. One of the first car races was called the Cobe Cup. The table shows various statistics from that race. Copy the table and change each number into a decimal. In this instance, why is it more sensible to record the times, distances, and miles per hour as decimal numbers?

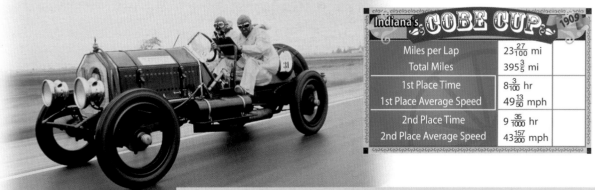

Indiana's COBE CUP 1909		
Miles per Lap	$23\frac{27}{100}$ mi	
Total Miles	$395\frac{3}{5}$ mi	
1st Place Time	$8\frac{3}{100}$ hr	
1st Place Average Speed	$49\frac{13}{50}$ mph	
2nd Place Time	$9\frac{35}{1000}$ hr	
2nd Place Average Speed	$43\frac{157}{200}$ mph	

1909 Buick racer Louis Chevrolet drove a Buick to a first place finish in the Cobe Cup.

3.8 Add and Subtract Decimals

"Lute Player"

Construct Meaning

The first musical instruments mentioned in the Bible are the harp and the flute in Genesis 4:21. Artifacts of stringed instruments resembling a lute have been excavated from the area that was ancient Babylonia. These instruments, dated at a time between 1900 and 1800 B.C., are the ancestors of the modern acoustic guitar.

Musical notes each have an individual frequency measured in Hertz (Hz). Low C has a frequency of 16.35 Hz. The next C, an octave higher, has a frequency of 16.35 + 16.35, which is 32.70 Hz.

low C   middle C   high C

C_0 — C_1 — C_2 — C_3 — C_4 — C_5 — C_6 — C_7 — C_8

16.35 Hz   32.70 Hz   261.60 Hz

To add or subtract decimals:
- Align the decimals and each place value.
- Add zeros after the decimal if needed.
- Add or subtract the digits.
- Write the decimal in the answer.

Determine the frequency of C_2.

$$\begin{array}{r} \overset{1}{} 32.70 \\ +\ 32.70 \\ \hline 65.40 \text{ Hz} \end{array}$$

What is the pattern of how the frequency changes from octave to octave?

Middle C has a frequency of 261.6 Hz and is 130.8 Hz greater than C_3, one octave below. What is the frequency of C_3?

Write an equation.
Let f = frequency of C_3.

$f + 130.8 = 261.6$
$f + 130.8 - 130.8 = 261.6 - 130.8$ Use inverse operations.
$f = 261.6 - 130.8$
$f = 130.8$

Write an expression.
The frequency of C_3 is the difference between 261.6 and 130.8.

$261.6 - 130.8$ Rewrite.

$$\begin{array}{r} \overset{0\ \ 1}{261.6} \\ -\ 130.8 \\ \hline 130.8 \end{array}$$

The frequency of C_3 is 130.8 Hz.

Decimal sums and differences can be estimated by rounding to the nearest whole number.

Ming had $135.25 in his checking account. He spent $35.41 on a guitar tuner and $17.89 on a guitar instruction book. Estimate the balance in his account after he purchased the items.

$135.25 – $35.41 – $17.89

$135 – $35 – $18   Round.

($135 – $35) – $18   Mentally group numbers that are easily subtracted.

$100 – $18 = $82 ⟵ Estimated checking account balance

Check Understanding

a. Why is the placement of the decimal in a problem important?

b. Explain how using an equation or an expression might help you solve a word problem.

Practice

Solve.

1. 1.748 + 0.62

2. 140.421 − 16.810

3. 42.005 + 0.361

4. 133 − 1.48 − 0.62

5. 0.049 + 0.162

6. 0.1894 − 0.0635

Round to the nearest whole number and use mental math to estimate.

7. 101.79 − 49.85

8. 50.1 + 70.36 + 25.03

9. 40.253 − 19.861

Use inverse operations to solve for x.

10. $x − 7.55 = 1.2$

11. $32.96 + x = 81$

12. $\$101.39 + x = \$199.99$

Apply

Use the check register for problems 13 and 14.

CHECK NUMBER	DATE	DESCRIPTION	(−) PAYMENT	(+) DEPOSIT	BALANCE
					$425.69
1321	3/1	Guitar strings	−12.95		
1322	3/4	Guitar body repair	−133.52		
1323	3/5	10 Guitar pics	−2.50		

13. Determine the ending balance of Jordy's checkbook.

14. How much did Jordy spend on his guitar hobby?

15. Gracie began with $100 in her savings account and has deposited $55.61, $44.99, and $113.60. Estimate and use mental math to determine if she has saved enough to purchase four fifty-dollar gift certificates at the bookstore.

16. Mr. Hansen used electronic calipers to measure the diameter of four pipes. The measurements were: 2.4215 cm, 2.1364 cm, 2.5012 cm, and 2.389 cm. What is the greatest difference between pipe diameters?

THE INVENTION STUDIO

As a research chemist, Stephanie Kwolek experimented with long molecules called polymers. Her work led her to discover a new, extremely strong and stiff fiber. The eventual result was Kevlar®, which is used to make bullet-resistant vests, firefighters' suits, helmets, canoes, skis, and other items.

	Before (kg)	After (kg)
1	11.439	11.461
2	10.691	10.490
3	12.638	11.500
4	10.941	10.836
5	9.421	9.400

17. Miss Buren weighed laboratory specimens before and after drying. Use the table to determine which specimen had the greatest weight loss.

Multiply and Divide Decimals

Construct Meaning

Alexander Cartwright and the members of his New York Knickerbocker Baseball Club devised the first rules and regulations for baseball in 1845. Baseball was based on the English game of rounders. By the 1860s, baseball was called America's national pastime.

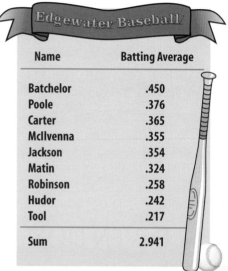

Edgewater Baseball

Name	Batting Average
Batchelor	.450
Poole	.376
Carter	.365
McIlvenna	.355
Jackson	.354
Matin	.324
Robinson	.258
Hudor	.242
Tool	.217
Sum	**2.941**

The Edgewater Baseball Team has nine members. The table shows each team member's batting average. Determine the team batting average by finding the sum of the individual averages and dividing by the number of team members.

$$2.941 \div 9$$

$$9\overline{)2.941} \rightarrow .326\overline{7} \leftarrow \text{Round to thousandths place value.}$$

The team batting average is .327.

Divide Decimals

$$0.4\overline{)12.38}$$
×10   ×10

Multiplying by 10 will move the decimal point one place to the right.

$$3.24\overline{)17.50}$$
×100   ×100

Multiplying by 100 will move the decimal point two places to the right.

- Multiply the dividend and divisor by the same power of 10 to remove the decimal point from the divisor.
- Write a zero when needed.
- Divide as with whole numbers.

Multiply Decimals

$$5.42 \times 2.2 = 11.924$$
3 decimal places

$$420.2 \times 1.961 = 824.0122$$
4 decimal places

Place the decimal point in the product by determining the sum of the number of decimal places in each factor.

Use a formula

The pitcher for the Edgewater Baseball Team can throw a baseball at a rate of 124.96 feet per second. The distance from the pitcher's mound to home plate is 60.5 feet. Use the formula $d = r \cdot t$ to determine the time t it takes the ball to go from the pitcher's mound to home plate.

$$\text{distance} = \text{rate} \times \text{time}$$

$$60.5 \text{ feet} = 124.96 \text{ feet per second} \cdot t$$

Substitute the numbers for the variables in the formula.

$$\frac{60.5}{124.96} = \frac{124.96}{124.96} \cdot t$$

Use inverse operations.

$$\frac{60.5}{124.96} = t$$

$$0.4842 = t$$

Round to the nearest hundredth.

$$0.48 \text{ sec} = t$$

It took 0.48 seconds for the ball to travel from the mound to home plate.

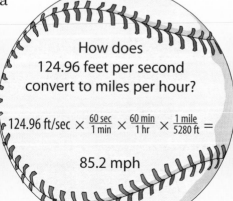

How does 124.96 feet per second convert to miles per hour?

$$124.96 \text{ ft/sec} \times \frac{60 \text{ sec}}{1 \text{ min}} \times \frac{60 \text{ min}}{1 \text{ hr}} \times \frac{1 \text{ mile}}{5280 \text{ ft}} =$$

85.2 mph

Check Understanding

a. How does the product of 0.02×0.03 compare to each factor?

b. Explain in your journal how to place the decimal point in the quotient to divide two decimal numbers.

c. Solve for s if $4.368 = 16.8 \cdot s$.

Practice

1. 1.364×1.2 **2.** 0.42×0.16 **3.** 450.15×10.8

4. 32.64×2.59 **5.** $3.5 \div 1.6$ **6.** $0.954 \div 1.8$

7. $0.29 \div 0.015$ **8.** $102.68 \div 3.4$

Solve for the variable.

9. $8.149 = 2.81 \cdot r$ **10.** $\frac{42}{5.6} = s$

11. $r \div 0.12 = 5.34$ **12.** $0.02 \times 0.08 = a$

13. $427.44 = 35.62 \cdot d$ **14.** $t \div 0.5 = 0.417$

Business Connection

In 1951, Bette Nesmith Graham was working as a secretary. She had an idea to make correction fluid out of white tempera paint and other ingredients. Within a few years she was running a business from her garage. In 1978 she sold her business to The Gillette Company for $47 million.

Apply

15. A first baseman catches a fly ball at first base and wants to get a runner out at third base. The distance d from first base to third is 127.28 feet. If he throws the ball at a rate r of 120.5 feet per second, how many seconds t will it take the ball to reach third base? Use the formula $d = r \cdot t$ and round your answer to the nearest hundredth.

16. Jared purchased 1.75 pounds of pears for his family. If each pear weighed $\frac{1}{8}$ of a pound, how many pears did Jared purchase?

17. Miss Creswell had 19 quarters, 38 dimes, and 16 nickels in her piggy bank. How much money was in her bank?

18. Coach McGuire replaced old equipment by purchasing four softball gloves for $12.95 each, two baseball bats for $15.86 each. He also paid $18.30 total for five softballs. If ten team members paid an $18.00 athletic fee, was the total cost for replacement equipment covered? What is the difference between the total fees collected and the total amount of the purchases?

Challenge

19. Candy bars are being sold three for a dollar, which is $\frac{1}{3}$ of $1.00 per bar. $\frac{1}{3}$ as a decimal is $0.\overline{3}$. How many cents is $0.\overline{3}$? When multiplying by a repeating decimal, how is the accuracy of an answer affected by the number of place values of the decimal?

Review

Estimate by rounding each decimal to the nearest whole number.

1. 7.3×7.8 **2.** 34.6×9.92 **3.** $15.36 \div 3.21$ **4.** $400.36 \div 80.19$

Problem Solving

Construct Meaning

The development of the automobile engine could not be accomplished until a simpler problem was solved. Metallurgists had to develop metals that were strong enough to make small, light parts, such as a bicycle chain. This led to the development of larger parts used in automobiles. Solving a simpler problem is often essential to solving more complicated problems.

The Bike Peddler Shop ships its bicycles overseas in shipping containers that measure $19\frac{1}{2}$ feet by 8 feet by 8 feet. The boxes used for each bike measure 1 foot by 2.5 feet by 3.8 feet. What is the greatest number of bike boxes that will fit in one container?

Draw a diagram and solve a simpler problem first.
Consider the way the boxes will be packed into the container. Start by determining how many boxes will fit in one end of the container.

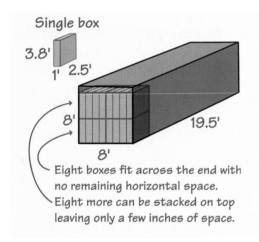

Single box

3.8'
1' 2.5'

8'
8'
19.5'

Eight boxes fit across the end with no remaining horizontal space.
Eight more can be stacked on top leaving only a few inches of space.

Sixteen boxes will fit in one end of the container. How much of the length of the container has been used?

think $\frac{2.5\ \text{ft}}{19.5\ \text{ft}} \approx \frac{2.5}{20} \approx \frac{1}{8}$

If 16 boxes fill about one eighth of the container, approximately how many will fill it entirely?
16 boxes × 8 = 128 boxes

Approximately 128 bicycle boxes fill the container.

In order to determine the exact number, complete the scale drawing. You can draw six additional sets of boxes like the first one, for a total of seven.
7 boxes × 8 boxes × 2 boxes = 112 boxes

The extra two feet of space at the end of the container can hold 12 more boxes positioned the other way in the 8 ft by 8 ft by 2 ft.
112 boxes + 12 boxes = 124 boxes

Exactly 124 bicycle boxes fill the container.

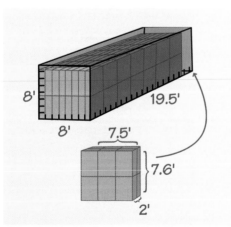

8'
8' 7.5'
7.6'
2'

19.5'

Can you estimate the number of boxes another way?
Can that method be used to calculate the exact number? Explain.

Apply

1. A certain type of copper piping is made with the following diameters: 0.68 cm, 0.83 cm, 1.03 cm, 1.28 cm. List the next three pipe diameters if the pattern is followed.

2. June purchased lettuce, grapes, and an avocado for $2.00. The cost of the grapes was $0.35 more than the cost of the lettuce. The cost of the avocado was half the cost of the lettuce. Let x = cost of the lettuce.
   a. Write an expression for the cost of the grapes.
   b. Write an expression for the cost of the avocado.
   c. Write an equation that shows the total cost in terms of x.
   d. If the cost of the lettuce, x, is $0.66, find the cost of the grapes.
   e. What is the cost of the avocado?
   f. How can you check your work?

3. Use a calculator to find two numbers having a sum of 15.5 and a product of 59.76.

4. Matt ordered the sockets for his ratchet wrench according to size. What will the size of the next socket be? $\frac{5}{32}$ $\frac{3}{16}$ $\frac{7}{32}$ ☐

5. Mr. Sahid purchased a fly rod for $89.90 and a reel for $41.50. Mr. Daley purchased a set of fly fishing flies for $15.65 and waders for $95.50. How much more than Mr. Daley did Mr. Sahid spend?

Playground Equipment			
Item	Total length	Length in ground	Resulting height
Basketball stand	15 ft		
Tetherball pole	11 ft		
Monkey bars	9 ft		
Fence posts	10 ft 6 in.		

6. A school is installing playground equipment. $\frac{1}{3}$ of the length of each item should be in the ground. Copy and complete the table to determine the length of each post that will be in the ground and its resulting height. Express your answers in feet and inches.

7. Mrs. Kim earns $0.30 per mile when she travels for her sales position. How much has she earned at the end of six weeks?

Week	1	2	3	4	5	6
Miles	260	140	300	80	316	243

8. The south side of the Westbrook family's property is the same length as the north side. The east side is the same length as the west side. The north side is 15 yards longer than the west side. The west side is 42.35 yards long. What is the perimeter of their property?

9. On their boat trip, the Smith family stopped three times for gasoline. They purchased 25.48 liters, 30.32 liters, and 20 liters of gasoline. If approximately 3.79 liters equal one gallon, how many gallons of gasoline did they purchase?

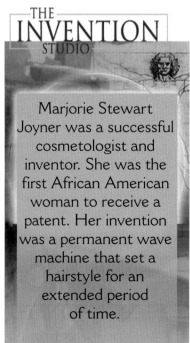

THE INVENTION STUDIO

Marjorie Stewart Joyner was a successful cosmetologist and inventor. She was the first African American woman to receive a patent. Her invention was a permanent wave machine that set a hairstyle for an extended period of time.

Somewhere in San Francisco

Try to locate the lost tourist who has stopped to rest and has called you, the tour guide, on his cell phone.

The befuddled tourist describes his position using a visible landmark. He says that he can see Alcatraz. Use the map to locate Alcatraz. The tourist might be anywhere within sight of Alcatraz. This sight area creates a circle where the tourist could be found. Is this enough information to find him?

You ask for another landmark. The tourist says that he can see Alcatraz and the Oakland Bay Bridge. Locate the Bay Bridge on the map.

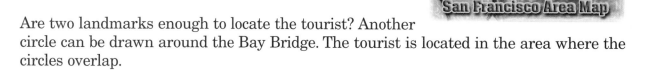

San Francisco Area Map

Are two landmarks enough to locate the tourist? Another circle can be drawn around the Bay Bridge. The tourist is located in the area where the circles overlap.

The lost tourist finally says that he can see Alcatraz to his left, the Bay Bridge to his right, and Coit Tower behind him.

Locate Coit Tower on the map. A third circle can be drawn. The overlap of the three circles shows the location of the tourist. This is similar to the way the Global Positioning System (GPS) works. However, instead of landmarks, it uses a system of 24 satellites that orbit the earth as points of reference. The GPS calculates the actual distance from three satellites to triangulate the position and uses a fourth satellite to factor out time errors. Triangulation is a technique that marks the relative postion of two or more points.

A hand-held GPS receiver would have given our lost tourist his latitude, longitude, and altitude in less than one second. The GPS can determine position to within 10 meters. To calculate the distance from a location to a satellite, the GPS uses the formula $d = r \cdot t$.

> **(example)** A satellite's signal travels at a rate of 186,000 miles per second and takes 0.06 seconds to reach the hand-held GPS receiver. How far away is the tourist from the satellite?
> $$d = r \cdot t$$
> distance = 186,000 mi/sec · 0.06 sec
> distance = ☐

Order the following fractions from least to greatest.   *Lesson 3.1*

1. $\frac{3}{4}$ $\frac{2}{5}$ $\frac{9}{15}$

Solve.

2. $\frac{8}{9} + \frac{1}{2}$ *Lesson 3.2*

3. $\frac{5}{12} + a = \frac{3}{4}$

4. $1\frac{1}{3} - \frac{5}{6}$ *Lesson 3.3*

5. $x - 1\frac{4}{9} = \frac{3}{4}$

6. $\frac{4}{7} \cdot \frac{1}{5}$ *Lesson 3.4*

7. $2\frac{1}{3} \cdot \frac{3}{4}$

8. $2\frac{2}{3} \div \frac{1}{3}$ *Lesson 3.5*

9. $4\frac{2}{5} \div 2\frac{2}{3}$

Oakland Bay Bridge

THE
INVENTION
STUDIO

The idea for the microwave oven began with Percy L. Spencer of the Raytheon Company. Mr. Spencer noticed that a chocolate bar in his pocket began to melt when he stood in front of a magnetron in the laboratory. He soon discovered that the microwaves produced by the magnetron would pop a bag of popcorn. The first microwave oven developed by Spencer and Raytheon weighed 750 pounds and was 5 feet 6 inches tall.

10. Kristi rode her bicycle for 4 hours at an average speed of $6\frac{1}{2}$ miles per hour. How far did she travel? Use the formula distance = rate × time.   *Lesson 3.6*

Change each fraction to a decimal.   *Lesson 3.7*

11. $\frac{7}{8}$ **12.** $\frac{10}{11}$

Change each decimal to a fraction.   *Lesson 3.7*

13. 0.26   **14.** 0.125

Solve for n.   *Lessons 3.8 and 3.9*

15. $n = 3.425 + 0.95$ **16.** $9.89 + n = 12.962$

17. $420.2 \times n = 13,820.378$

18. $n \div 3.25 = 2.25$

19. E Technology and Communication Satellite have a 50-50 partnership. They launched three GPS satellites at a cost of $4.26 million. How much did E Technology spend to launch one satellite?   *Lesson 3.10*

Fine-tuning Fractions

Write the letter of the definition that matches each numbered item.

1. Equivalent fractions

2. Write an equation.

3. Cross-cancellation

4. Triangulation

5. Reciprocal

> **a.** Method used to simplify multiplication of fractions
> **b.** One of two numbers having a product of 1
> **c.** Name the same number
> **d.** Strategy used to organize a problem
> **e.** A technique that marks the relative position of two or more points
> **f.** Having a fraction in the numerator and denominator

Order from least to greatest.

6. $8\frac{3}{4}$ $8\frac{5}{6}$ $8\frac{2}{3}$ $8\frac{3}{5}$

Write >, < or =.

7. $2\frac{3}{8} \bigcirc \frac{5}{2}$

8. $\frac{18}{5} \bigcirc \frac{36}{10}$

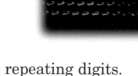

Solve.

9. $6\frac{2}{5} + \frac{9}{10}$

10. $\frac{7}{12} - \frac{8}{15}$

11. $\frac{4}{15} \cdot \frac{3}{4}$

12. $3\frac{7}{8} \cdot 2\frac{1}{2}$

13. $12\frac{1}{2} \div \frac{2}{3}$

14. $\frac{8}{9} \div \frac{4}{5}$

Convert each fraction to a decimal. Write a bar above repeating digits.

15. $\frac{3}{8}$

16. $\frac{5}{11}$

Convert each decimal to a fraction in simplest form.

17. 0.6

18. 17.75

Solve.

19. $2.841 + 0.59$

20. $178 - 55.89$

21. 6.32×3.5

22. 36.3×2.854

23. $13.95 \div 0.5$

24. $5.9 \div 1.18$

Find the value of the unknown term.

25. $\frac{5}{6} = x + \frac{1}{3}$

26. $4\frac{7}{9} + \frac{1}{2} = n$

27. $d - \frac{2}{7} = \frac{3}{4}$

28. $\frac{s}{7.8} = 0.6$

Round to the nearest whole number and use mental math to estimate.

29. $37.2 + 8.09 + 65.14$

30. $187.32 - 51.89 - 26.47$

Identify your strategy and solve each problem.

DRAW A DIAGRAM   WORK BACKWARD

WRITE AN EQUATION   USE A FORMULA

MAKE A TABLE

TRY AND CHECK

31. A box of Paula's favorite chocolates has two layers. Each layer is three pieces wide and five pieces across. How many pieces were eaten if $\frac{2}{3}$ of the box remains?

32. Jerry drives his car $6\frac{1}{2}$ miles one way to work. Tom drives his car $5\frac{3}{4}$ miles one way to work. After how many days will Jerry have driven exactly three more miles than Tom?

33. A dealer sold $\frac{1}{3}$ of the 48 sports cars at the dealership. How many remain?

CORVETTE
America's first sportscar

Chapter Theme:
Communication

4.1 | *Translating Numerical Expressions*

Construct Meaning

When God inspired people to write the Bible, they used the Hebrew, Greek, and Aramaic languages. Many people have worked to translate the Bible so others can read and hear what God wants to say to them. Mathematics is a universal language.

When solving problems, one may have to translate words into numerical expressions. A **numerical expression** is a mathematical phrase that contains numbers and operation symbols. An expression is similar to an equation. An **equation** is a mathematical sentence using an equal sign. It can show that two expressions are equal. Many words may state the operations used in an expression.

Addition	sum	greater than	more than	plus	increase
Subtraction	difference	minus	less than	decrease	fewer than
Multiplication	product	of	times	by	double
Division	quotient	per	divided by	half	separate equally

Write *3 times the sum of 21 and 12* as a numerical expression.

Phrase	Numerical expression
3 times the sum of 21 and 12	$3 \cdot (21 + 12)$

TRANSLATE the operation words into symbols. <u>Times</u> means *multiply* and <u>sum</u> means *add*.

Because the phrase says *3 times the sum of 21 and 12*, addition is done first. Parentheses show this order in the numerical expression.

Thom has one set of six socket wrenches. His collection was increased by two sets of eight. Write a numerical expression for the total number of socket wrenches in Thom's collection.

Phrase	Numerical expression
One set of 6 increased by 2 sets of 8	$6 + 2 \cdot 8$

TRANSLATE the operation words into symbols. <u>Increased by</u> means *add* and <u>of</u> means *multiply*.

The phrase *2 sets of 8* indicates grouping, which is performed first according to the order of operations. Parentheses are unnecessary.

To determine the number of wrenches, simplify the expression.

$6 + 2 \cdot 8 = 22$ **Thom has 22 wrenches.**

Intermediate Course A

Check Understanding
   a. Why is it important to consider order of operations when translating expressions?
   b. Write a phrase for the numerical expression $4 \div (8 + 2)$.

Write a numerical expression.
   c. Six more than the product of 10 and 3
   d. Four times the number that is 7 less than 12

Practice
Translate the following phrases into numerical expressions.
   1. One-half the sum of 42 and 8
   2. Ten less than twice eight
   3. Five times the number that is two less than ten
   4. Three more than double the sum of 14 and 2

Write a numerical expression and simplify.
   5. Twice the number that is three minus one-tenth
   6. Ten less than the quotient of 120 divided by 6

Write a phrase for the following numerical expressions.
   7. $30 + 2 - 14$ **8.** $\frac{(14 + 6)}{2}$ **9.** $4 \cdot (6 + 2)$

   10. $3 + 6 - 2$ **11.** $5 + 3(4 + 2)$ **12.** $\frac{1}{2} \cdot 4 \div 1$

Apply
Write a numerical expression. Simplify.
   13. Mrs. Simpchin ordered three Spanish-English dictionaries for $4 each and three French-English dictionaries for $5 each. How much did she pay for the dictionaries?

   14. Bill reads his Bible every morning. In July, he read twice as many chapters each day as the two previous months combined. He read two chapters each day in June and three in May. How many chapters did he read each day in July?

   15. Joseph ran two miles the first day of training, one and one-half times that on Day 2, and double Day 2's mileage on Day 3. What was his total mileage?

   16. The City Repair truck carried three sets of six rolls of telephone wire. By the end of the day, the number of rolls had decreased by two sets of three rolls. How many rolls of wire remained?

4.2 Translating Algebraic Expressions

Construct Meaning

Joel Borkert was educated in Christian schools. Today he knows that his life was impacted by the academic challenges he met there. Joel is a 2nd Lieutenant Infantry Army officer and uses mental math to determine distance, direction, and position.

To translate an idea from words into an algebraic expresion, think about what is being described. An **algebraic expression** is a mathematical phrase having numbers, variables, and operation symbols.

example Five times the sum of three and a number

Phrase	Algebraic expression
5 times the sum of 3 and a number	$5(3 + n)$

Consider the meaning and the order of operations. This expression means that the sum of 3 and *a number* must be found first, then multiplied by 5. Use parentheses to indicate that addition must be performed before multiplication.

Choose a letter to represent the unknown value. Let n represent *a number*.

Translate the operations in the phrase.

example Helena is three years older than her brother Dmitri. If you do not know how old Dmitri is, what algebraic expression could represent Helena's age?

Phrase	Algebraic expression
3 plus Dmitri's age	$3 + d$
or	
Dmitri's age plus 3	$d + 3$

Consider the meaning and the order of operations.
Choose a letter to represent the unknown.
Translate the operation.

Always check your algebraic expression to be sure the meaning is the same as the original phrase.

Consider each phrase to represent $2x - 3$.

• Twice a number minus 3
• The product of 2 and a number less 3
• Three less than twice a number

Explain why the final phrase most clearly represents the expression.

Check Understanding

a. Write the two phrases that correctly describe the algebraic expression $16(4 + n)$.

> 16 multiplied by the sum of 4 and a number
> 16 times four added to a number
> the product of 16 and the sum of 4 and a number

Translate each of the following pairs of phrases into expressions. State whether the two phrases describe the same idea.

b. The sum of 32 and a number; the sum of a number and 32

c. 20 less than 100; 100 less than 20

d. The product of 70 and a number; the product of a number and 70

Write a phrase for each algebraic expression.

e. $13 + 4n$ **f.** $5(n + 27)$

Practice

Translate the following phrases into algebraic expressions.

1. One-half more than a number

2. 82 decreased by a number

3. Four times the sum of a number and $\frac{3}{10}$

4. 21 less than twice a number

5. The square of twice a number

6. One-third of the sum of a number and 53

Write a phrase for each algebraic expression.

7. $205 - 3x$ **8.** $4.5y$ **9.** $n(2.25 + 10)$

10. $(m - 7)^3$ **11.** $\frac{(2b)}{12}$ **12.** $\frac{(x + 17)}{3}$

Apply

13. Write two different algebraic expressions to represent a number multiplied by itself.

14. Does b represent the same value each time it appears in the expression $b(13.2 + b)$?

15. Serena and Lydia have 14 schoolbooks. If Serena has b books, write an expression to represent the number of books Lydia has.

16. The monetary value of an antique phone is 3.5 times its original cost. Choose a variable to represent the original cost of the phone and write an algebraic expression describing the monetary value of the phone.

17. Write an algebraic expression that represents one-tenth of Sarah's salary. What letter did you use for the variable and why?

Challenge

18. Write a numerical expression describing the area of the larger rectangle and simplify. Write an algebraic expression for the area of the square. Finally, write an expression for the area of the shaded region.

73

Simplifying Expressions

Joel and Kimberly Borkert

Construct Meaning

Although careful translation has made it possible to read the Bible in your own language, it can still be difficult to understand what some passages mean. Studying the context of the passage as well as related verses can help us understand the truth of God's Word as it was originally communicated.

To **simplify** is to find a numerical value of an expression or to make an algebraic expression less complex by applying the order of operations. This does not change the original meaning or value of the expression.

Simplify the numerical expression.

$$3 + 2^2 \times (2 + 5)$$

$3 + 2^2 \times 7$	Do the operation in parentheses.
$3 + 4 \times 7$	Simplify the exponent.
$3 + 28$	Multiply.
31	Add.

Simplify the numerical expression.

$$\frac{12 + 3}{15 \div 3}$$

$\dfrac{15}{15 \div 3}$	Simplify the numerator.
$\dfrac{15}{5}$	Simplify the denominator.
3	Simplify the remaining expression by dividing.

Simplify the algebraic expressions.

★ $a(6 + 2^2)$

$a(6 + 4)$	Simplify the exponent in the parentheses.
$a(10)$	Add the values in the parentheses.
$10a$	Rewrite.

★ $(4 + 10) \div 7 + 10n$

$14 \div 7 + 10n$	Do the operation in parentheses.
$2 + 10n$	Divide.

★ $\dfrac{5^2 + 23}{6 \times 4} + 6x$

$\dfrac{25 + 23}{6 \times 4} + 6x$	Simplify the exponent in the numerator.
$\dfrac{48}{6 \times 4} + 6x$	Add the values in the numerator.
$\dfrac{48}{24} + 6x$	Simplify the denominator.
$2 + 6x$	Simplify the fraction by dividing.

Check Understanding

Simplify each expression.

a. $5 + 3^2 \times (4 + 6)$

b. $6b - \frac{6^2 - 6}{5 \times 3} + 10$

c. $29 + a(7 - 3) - 24$

Write *true* or *false* for each equation.

d. $14 \times 3^2 + 2 = 154$

e. $\frac{12 - 6}{2} + 3 = 6$

f. $(3 + 2)^3 \div 4 = 5$

Practice

Copy each problem and insert parentheses to make each equation true.

1. $35 + 3 \times 2 - 4 = 72$

2. $3 + 4^2 \times 2 + 5 = 115$

Simplify each numerical expression.

3. $(7 + 2) \cdot (6 - 2\frac{1}{2})$

4. 5.25×2^3

5. $7 + 2 \times (6 - 4)$

6. $5 \times (2^3 + 1)$

7. $\frac{3^2 + 1}{2 + 3}$

8. $\frac{4^2 \times (2 + 1)}{2 \times 3}$

Simplify each algebraic expression.

9. $30 - 4x + 2$

10. $a(14 - 3) + 7$

11. $2.2^2 + 10.5(2) + n$

12. $20 + 2b - 9$

13. $2^3 + 3^2 + t - \frac{9 + 12}{3}$

14. $b(49 \div 7) - 69$

Apply

15. A journalist traveled to Africa to gather material about the people and their culture. She will be paid $420.00 a week, plus $0.05 for every word she writes that is published. Suppose she publishes an average of 2400 words a week. Write a numerical expression to show her average weekly salary. Simplify your expression.

16. The transportation for a field trip to Grace and Truth Publications will cost $50.00 plus an additional $0.17 per mile. The cost will be divided among the 21 students and their teacher. Write an algebraic expression to represent the amount each person will pay. Let *m* equal the number of miles.

17. The publishing company told the class that two-thirds of their annual profits were given to organizations responsible for Bible translation work in areas where the gospel had not been preached. In addition, their employees gave an offering of $1245. Express the amount given as an algebraic expression, using *p* to represent the annual profit.

18. A team of Bible translators translated four more verses every day than their original goal of *v* verses. Write an expression representing the number of verses they translated in seven days.

Construct Meaning

"For what profit is it to a man if he gains the whole world, and loses his own soul?" Matthew 16:26a. God's Word helps us evaluate what is important. This wisdom along with the mathematical skill of evaluating can enable us to make good decisions.

e•vac′u•ate, 1. empty. 2. remove. 3. withdraw.

e•vade′, avoid by deceit or indirect answer.

e•val′u•ate, find the value.

e′van•gel′i•cal, of the Gospels or New Testament.

e•van′gel•ist, one who preaches the Gospels.

Shanika is determining which phone plan is the best value. Plan A charges $0.05 a minute plus a monthly fee of $5.00. Plan B charges $0.10 a minute with no monthly fee. If she normally uses 110 minutes per month, which plan is the better buy? Use m to represent the number of minutes.

Evaluating Expressions	Plan A	Plan B
• Begin with an algebraic expression.	$0.05m + 5$	$0.10m$
• Substitute a value for each variable. In this case let $m = 110$.	$0.05(110) + 5$	$0.10(110)$
• Simplify the resulting numeric expression.	$5.50 + 5 = \$10.50$	$\$11.00$

After evaluating these two expressions, you can see that Plan A would be cheaper.

In mathematics, to **evaluate** means to find the numeric value of an expression by replacing variables with numerals. Substitute a value for the variable and simplify.

Evaluate $3(n + 6)$ if $n = 8$.	$3(n + 6)$
Substitute the value for the variable.	$3(8 + 6)$
Simplify.	$3(14)$
	42

Evaluate $(a + b) \cdot (a - b)$ if $a = 7.5$ and $b = 2.5$.	$(a + b) \cdot (a - b)$
Substitute the value for each variable.	$(7.5 + 2.5) \cdot (7.5 - 2.5)$
Simplify.	$10 \cdot 5$
	50

Check Understanding

Evaluate each algebraic expression if $x = 4$, $y = 10$, and $z = 6$.

a. x^3 **b.** $(x + y)(x + z)$ **c.** z^x

d. 3^x **e.** $4(2z - y)^2$ **f.** $(x + 50z) + (12z - 8x)$

Practice

Evaluate each expression if $a = \frac{1}{2}$, $b = 5$, and $c = 100$.

1. $ac - b$

2. $b \cdot c(a - a)$

3. $b^2 + 2a + 1$

4. $10b + \frac{3}{5} \cdot b^2$

5. Rank the following expressions in order from least to greatest if $m = 4$ and $p = 6$.

a. $m + p^2$

b. $(m + p)^2$

c. $p^2 - m$

d. $(p - m)^2$

e. mp^2

f. $(mp)^2$

g. $m \div p^2$

h. $(m \div p)^2$

Evaluate each expression.

6. Find $(x + 0.25)^2$ if $x = 1.75$.

7. Find $\frac{3}{x} \cdot \frac{y}{2} - \frac{x}{3} \cdot \frac{2}{y}$ if $x = 1$ and $y = 4$.

Write >, < or = to show the relationship between each pair of expressions. Let $p = 0.25$, $q = 20$, and $r = 4$.

8. $q - (10 - r) \bigcirc q - 10 - r$

9. $p + 5(p + 1.25) \bigcirc (p + 5)p + 1.5$

10. $4(q + 2) \bigcirc 4q + 8$

11. $27 - 5r \bigcirc (27 - 5)r$

Apply

When you use a formula, you are evaluating an expression.

12. In the formula $r = \frac{d}{t}$, r is the rate, d is the distance, and t is the time. The table shows the time it took each engine to travel a certain distance. Use this formula to write an expression for the rate of each engine pictured and evaluate. Remember to label each answer. Which engine was the fastest?

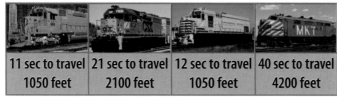

11 sec to travel 1050 feet	21 sec to travel 2100 feet	12 sec to travel 1050 feet	40 sec to travel 4200 feet

13. Use the formula $d = rt$ to write an equation and determine the distance traveled by a car moving at a rate of 60 mph for a time of $5\frac{1}{2}$ hours. Label your answer.

USING A CALCULATOR

14. Evaluate Einstein's formula $E = mc^2$ when m equals four kilograms and c equals 3×10^8 meters per second. Write your answer in scientific notation and label it *joules*, a metric measure of energy. (Hint: $E = mc^2$ means $E = m \cdot c \cdot c$.)

Problem Solving

Construct Meaning

Use the skills you have developed in this chapter to solve word problems.
A challenge in solving word problems lies in translating the expressions involved.

Iceland Bible Church hires a local printing company to produce the Sunday
bulletins. The printer charges $0.10 per bulletin, plus a $25.00 set-up fee. How can
the church calculate its weekly printing bill?

Step 1 Choose a variable for each unknown amount. Choose a letter that reminds
you of what it represents. Write what each variable represents.

b = the number of bulletins

Step 2 Translate the information from the problem into an
expression using the chosen variable.

$0.10 \cdot b + \$25$

> Think: *$0.10 per bulletin* means $0.10 · b
> for the basic cost. *Plus a $25 fee* means
> adding that amount to the basic cost.

This week the church requested 175 bulletins.
Find the cost.

Step 3 Substitute the given value for the variable.

$b = 175$
$0.10(175) + \$25$

Step 4 Simplify.
$17.50 + \$25 = \$42.50$

Step 5 Answer the question completely, using correct units.
The church will spend $42.50 on printing this week.

Check Understanding

Select a variable and state what it represents.
Write an algebraic expression and solve the problem. Show your work for each step.

  a. A web page designer charges customers a $100 base fee plus $20 for each hour of
  work. What expression does the designer use to calculate a bill? If a business
  needs five hours of work done, how much should they expect to pay?

  b. Pelé flies a plane for missionaries in South America. The plane gets 6 miles per
  gallon and currently has 36 gallons of fuel remaining. Show how to calculate the
  number of miles Pelé can travel. If the next scheduled flight is a 120-mile trip
  from Santos to Rio Claro, does he need to refuel before taking off? Fuel is
  available in Rio Claro.

Apply

Select a variable and state what it represents. Write an expression and solve.

1. A local car tax is calculated by adding a five-dollar public transportation fee to 1.2% of the value of the car. Write an expression to calculate a car tax based on the value of the car. (Hint: 1.2% = 0.012) How much is the car tax for a car valued at $10,100?

2. One inch is approximately the same length as 2.54 centimeters. Use this information to write an expression to convert inches to centimeters. What are the dimensions of an 8.5" by 11" sheet of paper in centimeters?

3. A radio station is building a sound room with special acoustical tiles. Each tile covers four square feet and costs $10. Write an expression to calculate the total cost. The radio station needs to cover 648 square feet of ceiling and walls. How much will this cost?

4. Each month Marcel gives 10%, which is 0.10, of his paycheck to his local church and deposits another 10% of his paycheck into savings. Write an expression to calculate the amount of money Marcel has left each month after tithing and saving. If Marcel makes $1258 per month, how much money does he have left after tithing and saving?

5. Hao is choosing between two Internet service providers. Plan A charges $17.50 a month for unlimited service. Plan B charges $10 a month for the first 20 hours a month, plus $1 for each additional hour. If Hao normally spends an hour using the Internet every night, which plan should he choose? Show all the expressions that you used and explain how you made your final decision.

6. Consider the trapezoid.
   a. Write an expression for the total area of both triangles.
   b. Write an expression for the area of the interior rectangle.
   c. Write an expression for the total area of the trapezoid.
   d. If the height of the trapezoid is 2 inches, what is the total area of the trapezoid?

   | Area Formulas |
   | Triangle $A = \frac{1}{2}(bh)$ |
   | Rectangle $A = bh$ |

   3 in.

   h

   1.5 in.

7. The Howard Box Factory makes 30 recycle boxes per minute. Write an expression for the number of boxes made in a certain number of hours. How many boxes are made in a 12-hour workday?

Construct Meaning

After Mitchell's dad finished moving loads of soil for a raised herb garden, Mitchell moved five additional loads using the wheelbarrow. Write an expression that shows the total number of loads.

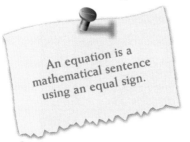

An equation is a mathematical sentence using an equal sign.

If n = number of loads moved by Mitchell's dad, then $n + 5$ = total number of loads.

Suppose they moved a total of 14 loads. Write an equation to show this relationship. Use the same method used for writing expressions.

sum of father's loads	and	son's loads	is	the total
n	+	5	=	14

To **solve** an equation containing a variable means to determine the value(s) of the variable that will make the equation true. A value that makes the equation true is a **solution**. How many loads did Mitchell's dad move?

Solve $n + 5 = 14$.

Determine the operation performed on the variable.	$n + 5 = 14$	 5 is added to the variable.
Perform the inverse operation on both sides of the equation to isolate the variable.	$n + 5 - 5 = 14 - 5$	 Subtract 5 from each side.
Simplify both sides of the equation.	$n = 9$	
Check the solution by substituting it back into the original equation.	$n + 5 = 14$ $9 + 5 = 14$ $14 = 14$ ✓	**Mitchell's dad moved nine loads.**

Solving an equation is similar to using a balance. The equal sign is the pivot point. Adding or subtracting equal amounts from both sides will not disturb the equality.

Solve $3 = r - 7$.

7 is being subtracted from r. Add 7 to both sides. Simplify.	$3 = r - 7$ $3 + 7 = r - 7 + 7$ $10 = r$	 
Substitute the value of r to check your solution.	$3 = 10 - 7$ $3 = 3$ ✓	Does $10 = r$ have the same meaning as $r = 10$?

Check Understanding

a. Draw a balance diagram to show $p + 7 = 9$. Show how to solve for p.

b. What would happen to the balance in the equation $n + 5 = 14$ if 5 was added instead of subtracted to both sides?

c. Explain how to solve $b + 150 = 313$ and determine the value of b.

d. Explain how to solve $219 = c - 16$ and determine the value of c.

Practice

Solve for the given variable. Check your solution.

1. $g - 14 = 29$

2. $42 = x + 11$

3. $5\frac{1}{3} = z - \frac{2}{3}$

4. $j + 42 = 1253$

5. $6\frac{3}{5} + n = 18\frac{4}{5}$

6. $h - 217 = 23$

7. $19.75 = y + 16.39$

8. $0 + m = 45.52$

9. $b + 17.3 = 97.5$

10. $\frac{7}{8} = k - \frac{5}{8}$

11. $\frac{17}{20} + p = 1$

12. $x - 49 = 100$

Apply

Identify the variable and write an equation that represents the problem. Solve the equation and check the solution.

13. Gabriella and her mom dismantled an old shed to move it to another location. They numbered each board as they removed it to make the reconstruction easier. Gabriella's mom numbered the ends of the first 42 boards and Gabriella numbered the rest. If they removed 180 boards, how many did Gabriella number?

14. After writing a check for $29.17, Corbin calculated that he had $642.28 left in his account. What was the balance in his account before he wrote the check?

Review

Write each fraction as a decimal.

1. $\frac{3}{5}$

2. $\frac{17}{100}$

3. $\frac{125}{200}$

4. $\frac{3}{8}$

5. $\frac{1}{3}$

Write each decimal as a fraction in lowest terms.

6. 0.875

7. $0.\overline{6}$

8. 0.8

9. 0.29

10. 0.25

Construct Meaning

Kalie used hollow logs for planters, putting three different herbs in each one. Write an expression that shows how many plants she used to fill the planters.

> The **coefficient** is a number by which a variable is multiplied. In the expression $3n$, 3 is the coefficient of the variable n.

If n = number of planters, then $3 \times n$ or $3n$ = total number of plants.

Suppose Kalie transplanted 18 plants. Write an equation to show this relationship.

plants in one planter	times	the number of planters	is	the total number of plants
↓	↓	↓	↓	↓
3	×	n	=	18

How many planters did Kalie fill?

Solve $3n = 18$.

Determine what operation is being performed on the variable.

$3n = 18$

The variable is multiplied by 3.

Perform the inverse operation on both sides of the equation to get the variable by itself.

$\dfrac{3n}{3} = \dfrac{18}{3}$

Divide each side by 3.

Simplify both sides of the equation.

$n = 6$

Check the solution by substituting it back into the original equation.

$3n = 18$
$3 \times 6 = 18$
$18 = 18$ ✓

Kalie filled six planters.

If both sides of an equation are divided by the same nonzero number, the two sides remain equal. Why can zero not be used? If both sides of an equation are multiplied by the same number, the two sides remain equal.

Solve $\dfrac{s}{3} = 5$.

$\dfrac{s}{3}$ means $\dfrac{1}{3}$ of s.

The variable s is divided by 3.

$\dfrac{s}{3} = 5$

Multiply both sides by 3.
Simplify.

$3 \cdot \dfrac{s}{3} = 5 \cdot 3$
$s = 15$

Draw a balance diagram to show the solution to this problem.

Substitute the value of the variable to check your solution.

$\dfrac{15}{3} = 5$
$5 = 5$ ✓

Check Understanding

a. Draw a balance diagram to show $4r = 20$. Show how to solve for r.
b. What happens to the equation $s \div 3 = 5$ if both sides are multiplied by 0?
c. Explain how to solve $14.4c = 57.6$ and determine the value of c.
d. Explain how to solve $\frac{d}{15} = 3$ and determine the value of d.

Practice

Solve for the given variable. Check your solution.

1. $5p = 75$ **2.** $96 = 16x$ **3.** $8.4 = z \cdot 4.2$ **4.** $m \div 5 = 12$

5. $\frac{r}{4} = 110$ **6.** $t \div 2.5 = 10$ **7.** $17q = 15.64$ **8.** $n \div \frac{1}{2} = 16$

9. $\frac{1}{4} = x \div 4$ **10.** $0.5n = 150$ **11.** $2 = c \div 0.75$ **12.** $9 = \frac{3}{4} \cdot x$

Apply

Identify the variable and write an equation that represents the problem. Solve the equation and check the solution.

13. At the fair, the price of roasted sweet corn is $0.75 per ear. How many ears can Alex purchase if he has $6.00 to spend?

14. Jacob and Laura worked for a local farmer during the summer. For every five bushels of sweet corn they picked, the farmer gave them a bonus of one dollar in addition to their hourly wage. At the end of one week, they each received a bonus of $8. How many bushels had they picked together that week?

15. Rick and Regan are planning a camping trip to Rocky Mountain National Park. The entrance fee for the park is $15 per vehicle. The camping spot is $12 per night. They will pay an additional $7 for an advance reservation. What is the total amount they will spend if they camp for three nights in the park?

Review

1. List the first ten prime numbers.
2. Write the prime factorization of 56.
3. Write 305 million in scientific notation.
4. Round 15.654 to the nearest tenth.
5. What is the least common multiple of 8 and 14?

Construct Meaning

A study of our world shows that God created everything in orderly patterns. Recognizing patterns and describing them in words and symbols enables us to make predictions and answer questions in many fields of science.

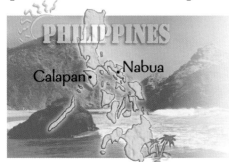

A meteorologist detected a storm in the Philippines traveling east from the town of Calapan at 3:15 P.M. The table below shows the distances the storm traveled after 3:15 P.M. Find the missing entry.

Hours after 3:15 P.M. (t)	0	2	5	6
Miles from Calapan (d)	0	30	75	

Study the pattern represented in the table to determine the relationship between t (time expressed in hours) and d (distance in miles). Is it an addition relationship?

$$2 + 28 = 30 \quad — but — \quad 5 + 28 \neq 75$$

Try multiplication.

$$2 \times 15 = 30 \quad — and — \quad 5 \times 15 = 75$$

The rule showing the relationship between the time and distance is *multiply by fifteen*.

distance = 15 × time

d (miles) = 15 (miles per hour) × t (hours)

Notice that the relationship is the rate, or speed, of the storm. Find the missing entry in the table by using the formula determined from the pattern.

$d = 15 \times t$
$d = 15 \text{ mi/hr} \times 6 \text{ hr}$
$d = 90 \text{ mi}$

IN SIX HOURS, THE STORM WILL BE 90 MILES FROM CALAPAN.

Since the meteorologist knows the rate of the storm, he can predict when the storm will hit Nabua, a town 150 miles east of Calapan, if it continues at the same rate.

Use the formula.

$d = 15 \times t$
$150 \text{ mi} = 15 \text{ mi/hr} \times t$
$\frac{150 \text{ mi}}{15 \text{ mi/hr}} = t$
$10 \text{ hr} = t$

THE STORM WILL REACH NABUA IN 10 HOURS.

m	3	5	■	9	10
g	1	3	5	■	8

Determine the relationship between the variables m and g. Write a formula and determine the missing values.

Check Understanding

Copy and complete the table. Write the rule for the pattern using the given variables.

a.

x	5	10	15	17
y	8		18	20

b. The formula for the cost of the taxi ride is $t = \$1.75 + \$0.90 \cdot m$, where m is the number of miles traveled. Using the formula, make a table to show the cost for traveling 2, 6, and 10 miles.

Practice

Copy and complete the table. Write the rule using the given variables.

1.

p	5	10	15	20
q	0.5	1		2

2.

v	2	4	6	7
w	3		35	48

3. Consider the pattern of squares. Copy and complete the table showing how the total number of small squares depends on the length of the side.

Length of side units (l)	1	2	3	4
Number of unit squares (n)	1		9	

4. Write the rule for the pattern represented in problem 3 using the given variables.

Apply

5. The circles show the number of slices in a pizza resulting from each cut through the center. Make a table relating the number of cuts to the number of slices. Write a rule describing the relationship. How many slices will result from 5 cuts?

6. Amir wants to buy a stereo system for 540 shekels. He decided to save 45 shekels per month. Complete the table showing the amount Amir still needed after each month. What amount did he still need after six months? When will he have enough money to buy the stereo?

Month	0	1	2
Amount needed	540	495	450

7. The table shows how far a flock of black-and-white warblers have traveled by a certain day during migration.

Days (t)	3	6	9	12
Miles (d)	36	72	108	144

a. What is the average rate the birds fly?
b. Write the rule that determines how far the flock has flown in a certain number of days.
c. Predict the distance the flock will have traveled after 20 days of migration.

Discovering Functions

Construct Meaning

A **function** is a rule that shows the relationship between a given number, input, and the resulting number, output, by defining the operation(s) performed.

A function machine can help you understand functions.Use each function machine to complete the table.

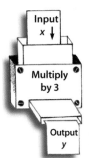

Input x	1	2	3	4	5	6
Output y	3	6	9			

Function: $y = 3x$

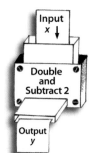

Input x	2	4	6	8	10
Output y					

Function: $y = 2x - 2$

Evaluating a function

The International Bible Society sells a case of softcover Bibles for $71.76. Shipping and handling is $15 for any order. The total cost y depends on the number of cases x purchased. Write this relationship as a function.

$$y = \$71.76 \cdot x + \$15$$

Use the function to determine the total cost for purchasing 4, 8, 12, and 15 cases of Bibles. Record the input and output in a table.

Input x	4	8	12	15
Output y	$302.04	$589.08	$876.12	$1091.40

Substitute the number of cases x into the function. Solve for y. Repeat for each x value.
$y = \$71.76 \cdot 4 + \$15 = \$302.04$ for 4 cases

Writing a function

Use the table to determine the function.

Input x	1	2	3	4	5	6
Output y	5	7	9	11	13	15

Find the relationship between the two variables by trial and error.

John tried adding 4 to each x value to find y.
$1 + 4 = 5 \qquad 2 + 4 \neq 7$

Caroline tried multiplying each x value by 5.
$1 \times 5 = 5 \qquad 2 \times 5 \neq 7$

Input x	1	2	3	4	5	6
2x	2	4	6	8	10	12
2x + 3	5	7	9	11	13	15
Output y	5	7	9	11	13	15

More than one operation may be involved. Try multiplying by 2. $1 \times 2 = 2, 2 \times 2 = 4 \ldots$

What additional operation needs to be performed to make $1 \times 2 = 5$? Add 3.

Substitute each x value in $2x + 3$ to check.

The function is $y = 2x + 3$.

Write the function.

Check Understanding

Use the function to copy and complete the table.

a. $t = 3s - 1$

Input s	1	2	3	4	5
Output t					

Use the table to write a function.

b.

Input m	1	2	3	4	5
Output r	0.5	2	4.5	8	12.5

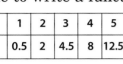

Practice

Copy and complete each table using the function.

1. $r = 4x$

Input x	1	2	3	4
Output r				

2. $a = t^2$

t	2	4	6	8
a				

3. $y = x + 5$

x	2	4	6	8	10
y					

4. $s = t^2 + 10$

t	1	3	5	7
s				

Use the table to write a function.

5.

Input x	1	2	3	4	5
Output y	1	3	5	7	9

6.

Input n	2	4	6	8	10
Output s	8	10	12	14	16

7.

h	4	8	12	16	20
b	13	25	37	49	61

8.

a	1	2	3	4	5
c	12	14	16	18	20

Apply

Write each relationship as a function. Copy and complete each table.

9. The cost of renting a snowmobile at Snow's Rentals is $30 plus $1.50 for each gallon of gas used. Let g = gallons of gas, and s = total rental cost.

g	2	4	6	8	10
s					

10. The cost of renting the day lodge located along the snowmobile trail is $5 per person. The total cost d depends on the number of people n.

n	2	4	5	6	8
d					

11. Lunches for the snowmobile trip cost $2.50 for each person plus $10 for beverages for the group, regardless of the number of people in the group. The total cost l depends on the number of lunches n purchased.

n	2	4	5	6	8
l					

Cryptography/Study Guide

Construct Meaning

Personal and financial security for individuals, businesses, and governments depends upon the mathematical science of cryptography. When information is encrypted, it is put into a secret code. The person on the receiving end must have the key, which is usually a very large prime number, to decode the information.

Developing and using an encryption process:

• Assign a number to each letter of the alphabet.

• Create a function for encoding.

Let n = number representing original letter.
Let c = number representing coded letter.

If 3 is added to the original letter, the function is $c = n + 3$. The function translates each letter into a coded letter.

• Encode the message.

Use the original numbering of the alphabet to find the new coded letters.

If the function goes past the end of the alphabet, continue counting from the beginning. If W is the original letter and the function is *add 10*, then W becomes G.

• To decode the message, use the opposite operation, which is $n = c - 3$ in this case. Then match the number with the letter.

FRPPXQLFDWH is COMMUNICATE.

Check Understanding

a. Encode WORD using $c = n + 6$.

b. Encode VICTORY using $c = n - 4$.

c. Decode XMFWJ using $n = c - 5$.

d. Decode GENAFYNGR using $n = r + 13$.

Chapter 4 Study Guide

Translate each phrase into an expression. *Lessons 4.1 and 4.2*

1. Forty-two plus the product of eighteen and two
2. One-half of the sum of a number plus one
3. One thousand and three more than twice a number

Simplify each numerical expression. *Lesson 4.3*

4. $235 + (50 + 2^2)$
5. $125.50 + 64 \cdot 3 - 284.45$

Simplify each algebraic expression. *Lesson 4.3*

6. $230 + x(0.5 + 30)$
7. $n(5 + 4) + 3^2 + 20$

Evaluate each expression. *Lesson 4.4*

8. $a(2a + 3p - 3p)$ if $a = 10$ and $p = 5$
9. $(a + b^2) \div a$ if $a = 100$ and $b = 200$

Use the figure at the right. *Lesson 4.5*

10. Write an expression for the area of a square.
11. Write an expression for the area of a triangle.
12. Write an expression for the total area of the figure.
13. If $b = 5$ cm and $h = 2$ cm, find the total area.

Solve each equation for the variable. Check your answer.

14. $21 + q = 47$ *Lesson 4.6*
15. $44.5 = r - 16$ *Lesson 4.6*
16. $26s = 104$ *Lesson 4.7*
17. $\frac{t}{19} = 3$ *Lesson 4.7*

Choose the correct rule for the pattern. Copy and complete each table. *Lesson 4.8*

18.

a	1	2	3	4
b	3	12	27	

   a. $b = a + 10$
   b. $b = 3a^2$
   c. $b = 9a$

19.

c	3	6	9	12
d	3	4		6

   a. $d = c \div 2 + 1$
   b. $d = c - 2$
   c. $d = c \div 3 + 2$

Use the function to complete the table. *Lesson 4.9*

20. $m = n^2 + 4$

n	1	2	3	4	5	6
m						

Speak the Truth

Translate the following expressions.

1. Two-tenths of the sum of five and a number

2. Twenty less than the square of ten

3. Eight times the sum of a number cubed and one

4. A number squared plus the product of ten and that number

Simplify each expression.

5. $67 - 7(3.18 + 4.32)$

6. $\dfrac{100 + 2 \cdot 36}{18 \div 9 \cdot 2}$

7. $50(17.2 - 7.2)^2 - 318$

8. $\frac{1}{2}(4^2 - 2) + 8$

9. $10 + x(4 + 2)$

10. $a(8 - 2) + 14 + 3^2$

Substitute the given value and evaluate.

11. $(n + 250m)(n - 250m)$ if $m = 2$ and $n = 1000$

12. $1.2q + 100(q - 3)$ if $q = 5$

13. $(12.5 - b)^2$ if $b = 5.5$

14. $27n - 13n$ if $n = 0.05$

15. Yousaref is hiring an electrician to help him remodel his home. One electrician charges $25 to visit the site plus $34.80 for each hour of work. Another electrician charges only $10 to come to the house, but $40 per hour of work. Write an expression to show the cost for each electrician to complete the work. Evaluate each expression if the job requires five hours of work. Which electrician will charge less?

16. Find the area of the irregular shape at right using the following steps.
   a. If the width of the rectangle is twice the height, write an expression for the area of the rectangle.
   b. Write an expression for the area of the semicircle in terms of h.
   c. Write the expression for the total area of the figure.
   d. If the height of the rectangle is 2 inches, find the total area.

Area of a circle = πr^2
$\pi \approx 3.14$
r = radius
$r = \frac{1}{2}h$

Solve each equation for the variable. Check your answer.

17. $19 = 7 + p$

18. $n - 15 = 37.5$

19. $5.4 = 27m$

20. $k \div 4 = 16$

Complete each table and write a function for each pattern.

21.

a	1	2	3	4
b	20	21		23

22.

t	5	10	15	20
n	15	90	215	

23.

h	2	4	6	8
r	8	12		20

Complete the table by using the given function.

24. $y = x^2 + 9$

x	1	2	3	4
y				

25. $b = \frac{4a}{2}$

a	4	8	12	16
b				

Evaluate each function for the given values.

26. $y = x^3 - 3x$ if $x = 3$

27. $a = 2(b^2 - 1)$ if $b = 8$

28. $t = (h^3 + 1) \cdot s$ if $h = \frac{1}{2}$ and $s = 10$

29. $m = 12 + 2 \cdot (n + n^2 + y^2)$ if $n = 6$ and $y = 1.1$

30. By noon Rachelle had already traveled 30 miles. If she continues at an average speed of 55 miles per hour, the total distance traveled can be calculated by the function $d = 55h + 30$ where h is the number of hours after noon. If Rachelle reaches her destination by 5 P.M., how far will she have traveled that day?

31. Joe works for the telephone company for $10.25 an hour. For each hour over 40 hours per week, he receives an additional $5 as an overtime bonus. If Joe works 45 hours in one week, how much will he be paid? Write a function to show the relationship and evaluate.

32. The CRZ communications team has 55 TV wall monitors. In addition, each team member has two monitors on his or her desk. If there are 14 team members, how many TV monitors does the communications team use? Write a function to show the relationship and evaluate.

33. Lars purchased a satellite dish for his business for $540. He will make a $67.50 payment each month until the total amount is paid. Copy and complete the table showing the amount Lars owed after each month. How long will it take for him to pay the debt?

Months	0								
Amount Owed	$540								

Chapter Theme:
The Ocean

5

Chapter

Integers

Properties of Integers

Construct Meaning

The summit of Diamond Head rises approximately 760 feet above sea level on the Hawaiian island of Oahu. Beneath the surface of the ocean, scientists have identified three zones, based on the amount of light each receives. The numbers for height and depth show a relationship with sea level, which is considered 0 feet.

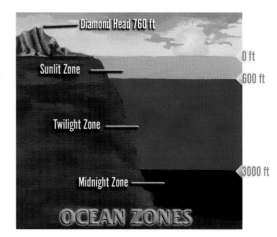

The set of integers includes 0 and all of the whole numbers greater than zero and their opposites. {. . . −5, −4, −3, −2, −1, 0, 1, 2, 3, 4, 5, . . .}

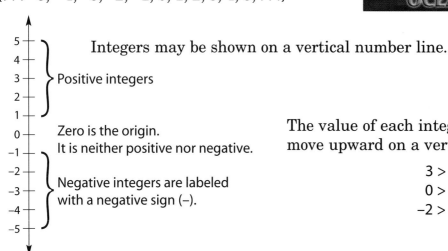

Integers may be shown on a vertical number line.

Positive integers

Zero is the origin.
It is neither positive nor negative.

Negative integers are labeled with a negative sign (−).

The value of each integer is greater as you move upward on a vertical number line.

$$3 > 2$$
$$0 > -1$$
$$-2 > -4$$

The integer value increases as you move right on a horizontal number line. As you move left, each integer decreases in value.

−5 < −4   −3 < 1   −1 < 0   2 < 5

Opposites are numbers that are the same distance from 0.

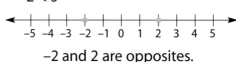

−2 and 2 are opposites.

The **absolute value** of an integer is determined by its distance from 0. An integer and its opposite have the same absolute value.

$|5| = 5$ $|-5| = 5$ $|-4| = 4$ $|4| = 4$

To compare and order integers:
• Consider the sign.
• For a negative integer, the greater the distance from 0, the less its value.
• For a positive integer, the greater the distance from 0, the greater its value.

|8| is read "the absolute value of eight."
|−8| is read "the absolute value of negative eight."

Check Understanding

Write *true* or *false*.
  a. The absolute value of a negative integer is its opposite.
  b. The set of integers between 1 and −5 are all negative.
  c. The absolute value of a positive integer is the integer itself.
  d. The least integer in a set of negative integers has the greatest absolute value.
  e. If 0 is the least integer in a set of ten integers, another element of the set may be negative.

Maritime Moments

Each of the eight deepest ocean trenches of the world is deep enough to submerge Mount Everest.

Practice

Write the opposite of each integer.
  1. −12   **2.** 8   **3.** 15   **4.** −7   **5.** −20

Write the absolute value.
  6. $|9|$ **7.** $|19|$ **8.** $|-10|$ **9.** $|-2|$ **10.** $|2|$

Compare using >, < or = .
  11. 16 ◯ 32   **12.** −16 ◯ −32   **13.** 0 ◯ −12
  14. 10 ◯ −2   **15.** −4 ◯ −3

Write each set of integers.
  16. Integers between 1 and 9
  17. Negative integers greater than −3
  18. Positive integers less than or equal to 12
  19. The greatest negative integer
  20. An integer neither positive nor negative

Alaska's Mount Russell

Apply

21. Which point lies at a greater distance from sea level, the 11,670-foot summit of Mount Russell or the bottom of the Japan Trench at a depth of 24,599 ft?

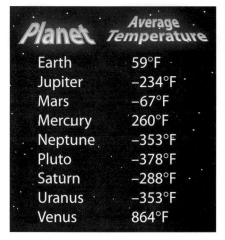

Planet	Average Temperature
Earth	59°F
Jupiter	−234°F
Mars	−67°F
Mercury	260°F
Neptune	−353°F
Pluto	−378°F
Saturn	−288°F
Uranus	−353°F
Venus	864°F

22. Identify each statement that could be true if a is a positive integer and b is a negative integer.
  $|a| = |b|$ $b > a$ $a > b$ $b = a$

23. The chart lists the average surface temperature on each of the nine planets of our solar system. Order the temperatures from least to greatest.

Adding Integers

Construct Meaning

The wreck of the *Titanic* lies about nine hundred sixty-three miles northeast of New York at a depth of 12,468 feet. The site has been explored by people who descended in a submersible made of titanium and steel.

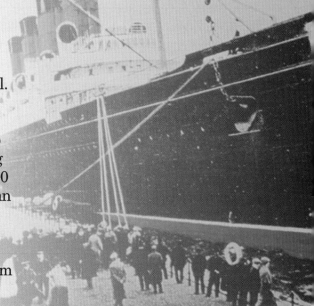

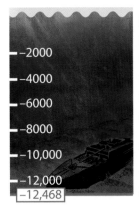

Suppose the submersible has made the two and one-half hour descent to the *Titanic* site and is now returning to the surface. If it has ascended 1500 feet, how far below the Atlantic Ocean surface is it presently located?

The expression may be written −12,468 + 1500. You may find the sum if you know how to add integers.

Rules of Integer Addition

The sum of any number and its additive inverse is 0.

Two integers that are opposites are called **additive inverses**.

$-3 + 3 = 0$
This is called the **Additive Inverse Property**.

The sum of two positive integers is positive.

Move right to add a positive integer on the number line.

Solve 1 + 3. Begin at 1 and move right 3 units.
$1 + 3 = 4$

The sum of two negative integers is negative.

Move left to add a negative integer on the number line.

Solve −2 + (−2). Begin at −2 and move left 2 units.
$-2 + (-2) = -4$

The sum of integers with different signs may be positive or negative.

To add integers with different signs, find the difference between their absolute values.

- The sum is positive if the positive integer has the greater absolute value.

  Solve 10 + (−5). $|10| = 10$ $|-5| = 5$ $|10| > |-5|$ The sum will be positive.
  The difference between $|10|$ and $|-5|$ is 5.
  $10 + (-5) = 5$

- The sum is negative if the negative integer has the greater absolute value.

  Solve −20 + 15. $|-20| = 20$ $|15| = 15$ $|-20| > |15|$ The sum will be negative.
  The difference between $|-20|$ and $|15|$ is 5.
  $-20 + 15 = -5$

Check Understanding

a. Will the sum of −12,468 + 1500 be a positive or negative integer? Explain.

b. Simplify −12,468 + 1500.

c. The Additive Inverse Property states that $-a + a = \square$.

d. On a number line, which direction do you move to add a positive integer?

e. Which direction do you move on a number line to add a negative integer?

Practice

Identify the additive inverse of each integer.

1. −9   **2.** 100   **3.** −13   **4.** −19   **5.** −1

Tell if the sum will be *positive*, *negative*, or *0*.

6. −7 + 5   **7.** −14 + (−10)   **8.** −1 + (−4)   **9.** 10 + (−9)   **10.** 56 + (−56)

Write the addition equation shown on each number line.

11.    **12.**

Find each sum.

13. −7 + (−3)   **14.** 1 + (−1)   **15.** 30 + (−8)   **16.** −21 + 5

17. 0 + (−29)   **18.** 100 + (−25)   **19.** −100 + 25   **20.** 8 + (−17)

21. 5 + (−4)   **22.** 6 + (−10)

Write *always*, *sometimes*, or *never*.

23. The absolute value of an integer is negative.

24. The sum of two integers is greater than either addend.

25. If a and b are integers, then $a + b = b + a$.

Apply

26. The Covenant Christian Stallions began the football game with a loss of five yards on the first play. The second play resulted in a gain of eight yards. What was the net gain or loss after two plays?

27. A tide table predicts −2 feet as the figure for the low tide that will occur at 7:05 P.M. on Thursday. The figure for the high tide at 1:54 A.M. Friday is predicted to be 8 feet. By what amount is the tide expected to rise between 7:05 P.M. and 1:54 A.M.?

Subtracting Integers

Construct Meaning

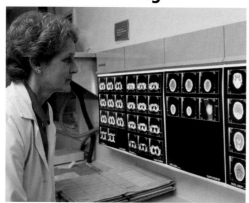

After reading the CT scan in the fifth floor laboratory, Dr. Andrews took the stairs down to her car parked three levels below the ground level. How many flights of stairs did she walk?

Let 0, 1, 2, 3, 4, 5 represent the ground level and the first five floors. Then −1, −2, −3 will represent the three levels of the parking garage below ground level.

To show the difference between 5 and −3, write the equation as $5 - (-3) = 8$. Dr. Andrews walked down 8 flights of stairs.

Consider the relationship between subtracting integers and adding integers.

Compare 5 − 2 with 5 + (−2).
On each model, ⊕ = 1 and ⊖ = −1.
Since 1 + (−1) = 0, ⊕ and ⊖ = 0.

Match one ⊕ and one ⊖ to make each zero pair. Each zero pair equals 0.

Show 5 − 2 = 3.

⊕ ⊕ ⊕ ⊕ ⊕

Show 5 + (−2) = 3.

⊕ ⊕ ⊕ ⊕ ⊕
⊖ ⊖
zero zero
pair pair

The models show 5 − 2 = 5 + (−2).

To subtract an integer, add its opposite.

Change the sign.

$$a - b = a + (-b)$$

Write the opposite.

Solve 6 − 7.
$6 - 7 = 6 + (-7) = -1$

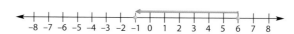

Solve −3 − 5.
$-3 - 5 = -3 + (-5) = -8$

Solve 2 − (−1).
$2 - (-1) = 2 + 1 = 3$

Solve − 8 − (−4).
$-8 - (-4) = -8 + 4 = -4$

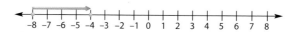

Check Understanding

a. Explain why subtracting a negative integer results in a greater integer.
b. Rewrite $-9 - (-3)$ as an addition expression and find the sum.
c. If you subtract -13 from 20, is the difference positive or negative? Explain.
d. For which type of integers is the following statement true: My opposite and my absolute value are the same number.

Practice

Write *positive* or *negative* to describe each difference. Do not solve.

1. $17 - 18$ 2. $-5 - (-8)$ 3. $-10 - 5$ 4. $25 - (-25)$

Rewrite each subtraction problem as an addition problem. Solve.

5. $-4 - 3$ 6. $0 - 6$ 7. $0 - (-6)$ 8. $-5 - (-9)$
9. $4 - 14$ 10. $9 - (-16)$ 11. $-30 - 7$ 12. $15 - (-8)$

Select the problem shown on the number line.

13.
-9 -8 -7 -6 -5 -4 -3 -2 -1 0 1 2 3 4 5 6 7 8 9

a. $9 - 7 = -2$ b. $9 - (-7) = 2$ c. $9 - 11 = -2$ d. $9 - (-11) = -2$

14.
-9 -8 -7 -6 -5 -4 -3 -2 -1 0 1 2 3 4 5 6 7 8 9

a. $-5 - 4 = 1$ b. $-5 - (-4) = -1$ c. $-5 + (-4) = -1$ d. $-5 - 4 = -1$

Apply

15. The cliff divers near a resort in Mexico plunge into the water from a height of approximately 105 feet above the normal water level. They must dive as a wave comes in because normally the inlet is only about 12 feet deep and 21 feet wide. What is the difference between the point where the dive begins and the bottom of the inlet?

16. Profit is defined by the amount taken in (income) less the amount spent (expenses). A loss occurs when profit is negative. Review the finances of the student snack shop and answer the questions. Remember, profit equals income minus expenses.

	JANUARY	FEBRUARY	MARCH	APRIL	MAY
EXPENSES	$570	$500	$450	$485	$500
INCOME	$435	$475	$575	$630	$680

a. During which months did the shop experience a loss?
b. Which month shows the greatest profit?
c. Compare the total figures for five months and determine the amount of gain or loss the shop experienced.

Construct Meaning

The pelican eel, also known as the "umbrellamouth gulper," lives in the world's oceans at an approximate depth of 6500 feet. A fish called fangtooth is found thousands of feet below where the pelican eel lives. Because fangtooth is found 9500 feet deeper than the pelican eel, that depth can be expressed as $-6500 + (-9500)$.

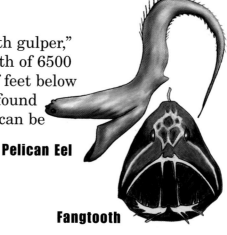

Pelican Eel

Simplify the numerical expression.
$-6500 + (-9500) = -16,000$
The fangtooth lives near a depth of 16,000 feet.

Fangtooth

To evaluate expressions having positive and negative integers, use the rules for integer operations.
Evaluate $a + 30$ if $a = -16$.
Substitute the value of a. $-16 + 30$ Simplify. $-16 + 30 = 14$

To solve algebraic equations with integers, use the rules for solving equations having a variable.
- Isolate the variable on one side of the equation by using inverse operations.
- If an operation is performed on one side, it must be performed on the other.

Solve $x - 8 = 20$.
$x - 8 + 8 = 20 + 8$
$x = 28$

The two sides remain equal if the same number is added to each side.

Check the solution by substituting it back into the original equation.
$28 - 8 = 20$
$20 = 20$ ✓

Solve $x - 6 = -4$.
$x - 6 + 6 = -4 + 6$
$x = 2$
Check the solution.
$2 - 6 = -4$
$-4 = -4$ ✓

Solve $x + 17 = 33$.
$x + 17 - 17 = 33 - 17$
$x = 16$

The two sides remain equal if the same number is subtracted from each side.

Check the solution by substituting it back into the original equation.
$16 + 17 = 33$ ✓

Solve $x + 22 = 11$.
$x + 22 - 22 = 11 - 22$
$x = -11$

Think
$11 + (-22)$

Check the solution.
$-11 + 22 = 11$
$11 = 11$ ✓

Check Understanding

a. Explain the steps needed to solve $x + 1 = -9$. Solve for x.

b. What should be done to check your solution to an equation?

c. Write an addition or subtraction equation using a positive and a negative integer that has -3 as its solution.

Practice

Evaluate each expression.

1. $s + -8$ if $s = -9$ **2.** $2 + r$ if $r = -11$ **3.** $|t|$ if $t = -52$

4. $-6 + c$ if $c = 7$ **5.** $x + 12$ if $x = -65$ **6.** $y - 15$ if $y = 10$

7. $a - (-5)$ if $a = 2$ **8.** $b - 19$ if $b = 87$

Evaluate each expression if $a = -12$ and $b = 24$.

9. $a + b$ **10.** $a - b$ **11.** $b - a$ **12.** $a - a$

Solve for the given variable. Check your solution.

13. $n + 67 = 129$ **14.** $9 = b - 46$ **15.** $13 + r = 8$

16. $t - 15 = -6$ **17.** $y + 100 = 60$ **18.** $3 + x = -7$

19. $c - 7 = -21$ **20.** $-3 = q - 9$

Challenge

Solve for the given variable. Check your solution.

21. $s - (-14) = 40$ **22.** $w - (-25) = -75$

23. $g - (-10) = -15$

Hint: Rewrite each equation to show adding the opposite.

Determine the number needed to make each equation true.

24. $6 + (-8) + 4 = 9 + 5 + \square$ **25.** $\square + (-7) + 10 = -5 + 25 + (-10)$

26. Negative 20 is the sum of a number and -6. Choose the correct equation and solve.

  a. $n + (-6) = -20$ **b.** $n - (-6) = -20$

27. A number decreased by 8 is -12. Choose the correct equation and solve.

  a. $n - 8 = 12$ **b.** $n - 8 = -12$

Apply

28. The temperature at sunrise was $-2°F$. At noon, the temperature was $30°F$. Write a subtraction equation to show how to find the difference t between the temperatures. Solve the equation for t.

29. A high-tech underwater robot called JASON can descend 20,000 feet under the ocean's surface. JASON was used to explore the shipwreck of the *Isis*, which lay undisturbed in the Mediterranean Sea from A.D. 355 until 1989. Compare that to a scuba diver's deepest dive, which is 130 feet. Complete the equation to determine x if x is the difference between the two depths. Solve for x. Use $\square - (-130) = x$.

Integers and Mathematical Properties

Construct Meaning

The Tanks A Lot Aquarium Shop purchased 25-gallon, 50-gallon, and 80-gallon aquariums from a wholesaler. The table shows the store's profit and loss on the retail sales of each type of aquarium at the end of the fiscal year.

Aquarium size	Profit	Loss
25-gallon	$1700	
50-gallon		$500
80-gallon		$1000

What was the profit or loss from the total sales of the aquariums?
Express the profit as a positive integer and each loss as a negative integer.

Tanks A Lot made a profit of $200 on the sales.

$1700 + (–$500) + (–$1000)   Use the Associative Property of Addition.

$1700 + (–$1500) = $200   Add.

The sum has the same sign as the integer with the greater absolute value.

To simplify expressions with integers:
- Rewrite subtraction as the addition of the opposite.
- Regroup using the Commutative and/or Associative Properties of Addition.
- Use the rules for adding integers to determine the sum.

Example 1

Simplify the expression.	$4 - 2 - 9 + 6$
Rewrite to add opposites.	$4 + (-2) + (-9) + 6$
Use the Commutative Property.	$4 + 6 + (-2) + (-9)$
Use the Associative Property and add.	$10 + (-11) = -1$

Example 2

Simplify the expression.	$-3 + 5 - |-7| + 2 + (-8)$
Substitute the absolute value.	$-3 + 5 - 7 + 2 + (-8)$
Rewrite to add opposites.	$-3 + 5 + (-7) + 2 + (-8)$
Use the Commutative Property.	$5 + 2 + (-3) + (-7) + (-8)$
Use the Associative Property and add.	$7 + (-18) = -11$

Example 3

Simplify.	$4 - 15 + y - (-17)$
Rewrite.	$4 + (-15) + y + 17$
Regroup.	$y + 21 + (-15)$
Add.	$y + 6$

Check Understanding

a. Why do you have to rewrite subtraction of integers to use the Commutative and Associative properties?

b. Name one or more ways that integers can be regrouped to make the addition easier.

c. Determine which equation is true and explain your choice.

$$6 - |-5| = 6 + (-5) \qquad\qquad 6 - |-5| = 6 + 5$$

Practice

Simplify each numerical expression.

1. $-1 + 14 - 5$

2. $4 - 10 + 8 - 12$

3. $-3 + 18 + (-4) - 2$

4. $3 - 9 - (-5) + (-4)$

5. $-6 - 1 - (-18) + (-3)$

6. $-7 + |15| - (-6)$

7. $7 - 8 - |-4| - 2 + 9$

8. $-4 - 13 - (-9) + (-6) + 3$

9. $|-16| - 9 + 3 + (-7)$

Simplify each algebraic expression.

10. $-2 + k + (-7) + 1$

11. $12 - s + 10 - 5$

Evaluate each algebraic expression.

12. $-7 - m + 11 + n$ if $m = 5$ and $n = -4$

13. $5 - |x| + y + (-9)$ if $x = -8$ and $y = 3$

New England Aquarium, Boston

Apply

14. Andrew began his visit to the aquarium with two twenty-dollar bills in his pocket. He received a $2.00 discount on the $7.00 admission fee. He was able to use a "$3.00 off" coupon when he purchased a book about whale watching priced at $12.00. The cost of his fish-and-chips lunch was $7.00. Write an addition expression to represent his financial expenditures on the trip. Simplify the expression to determine the amount of money he had left at the end of his aquarium trip.

15. Mrs. Martinez gave each of the triplets ten dollars to spend at the book fair. At the end of the day, the total amount she received back from them was six dollars. She knows that one of the triplets spent his entire ten dollars on a book. What are the four possible whole dollar combinations that the two other triplets could have spent?

Multiplying Integers

Construct Meaning

On May 6, 2001, Tanya Streeter set a world record in the sport of freediving. While holding her breath, she descended at an approximate rate of 3 feet per second for a period of 1 minute and 16 seconds. What was the depth of her dive?

Use -3 to represent a descent of 3 feet per second.
1 min 16 sec = 76 sec
$$76 \cdot (-3) = -228$$

What type of integer resulted when -3 was multiplied by the positive integer 76?

Tanya Streeter's actual record-setting dive was to a depth of 230 feet.

 The product of one negative integer and one positive integer is negative.

$2 \cdot (-3)$ represents 2 groups of -3, which is -6.

 The product of two positive integers is positive.

$$2 \cdot 3 = 6$$

 The product of two negative integers is positive.

$$-2 \cdot (-3) = 6$$

What pattern do you observe in the products?

$$2 \cdot (-3) = -6$$
$$1 \cdot (-3) = -3$$
$$0 \cdot (-3) = 0$$
$$-1 \cdot (-3) = 3$$
$$-2 \cdot (-3) = 6$$

Remember:
If the signs of two factors are the same, the product is positive.

Maritime Moments

Freediving is a diving sport scored on time and depth. The dive is made all on one breath, and underwater breathing equipment is not allowed.

Problems with More Than Two Factors

Evaluate $5 \cdot (-2) \cdot (-3)$.

$$5 \cdot (-2) \cdot (-3)$$ Multiply the first two factors.
$$-10 \cdot (-3) = 30$$ Multiply their product by the next factor.

Check Understanding

a. Explain what you know about two factors if their product is negative.

Use the number line to determine if each product is positive, negative, or 0.

b. $w \cdot z$ **c.** $x \cdot w$ **d.** $y \cdot z$ **e.** $x \cdot y$

Practice

Write whether each product is *positive*, *negative*, or *0*.

1. $5 \cdot 16$ **2.** $-8 \cdot 9$ **3.** $9(-8)$ **4.** $-7 \cdot 0 \cdot 4$ **5.** $-12 \cdot (-11)$

6. $-4(-5)$ **7.** $100 \cdot (-2)$ **8.** $(-2)(1)(-5)$ **9.** $2(-1)5$ **10.** $4 \cdot (-7)$

Find each product.

11. $21 \cdot (-3)$ **12.** $(-8)(-8)$ **13.** $15 \cdot 32$ **14.** $-9 \cdot (-4) \cdot (-2)$ **15.** $-6(-11)$

16. $3 \cdot 4 \cdot (-7)$ **17.** $-2 \cdot (-6) \cdot 3$ **18.** $-6 \cdot (-7)$ **19.** $7(7)(-5)$ **20.** $-8(12)$

Copy and complete each pattern.

21.
$6 \cdot 4 = 24$
$6 \cdot 3 = 18$
$6 \cdot 2 = 12$
$6 \cdot 1 = 6$
$6 \cdot 0 = 0$
$6 \cdot (-1) =$
$6 \cdot (-2) =$
$6 \cdot (-3) =$
$6 \cdot (-4) =$

22.
$8 \cdot (-4) = -32$
$8 \cdot (-3) =$
$8 \cdot (-2) = -16$
$8 \cdot (-1) =$
$8 \cdot 0 =$
$8 \cdot 1 =$
$8 \cdot 2 =$
$8 \cdot 3 =$
$8 \cdot 4 =$

23.
$-9 \cdot 4 = -36$
$-9 \cdot 3 =$
$-9 \cdot 2 =$
$-9 \cdot 1 =$
$-9 \cdot 0 =$
$-9 \cdot (-1) =$
$-9 \cdot (-2) =$
$-9 \cdot (-3) =$
$-9 \cdot (-4) =$

Determine whether each equation is true or false. Write *true* or copy and insert parentheses to make the equation true.

24. $5 \cdot 6 - 4(-2) = 38$ **25.** $14 - 2 \cdot (-3) = -36$ **26.** $8 \div 4 \cdot (-1) = -2$

Apply

27. A submarine may dive from the ocean's surface at a rate of 72 feet per minute. Write an expression using one negative integer and one positive integer to describe the location of the submarine after three minutes of descending at this rate. Simplify the expression.

28. Ted's watch has been losing time at a consistent rate of twenty seconds per day. He has just set his watch to the exact time. How many days will it be until his watch is off by 5 minutes?

Canadian Submarine

Dividing Integers

Construct Meaning

A scuba diver exploring the Red Sea may see magnificent evidence of God's creative power as giant anemones, black emperor fish, and unicorn fish come into view. The chart below shows the depths of some popular Red Sea dive sites. Find the average depth of the four dive sites.

Site Name	Abu Hashish	Elphinstone	Panorama Reef	Salem Express
Depth in feet	−50	−132	−110	−120

- Add the integers.
  $-50 + (-132) + (-110) + (-120) = -412$
- Divide the sum by 4 since there are 4 addends.
  $-412 \div 4 = x$ where x is the average depth.

think

Will x be a positive or negative integer if it represents depth?

$-412 \div 4 = -103$ The average depth is −103.

To understand dividing integers, relate division to multiplication.
Multiplication and division are inverse operations.

If $6 \cdot 8 = 48$
then $48 \div 8 = 6$ The product of two positive integers is positive.
The quotient of two positive integers is positive.

If $-6 \cdot 8 = -48$
then $-48 \div 8 = -6$ The product of a negative integer and a positive integer is negative.
The quotient of a negative integer and a positive integer is negative.

If $-6 \cdot 8 = -48$
then $-48 \div (-6) = 8$ The quotient of two negative integers is positive.

Same Signs = Positive Quotient
$30 \div 5 = 6$ $-30 \div (-5) = 6$
$\frac{30}{5} = 6$ $\frac{-30}{-5} = 6$

Different Signs = Negative Quotient
$-40 \div 2 = -20$ $40 \div (-2) = -20$
$\frac{-40}{2} = -20$ $\frac{40}{-2} = -20$

Zero in Division
$0 \div 2 = 0$ because $0 \cdot 2 = 0$.
$2 \div 0 = x$ is undefined because there is no value for x where $x \cdot 0 = 2$.

Check Understanding

Red Sea Anemone

State whether each quotient is *positive*, *negative*, *zero*, or *undefined*.

   a. $-2 \cdot 19$ **b.** $-28 \div (-7)$
   c. $\frac{364}{0}$ **d.** $-90 \cdot 0$
   e. Write two division equations related to $7 \cdot (-9) = -63$.

Practice

Write *true* or *false* for each statement.

1. If a nonzero integer is divided by its opposite, the quotient is 1.

2. The quotient of two negative integers is negative.

3. To find the average of five integers, find their sum and divide by 5.

4. If a negative integer is divided by another negative integer, the quotient will be greater than each of the integers.

Find each quotient.

5. $-21 \div (-7)$ **6.** $\frac{15}{-5}$ **7.** $-720 \div 8$ **8.** $\frac{-144}{-12}$ **9.** $-135 \div 15$

10. $\frac{-35}{5}$ **11.** $-65 \div (-5)$ **12.** $\frac{-20}{-2}$ **13.** $72 \div (-6)$ **14.** $-72 \div 6$

15. $0 \div (-10)$ **16.** $-120 \div 5$ **17.** $-400 \div (-20)$ **18.** $63 \div (-9)$ **19.** $\frac{108}{-9}$

Apply

20. Explain why $\frac{-75}{25} = \frac{75}{-25}$ is true.

21. Explain why it is easy to use mental math to solve $\frac{-5 + 1 + (-1) + 5}{5}$.

Date	Jan 1	Jan 2	Jan 3	Jan 4	Jan 5	Jan 6	Jan 7
High Temperature	−13°F	−13°F	−14°F	−12°F	−16°F	−15°F	−15°F

22. The chart above shows the daily high temperature for a period of one week in the Far North region of Alaska. What was the average temperature for the week?

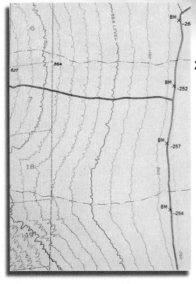

23. A topographical map shows the variations in elevation of the land represented on it. While studying a topographical map of Death Valley, California, Lynda and Tom noticed many negative integers representing the number of feet below sea level of certain locations. They listed −282, the number that represents the lowest elevation in the United States, along with −257, −226, −202, −248. Find the average of the integers they listed.

Multiplication and Division Equations

Construct Meaning

In 1620, a submarine built by Danish doctor Cornelius Van Drebbel was rowed underwater at a depth of 15 feet. In 1977, the research submersible ALVIN happened upon a hydrothermal vent while diving 7995 feet below the Pacific Ocean surface. How many times greater was ALVIN's depth than that of the early submarine?

Write an equation showing each depth as a negative integer. Solve for the variable.

$$-15 \cdot a = -7995$$
$$\frac{-15 \cdot a}{-15} = \frac{-7995}{-15}$$
$$a = 533$$

The two sides remain equal if they are both divided by the same number.

Check your solution.
$$-15 \cdot 533 = -7995$$
$$-7995 = -7995 \checkmark$$

> ALVIN was capable of diving 533 times deeper than the early submarine.

Solve $\frac{x}{3} = -53$ for x.

$$\frac{x}{3} \cdot 3 = -53 \cdot 3 \qquad \text{Multiply both sides by 3.}$$
$$x = -159 \qquad \text{Simplify.}$$
$$\frac{-159}{3} = -53 \qquad \text{Check your solution.}$$
$$-53 = -53 \checkmark$$

The two sides remain equal if they are both multiplied by the same number.

Expressions with Positive and Negative Integers

To evaluate multiplication and division expressions with integers, recall how the signs are determined.

> The product or quotient of two numbers with the same sign is positive.
> The product or quotient of two numbers with different signs is negative.

Evaluate $\frac{a}{bc}$ if $a = 40$, $b = 2$, and $c = -5$.
Write the values in the expression.

$$\frac{40}{2 \cdot (-5)}$$

Complete any operation above or below the fraction bar.

$$\frac{40}{-10}$$

Divide to simplify the expression.

$$-4$$

Check Understanding

a. Explain the steps needed to solve $b \div 3 = -16$. Solve for b.

b. Write a multiplication or division equation that has -8 as the solution.

c. Evaluate $\frac{152}{y}$ if $y = -4$.

Practice

Write whether the solution is *positive* or *negative*. Do not solve.

1. $y \div 15 = 10$

2. $x(-9) = -81$

3. $\frac{s}{-5} = 25$

4. $8x = -56$

5. $-30 \div y = 10$

6. $-7a = -140$

7. $-11 \cdot b = 66$

8. $c \div (-5) = -50$

9. $44 \div x = 2$

10. $165 \div x = -33$

Evaluate each expression for $x = -6$, $y = 9$, and $z = -24$.

11. xy **12.** $z \div x$ **13.** xz **14.** $\frac{z}{x} \cdot y$ **15.** zy

Solve for x.

16. $x \cdot (-14) = 126$

17. $x \div 82 = 3$

18. $x \div (-3) = -104$

19. $\frac{x}{55} = 6$

20. $x \div (-6) = -84$

21. $-16x = 112$

22. $x \cdot (-2) = -150$

23. $x \cdot (-4) = -380$

24. $x \div (-16) = 16$

25. $\frac{x}{-20} = 800$

Write the correct equation and solve for the variable.

26. A number divided by −10 equals 100.

27. A number divided by 3 is −28.

Write the correct equation and use math reasoning to solve for the variable.

28. The product of a number and −1 is 15.

29. A number and its opposite result in a product of −49.

Apply

30. Michael borrowed $280 from his sister to pay for books for college classes. He paid $40 a month until the interest-free loan was repaid. Write and solve a multiplication equation to show the number of months it took Michael to pay the debt. Use negative integers to represent the amount of the loan and the amount of the monthly payment.

Villanova University
Pennsylvania

5.9 Expressions with Integers

Construct Meaning

On Monday, Hannah repaid a debt of $3 to her sister. On each of the next seven days, she earned $4 babysitting and used the money to repay a debt to her mother. What was the total amount of Hannah's original debt?

If negative integers represent debt amounts, the expression may be written: $-\$3 + 7 \times (-\$4)$.

If the expression is evaluated from left to right, the total debt appears to be $-\$16$. Is that correct?

Integer expressions with more than one operation must be evaluated using the order of operations.

Review Order of Operations

1st Complete operations within grouping symbols, such as parentheses, absolute value symbols, or above or below a division bar.

2nd Simplify exponents.

3rd Multiply and divide left to right.

4th Add and subtract left to right.

Evaluate using the order of operations.
$$-\$3 + 7 \times (-\$4)$$

$$-\$3 + (-\$28) \qquad \textbf{Multiply.}$$
$$-\$31 \qquad \textbf{Add.}$$

Hannah's original debt was $31.

WORKING WITH NEGATIVE INTEGERS AND EXPONENTS

Is $(-2)^4$ equal to -2^4?

Use your scientific calculator.

For $(-2)^4$ enter

((−) 2) ∧ 4 =

Answer 16

For -2^4 enter

(−) 2 ∧ 4 =

Answer −16

$(-2)^4$ is read, "Negative two to the fourth power."
The base is -2. The exponent is 4.
$(-2) \cdot (-2) \cdot (-2) \cdot (-2) = 16$

-2^4 is read, "The opposite of two to the fourth power."
The base is 2. The exponent is 4.
$2 \cdot 2 \cdot 2 \cdot 2 = 16$ and the opposite of 16 is -16.

Compare $(-3x)^2$ to $-3x^2$.

$(-3x)^2 = (-3x) \cdot (-3x) = 9x^2$ ◄ The expressions are not equivalent. ► $-3x^2 = -3 \cdot x^2$

Discuss how the order of operations is used to evaluate each expression.

$15 - 2^3 \div (-4)$	$-6(7 - 11 + 3)^2$	$9 + 4 \cdot \|5^2 - 2^5\|$	$\dfrac{3 + 3^3}{6 - a}$ if $a = -9$
$15 - 8 \div (-4)$	$-6(-1)^2$	$9 + 4 \cdot \|25 - 32\|$	$\dfrac{3 + 27}{6 - (-9)}$
$15 - (-2)$	$-6(1)$	$9 + 4 \cdot \|-7\|$	$\dfrac{30}{15}$
17	-6	$9 + 4 \cdot 7$	2
		$9 + 28$	
		37	

Check Understanding

a. Simplify $(-3)^2$, $(-3)^3$, $(-3)^4$, and $(-3)^5$. How does the pattern of integers in the answers relate to the exponents?

Evaluate each expression if $x = -6$ and $y = 2$.

b. $\frac{y(x)^2}{2x}$ **c.** $\frac{x - y}{|x - y|}$ **d.** $-x^3$ **e.** $(x)^3$

Practice

Evaluate each expression.

1. $10 - 20 \div (-5)$ **2.** $20 - (-5)^3$ **3.** $-7 + (8 - 12)^2$

4. $\frac{-3 + (-5)}{(-2)^3}$ **5.** $\frac{-9 \cdot (-5)}{-2^2 + 1}$ **6.** $(10 - 5^2 + 6)^2$

7. $\frac{-12 \cdot 6 \div (-2)}{-9 - 3}$ **8.** $7 \cdot (-1) - 1 - (-12) \div 3$ **9.** $\frac{11 - 5^2}{|-2| - |-4|}$

Evaluate.

10. $15c - d^2$ for $c = 2$ and $d = (-4)$ **11.** $\frac{9a - b}{|ab|}$ for $a = -1$ and $b = -3$

12. $\frac{-a + 8b}{|a + b|}$ for $a = -6$ and $b = 3$ **13.** $6s - t^3$ for $s = -5$ and $t = -3$

14. $\frac{x^y}{5 - xy}$ for $x = -10$ and $y = 2$ **15.** $-10v - 3w$ for $v = -5$ and $w = 7$

Write *true* or *false* for each equation.
If the statement is false, insert parentheses to make it true.

16. $8 \cdot 5 + (-2) = 24$ **17.** $2 - 9^2 + 7 = -72$

Apply

18. Water Wonderland spent $124,000 to construct a new ride. During its first season of operation, 29,012 rides were sold at the price of $4 each. Write and solve an expression to show the difference between the cost of construction and the total amount received from ticket sales. How many additional tickets needed to be sold to cover the construction costs?

Review

Simplify each algebraic expression.

1. $25 - y + 16$ **2.** $4^2 + 5^2 + y + 3$

3. $40 + 3(x - 2)$ **4.** $2(a - 4) - 9$

Construct Meaning

The needle of a compass points to the <u>magnetic</u> North Pole, which differs from true (geographic) north. The angular distance between true north and magnetic north at a given location is called **magnetic declination**.

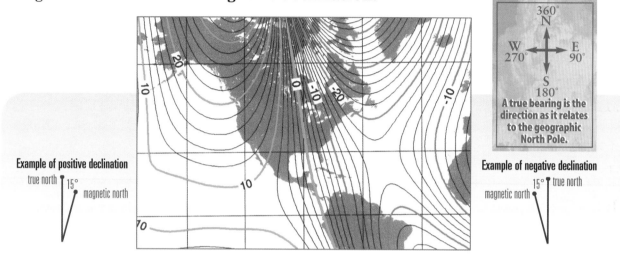

Example of positive declination
true north 15° magnetic north

A true bearing is the direction as it relates to the geographic North Pole.

Example of negative declination
15° true north
magnetic north

Suppose you are sailing off the coast of Florida and want to head directly east to an island. True east is a 90° true bearing. Your magnetic compass gives you the magnetic bearing, which is not the same as the true bearing. Using a formula will enable you to navigate correctly with your compass.

true bearing – magnetic declination = magnetic bearing

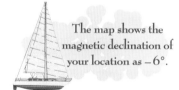

The map shows the magnetic declination of your location as –6°.

$90° - (-6°) = 96°$
You are headed in the direction of the island if your compass shows a magnetic bearing of 96°.

Airplane pilots must distinguish the true bearing from the magnetic bearing. A biplane landed to the south on a runway parallel to true north and south. The magnetic declination was –16° at this New England location. The true bearing of south is 180°. What was the reading on the pilot's magnetic compass?

$180° - (-16°) = 196°$

The magnetic reading was 196°.

Check Understanding

Refer to the map showing magnetic declination.

a. In 2000, the magnetic declination in Halifax, Nova Scotia, was approximately –20°. To travel true east from Halifax, your compass should read ☐.

b. Suppose you are in Colorado where the magnetic declination is 10° and your plane just landed on a runway having a magnetic bearing of 170°. What is the true bearing?

1. Two integers have the same absolute value if they are the same distance from ☐ .
Lesson 5.1

2. Order the integers from least to greatest. *Lesson 5.1*
39, –12, 0, –18, –50, 100, –2, 5

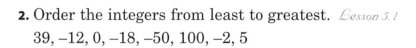

Tell if the sum will be *positive*, *negative*, or *zero*. *Lesson 5.2*

3. –2 + 1   **4.** 8 + (–10)   **5.** –24 + 24

6. 12 + (–5)   **7.** 141 + (–220)

Rewrite each problem as an addition problem and solve. *Lesson 5.3*

8. 5 – 20   **9.** 0 – 10   **10.** 0 – (–10)   **11.** 8 – 5   **12.** –9 – (–30)

Solve each equation for *x*. *Lesson 5.4*

13. 32 + x = 19   **14.** x – 14 = –2   **15.** x + 88 = 43

Use mathematical properties to simplify each expression. *Lesson 5.5*

16. 5 – 8 – 9 + 30   **17.** |8| + 7 – |2| + 16 + (–4)   **18.** 3 – 6 + x – (–10)

Evaluate each numerical expression. *Lesson 5.6*

19. 9 · (–20)   **20.** –6 · (–6)3   **21.** 5 · 7(–2)(–4)

Find each quotient. *Lesson 5.7*

22. 210 ÷ (–42)   **23.** $\frac{-68}{-4}$ **24.** –81 ÷ 3

25. Solve 9x = 207 for *x*. *Lesson 5.8*

26. Evaluate $\frac{a}{b} \cdot c$ for a = 6, b = –2, c = –7. *Lesson 5.8*

27. Use the order of operations to evaluate $\frac{(6 + 2) \cdot |3^2 - 5^2|}{-20 + 16}$. *Lesson 5.9*

28. Write and evaluate the numerical expression for three to the fourth power added to negative two squared. *Lesson 5.9*

29. The Badwater Ultramarathon is a 135-mile race from Badwater in California's Death Valley, where the elevation is 282 feet below sea level, to the 8360-foot summit of Mount Whitney. Use a positive and negative integer to write an equation showing the elevation gain of a runner completing the race. *Lesson 5.9*

Oceans of Integers

In each expression tell whether m is *positive* or *negative*. Do not solve.

1. $-5m = 15$　　　　**2.** $m - 6 = 7$　　　　**3.** $\frac{-27}{m} = -3$

Compare using >, < or = .

4. $|-2| \bigcirc -|4|$　　　　**5.** $7 - (-4) \bigcirc -3 + 12$

6. $2 \cdot (-3) \bigcirc -8 - (-2)$　　**7.** $-14 \div (-7) \bigcirc 2^2 - 6$

Evaluate each expression.

8. $-6 - (-4) + 3$　　　　**9.** $-3 \cdot (-6) \cdot 4$

10. $(-5) \cdot (-9) \div (-3)$　　**11.** $5 \cdot (-9) - 18 \div (-6)$

12. $-5^2 \cdot 6 \div (-15)$　　　**13.** $(-3)^3 + 3$

14. $\frac{6(-8)}{16 - (-8)}$　　　　**15.** $\frac{27 + |-3|}{-6}$

This chart shows the air temperature one winter day in Salina, Kansas.

3 A.M.	6 A.M.	9 A.M.	12 noon	3 P.M.	6 P.M.
–9°F	–7°F	15°F	34°F	40°F	32°F

16. During which three-hour period did the temperature rise the most?

17. Write an equation showing the difference between the highest and lowest temperatures that day. Label your answer.

Solve for n.

18. $n + 8 = 6$

19. $6 - n = 10$

20. $2n = -4$

21. $n \cdot (-5) + 3 = 18$

22. $\frac{12}{n} = -2$

23. $\frac{12}{2 + n} = -3$

Evaluate each expression if $a = 3$, $b = -4$, and $c = 7$.

24. $b - a + c$

25. $|a + b|$

26. $\frac{c}{a - b}$

27. $\frac{a - b + c^2}{2^3}$

28. $\frac{-4b - c}{a}$

The tallest mountain in Israel is Mount Hermon with an elevation of 9232 feet. The snow on Mount Hermon melts into the headwaters of the Jordan River, which flows into the Sea of Galilee. The Sea of Galilee is situated 696 feet below sea level. From the Sea of Galilee the Jordan River continues south, where it empties into the Dead Sea. The Dead Sea is the lowest spot on the earth's surface at an elevation of 1349 feet below sea level.

29. A pair of hikers descended from the summit of Mount Hermon and ended their hike at the shore of the Sea of Galilee. Write an equation to show the change of altitude from the beginning to the end of their hike. Label your answer.

30. Write an equation to show how far the Jordan River drops between the Sea of Galilee and the Dead Sea. Label your answer.

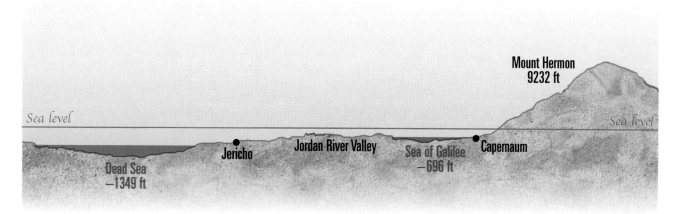

Chapter Theme:
Careers

6 Chapter

Equations and Inequalities

Graphing on a Number Line

Construct Meaning

Mark works for a Christian hunger relief organization, Shari teaches at a school for missionary children, and Xiao translates Bible study materials from English into a tribal language. Although these three people each have a different job, they all are working toward the same goal of leading others to Christ. God uses many people to build His kingdom.

In mathematics, there are often different ways of expressing the same idea.

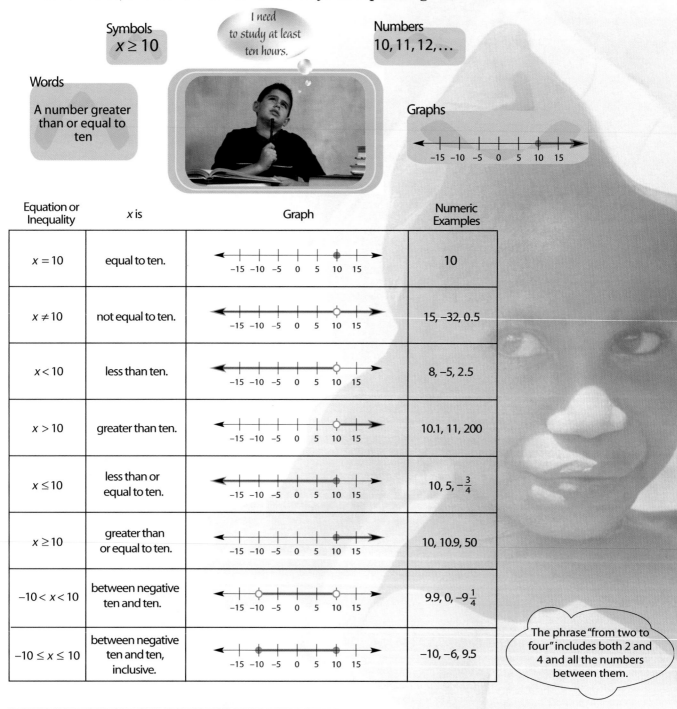

Symbols
$x \geq 10$

I need to study at least ten hours.

Numbers
$10, 11, 12, \ldots$

Words
A number greater than or equal to ten

Graphs

Equation or Inequality	x is	Graph	Numeric Examples
$x = 10$	equal to ten.		10
$x \neq 10$	not equal to ten.		$15, -32, 0.5$
$x < 10$	less than ten.		$8, -5, 2.5$
$x > 10$	greater than ten.		$10.1, 11, 200$
$x \leq 10$	less than or equal to ten.		$10, 5, -\frac{3}{4}$
$x \geq 10$	greater than or equal to ten.		$10, 10.9, 50$
$-10 < x < 10$	between negative ten and ten.		$9.9, 0, -9\frac{1}{4}$
$-10 \leq x \leq 10$	between negative ten and ten, inclusive.		$-10, -6, 9.5$

The phrase "from two to four" includes both 2 and 4 and all the numbers between them.

How can you check the graph of an inequality?

Check Understanding

Draw and label a number line with an appropriate scale. Graph each inequality.

a. $r > 608$ **b.** s is at most -23.   **c.** $n \leq 20.5$ **d.** p is between -6 and 3.

e. How can you draw a number line graph to represent the set of numbers that are greater than ten or less than five?

f. Compare the graph of $x > 16$ with the graph of $16 < x$.

Practice

Draw and label a number line with an appropriate scale. Graph each inequality.

1. $x \geq 3250$ **2.** y is at least 120.

3. z is more than -0.5.   **4.** $0 \leq m \leq 60$

5. n is a number between 12 and 32.   **6.** p is negative.

Write an inequality to describe what is represented on each graph.

7.

8.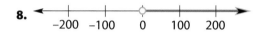

9.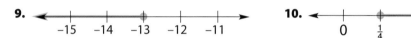

10.

Apply

11. The weather report lists the daily high temperature as 74°F and the current low as 40°F. Write an inequality to show the range of temperatures for today. Draw a number line graph to show the range.

12. Lynette signed an apartment lease for $550 per month. She has a budget of $120 per month for food and $150 for utilities. Write an inequality to show the minimum monthly salary Lynette needs to earn just for living expenses. Graph your answer.

13. On certain lakes, the state of Minnesota imposes experimental fishing regulations designed to increase fish populations by protecting certain sizes of a species. The fishing regulations for Crane Lake state that all walleye less than 13 inches long or larger than 17 inches must be released, except one fish over 23 inches may be kept as part of the daily limit of six walleye. Draw a graph on a number line to show the sizes of walleye that may be kept.

Solving Two-Step Equations

Construct Meaning

Erin is interested in a career in forest management. She is planning to take classes at a college where the tuition is $135 per hour with an activity fee of $95. How many hours of classes can Erin take if she spends $1175? Write an equation to show the relationship.

x = the number of hours of classes

cost per hour	number of hours	fee	amount spent
$135 $\cdot$	x	+ $95 =	$1175

Solve $135x + 95 = 1175$.

Determine the operation performed on the variable.	$135x + 95 = 1175$	x is multiplied by 135 and 95 is added.
Perform the inverse operation on both sides of the equation to isolate the variable. Since we are "undoing," we need to reverse the order of operations. Addition and subtraction will be done before multiplication and division.	$135x + 95 - 95 = 1175 - 95$ $$135x = 1080$$ $$\frac{135x}{135} = \frac{1080}{135}$$ $\boxed{x = 8}$	Subtract 95 from both sides. Divide both sides by 135. Simplify.
Check the solution.	$135(8) + 95 = 1175$ $1080 + 95 = 1175$ $1175 = 1175$ ✔	Check.

🌲 $\boxed{\text{Erin can take 8 hours of classes.}}$

Solve $\frac{c}{5} - 27 = 19$.

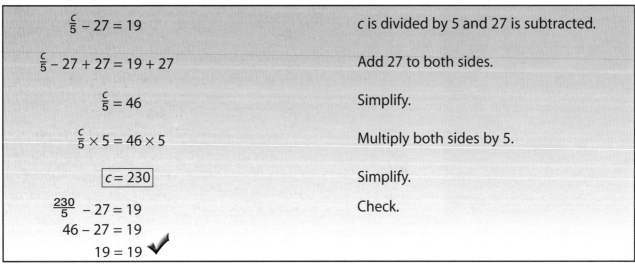

$\frac{c}{5} - 27 = 19$	c is divided by 5 and 27 is subtracted.
$\frac{c}{5} - 27 + 27 = 19 + 27$	Add 27 to both sides.
$\frac{c}{5} = 46$	Simplify.
$\frac{c}{5} \times 5 = 46 \times 5$	Multiply both sides by 5.
$\boxed{c = 230}$	Simplify.
$\frac{230}{5} - 27 = 19$ $46 - 27 = 19$ $19 = 19$ ✔	Check.

Check Understanding

a. Eduardo was attempting to solve an equation, but his answer did not check. What was his mistake?

b. Find the correct solution to Eduardo's problem.

c. Solve $(y \div 2) + 1.7 = 7.5$. Check your solution.

$$5x - 10 = 25$$
$$\frac{5x}{5} - 10 = \frac{25}{5}$$
$$x - 10 = 5$$
$$x - 10 + 10 = 5 + 10$$
$$\boxed{x = 15}$$
$$5(15) - 10 = 25$$
$$75 - 10 = 25$$
$$65 \neq 25$$

Practice

Solve each equation for the given variable. Check your answer.

1. $15 + 4r = 31$

2. $8 = 3s - 7$

3. $\frac{a}{5} + 2 = 9$

4. $4 = (b \div 2) - 16$

5. $0.75 + 2.25x = 12$

6. $2y + 9 = 17$

7. $1\frac{1}{2} = 3u + \frac{3}{4}$

8. $\frac{v}{6} - 15 = 5$

9. $(k \div 4) - 4.2 = 11.8$

Apply

10. Jenna has $11 to purchase a gift for her mother. If she chooses a candleholder for $2.25, how many candles priced at $1.75 can she purchase? Identify the variable. Write an equation to represent the problem and solve it.

11. José wants to join a swim club with a membership fee of $25 plus a charge of $1.25 each time he uses the pool. How many times can he swim before he has spent the $100 his grandparents gave him for his birthday? Identify the variable. Write an equation to represent the problem and solve it.

12. If José plans to swim 20 times during the summer, would it be less expensive to join the swim club or go to the public pool that charges $2.25 per swim? What if he plans to swim 45 times?

Two-Step Equations with Integers

Construct Meaning

Japanese farmers have been catching grasshoppers from their rice fields for centuries. Not only does it save the tender rice plants, but it provides two crops—pesticide-free rice and the grasshoppers, cooked and eaten in teriyaki sauce. Insect cuisine is gaining popularity even in the United States. Entomologists, scientists who study insects, have done studies to show the health benefits of eating larvae and bugs. Are you ready for stir-fry crickets or mealworm pie?

Dennis and Dan attended an insect fair at the city zoo. Many samples of edible insects were available. Dennis paid for both admissions but had to borrow $2 from Dan to cover the $4 cost of the three-bee salad and chocolate cricket cookies. How much is a single zoo admission if Dennis started the day with $20?

| starting amount | − | tickets | − | food cost | = | remaining amount |

$$\$20 - 2x - \$4 = -\$2$$

$20 - 4 - 2x = -2$	Use the Commutative Property.
$16 - 2x = -2$	Simplify.
$16 - 2x - 16 = -2 - 16$	Subtract 16 from both sides.
$-2x = -18$	Simplify.
$\dfrac{-2x}{-2} = \dfrac{-18}{-2}$	Divide both sides by −2.
$x = \$9$	
$\$20 - 2(\$9) - (\$4) = -\$2$	Check.
$\$20 - \$18 - \$4 = -\$2$	
$-\$2 = -\$2 \checkmark$	A single zoo admission is $9.

Solve.
$$\frac{n}{5} + 16 = 9$$
$$\frac{n}{5} + 16 - 16 = 9 - 16$$
$$\frac{n}{5} = -7$$
$$\frac{n}{5} \cdot 5 = -7 \cdot 5$$
$$n = -35$$

Check.
$$\frac{-35}{5} + 16 = 9$$
$$-7 + 16 = 9$$
$$9 = 9 \checkmark$$

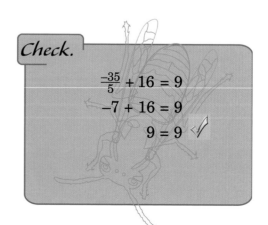

Check Understanding

a. What is the first step needed to solve the equation $-6 + 14 - 2 + 3x = -15$?

b. Solve the equation in problem a. Check your answer.

c. What would happen in the last step of this problem if you divided by 2 instead of −2?

$$\frac{-2x}{-2} = \frac{-18}{-2}$$

$$x = 9$$

Practice

Solve each equation for the given variable. Check your answer.

1. $4 = 2m + 6$

2. $3n - 5 = -17$

3. $\frac{b}{6} - 2 = -11$

4. $-5 = (c \div 5) - 12$

5. $5x - 4 = -19$

6. $11y + 21 = -12$

7. $\frac{w}{9} + 2 = -2$

8. $15 = 27e + 15$

9. $(t \div 10) + 16 = 14$

Apply

10. Rachelle bought six copies of the *Eat-a-Bug Cookbook* by David Gordon. She has a coupon for $5 off her total order. If her bill came to $85, what was the original price of each cookbook? Write an equation to represent this problem. Identify the variable and solve.

11. Daren said that the current temperature of −7°F was five degrees warmer than twice the morning low temperature. Stephanie said that the current temperature is one degree colder than the morning low. Can they both be correct? Explain.

Challenge

12. Use the equation $F = \frac{9}{5}C + 32$ to calculate the temperature in degrees Celsius for −4°F.

Writing Inequalities

Construct Meaning

Wes and Danny are planning to make nachos to sell at the Lifeguard Competition. Their expenses are $20 for cheese sauce, $16 for tortilla chips, and $5 for plates. Assume that they have just enough supplies to make 100 servings and that they sell all of the servings. How much should they charge per serving if they want to make a minimum profit of $50?

Identify the variable.

   n = price of one serving of nachos

Write an **inequality**, a mathematical sentence using an inequality sign, to represent the situation.

money from sales	−	expenditures	≥	desired profit
$100 \cdot n$	−	($20 + $16 + $5)	≥	$50
Simplify. $100n$	−	$41	≥	$50

Values that make an inequality true are **solutions** of an inequality.

Wes thought that $0.75 might be an appropriate price. Try it in the inequality to see if it would give the desired profit.

$$100n - \$41 \geq \$50$$
$$100(\$0.75) - \$41 \geq \$50$$
$$\$75 - \$41 \geq \$50$$
$$\$34 \geq \$50 \quad \text{Is this true?}$$

Since $34 is not greater than or equal to $50, $0.75 is not a solution to the inequality. Wes and Danny decided that $1.00 would be a fair price that would give them the desired profit. Are they right?

$$100n - 41 \geq \$50$$
$$100 \times \$1.00 - \$41 \geq \$50$$
$$\$100 - \$41 \geq \$50$$
$$\$59 \geq \$50$$

Check Understanding

Write *true* or *false*. In order to be true it must be true for any value of x.

a. $3x > x$ **b.** $x^2 > x$

c. $x < x + 3$ **d.** $x > -x$

CANOE MANNED BY VOYAGEURS

Practice

For each inequality, determine if the value given for the variable is a solution. Write *yes* or *no*.

1. $25 - p \geq 19$
$p = 5$

2. $\frac{s}{2} + 2 < 6$
$s = 4$

3. $-15 < k + 1 < 15$
$k = 14$

4. $64 \leq 16n$
$n = 3$

5. $\frac{x}{6} \leq -15$
$x = -45$

6. $-8 < y + 2$
$y = -2$

7. $15 + w < 60$
$w = 45$

8. $-5 < v < 5$
$v = 0$

9. $11 < |z| < 29$
$z = -13$

Write an inequality to represent each of the following.

10. Twice the sum of 3 and a number is less than 25.

11. Four times the square of a number is greater than or equal to 100.

12. The sum of a number and 19 is between 30 and 60.

13. The square of a number is greater than or equal to the number.

14. A number is less than the absolute value of the number.

15. One-half of a number is greater than zero and less than or equal to ten.

16. After paying her rent r, Jessica needs to have at least $1800 left for other monthly expenses and savings. Her monthly paycheck is $2575.

17. Brett did not want to go swimming unless the temperature t was greater than 75°F.

18. When planning a trip, Jennifer found that the price p for an airline ticket from Boston to Los Angeles varied from $319 to $702.

Review

Write an inequality to describe what each graph represents.

1.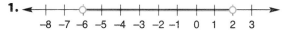

2.

3.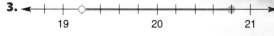

4.

Draw and label a number line with an appropriate scale. Graph each inequality.

5. w is greater than -2.

6. $0 \leq p < 6$

7. x is an integer between 6 and 10.

8. $y \leq -10$

Solving Inequalities

Brick kiln worker

Construct Meaning

Mark is a building consultant in India. He is also a missionary. This year, he delivered more than twice as many Bibles to villages than he did last year. If Mark delivered 2500 Bibles this year, how many did he deliver last year? Identify the variable and write an inequality to represent the problem. Solve by using the same method used to solve an equation.

Let b = the number of Bibles delivered last year.

$$2500 > 2b$$

$$\frac{2500}{2} > \frac{2b}{2} \qquad \text{Divide both sides by 2.}$$

$$1250 > b \qquad \text{Simplify.}$$

$$b < 1250 \qquad \text{Rewrite by reversing the inequality sign and the two sides.}$$

Mark delivered less than 1250 Bibles last year.

Does the solution to the inequality give an exact number of Bibles? The solution is a range of values. In this case, it would be the set of integers between 0 and 1250. Obviously, the number of Bibles cannot be a negative number or a decimal even if that value made the inequality true.

Solve.

$$3x + 2 \le -7$$
$$3x + 2 - 2 \le -7 - 2 \qquad \text{Subtract 2 from both sides.}$$
$$3x \le -9 \qquad \text{Simplify.}$$
$$\frac{3x}{3} \le \frac{-9}{3} \qquad \text{Divide both sides by 3.}$$
$$x \le -3 \qquad \text{Simplify.}$$

$$x \le -3 \qquad \text{Check the endpoint for equality, where } x = -3.$$
$$-3 = -3 \checkmark \qquad \text{The endpoint is part of the solution since } -3 \le -3 \text{ is true.}$$
$$-5 \le -3 \checkmark \qquad \text{Check another value for the variable by choosing a number less than } -3.$$

Graph the solution.

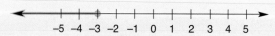

$$-5 \ -4 \ -3 \ -2 \ -1 \ \ 0 \ \ 1 \ \ 2 \ \ 3 \ \ 4 \ \ 5$$

Check Understanding

a. The equation $x = 4$ is the same as $4 = x$. Is this true for inequalities such as $x < 4$ and $4 < x$? Write an inequality that means the same as $x < 4$.

b. Which of the following is not a solution for $22 - x \leq 10$?
$x = 19$ $x = 15$ $x = 12$ $x = 9$

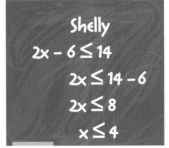

Shelly
$2x - 6 \leq 14$
$2x \leq 14 - 6$
$2x \leq 8$
$x \leq 4$

c. Shelly checked her work and found that her endpoint was incorrect. Find her mistake.

Practice

Solve each inequality. Graph your solution. Check your answer by trying both the endpoint and one other value for the variable.

1. $3r \leq 45$

2. $20s < -640$

3. $n - 19 > 15$

4. $p + \frac{1}{2} < \frac{5}{2}$

5. $\frac{k}{20} + 2 \geq 6$

6. $9 < x + 2$

7. $19.7 + m < -3.2$

8. $(z \div 5) + 2 > 0$

9. $0 \geq b$

Apply

Write an inequality to represent each situation. Solve and check.

Geyser in New Zealand

10. The average production worker in New Zealand in 1999 made less than half the hourly wage of the average American production worker. How much did the American worker make if the New Zealand worker made $9.14 per hour?

11. Roshanda and her family need to save at least $20,000 for her college tuition. She has $5360 and plans to start college in six years. How much needs to be saved each year?

Compound Inequalities

Construct Meaning

Dr. Daniel Egeler works with international schools that are members of the Association of Christian Schools International. He served as a school administrator at Alliance Academy in Ecuador for many years. In his career, Dr. Egeler uses math to calculate appropriate tuition rates, to construct million dollar budgets, and to exchange currency when traveling to other countries. He grew up in Tanzania, Africa, and attended Rift Valley Academy, a school for missionary children.

For a trip to the country in which he was raised, Dr. Egeler wants to have at least 495,000 Tanzanian shillings but not more than 792,000 shillings. How many US dollars should he plan to take? For each US dollar, he will receive 990 shillings at the currency exchange. Let x = number of US dollars.

Write each inequality. $495{,}000 \le 990x$ and $990x \le 792{,}000$

Rewrite as a compound inequality. $495{,}000 \le 990x \le 792{,}000$

Solve each inequality.

$495{,}000 \le 990x$	$990x \le 792{,}000$
$\dfrac{495{,}000}{990} \le 990x$	$990x \le \dfrac{792{,}000}{990}$
$500 \le x$	$x \le 800$

Rewrite as a compound inequality. $500 \le x \le 800$

Tanzania

Dr. Egeler needs to take from $500 to $800 in American currency.

Note that this compound inequality is an *and* relationship. A value must make *both* inequalities true in order to be a solution. This is the <u>intersection</u> of the two sets of numbers, as shown on the second graph.

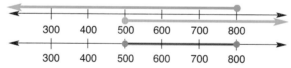

How can you check the solution to a compound inequality?

A compound inequality is an *or* relationship when it is the <u>union</u> of two sets of numbers. A value that makes *either* inequality true is a solution.

Consider the relationship where twice a number n is greater than 20 or less than zero.

Write each inequality. $2n < 0$ or $2n > 20$

Since this is an *or*, the inequalities   ~~$0 > 2n > 20$~~   **2n is not between 0 and 20.**

cannot be rewritten as one. $2n < 0$ or $2n > 20$

Solve each inequality. $n < 0$ or $n > 10$

Graph the union of the two inequalities.

What points would you check to see if they make the compound inequality true?

Check Understanding

Write *and* or *or* for each situation described. Explain your reasoning.

a. x is between 49 and 52.

b. $|y| > 4$

c.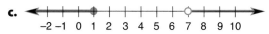

d.

Write an inequality to represent each of the following.

e. The daily low temperature was –5°F and the high was 40°F.

f. A package can be sent by express delivery that is guaranteed to arrive within two days. The package could be sent by regular mail that takes at least five days.

Dan surfing off the east coast of Africa

Practice

Solve each compound inequality and graph the solution.

1. $-7.5 < \frac{x}{10} < -2.5$

2. $15 \leq 5x \leq 500$

3. $x - \frac{3}{4} < 3$ or $x - \frac{3}{4} > 12$

4. $5 + x > 7$ or $5 + x \leq 2$

Write the inequality described by each graph.

5.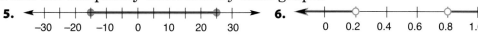

6.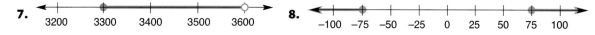

7.

8.

Apply

Write a compound inequality to represent each situation. Solve and check.

9. If James is able to earn an extra $200 this weekend, his monthly income will be between $1500 and $2000 for his job at a local restaurant. What is the normal range of James monthly income? Let i = James' monthly income.

10. Huoth is looking at apartments that rent from $600 to $700 per month. If he wants to spend about 30% (0.30) of his monthly salary for housing, what is his monthly salary s?

Sand dollar from the Indian Ocean

Challenge

11. The value of a is 5. The value of b is either more than $2a$ or less than $\frac{9}{2}$. The value of b is between a and $\frac{5a}{2}$. If b is an integer greater than 11, what is b?

Problem Solving

Construct Meaning

Use the Problem-Solving Guide to systematically solve real-life problems. Taking the time to review the step-by-step approach for simple problems will help you remember the techniques necessary for solving more complex problems.

Read and analyze.

Elisa plans to have between $150 and $200 to spend for Christmas gifts. She needs to purchase gifts for eight people. How much should she spend for each gift?

What information is given?
She has between $150 and $200 to buy eight gifts.
What am I asked to find?
Find the amount she should spend on one gift.

Select a strategy.

What method will help solve the problem?
Since a range of money is given, an inequality can be written.

Apply the selected strategy.

Choose a variable and write the inequality.
Let s = amount spent on one gift.
$$\$150 < 8s < \$200$$

Solve.

$\$150 < 8s$	$8s < \$200$
$\frac{150}{8} < \frac{8s}{8}$	$\frac{8s}{8} < \frac{200}{8}$
$\$18.75 < s$	$s < \$25.00$

$$\boxed{\$18.75 < s < \$25.00}$$

Elisa can spend between $18.75 and $25.00 on each gift.

Check for reasonableness.

Check each endpoint.
$$\$150 < 8s < \$200$$
$$\$150 = 8 \times \$18.75 \quad | \quad 8 \times \$25.00 = \$200$$
$$\$150 = \$150 \checkmark \quad | \quad \$200 = \$200 \checkmark$$

Choose one value between the endpoints and check. Use $s = \$20$.
$$\$150 < 8 \times \$20 < \$200$$
$$\$150 < \$160 < \$200 \checkmark$$

Is it reasonable that she would spend that amount?

Check Understanding

Write the equation or inequality that correctly represents each problem.

a. Twice the sum of a number and five is 37. $2n + 5 = 37$ $2(n + 5) = 37$

b. Two-thirds of a number is less than 63. $\frac{2}{3}m < 63$ $m < \frac{2}{3} \times 63$

c. Twenty-seven more than a number is less than 50 and more than −20. $50 < p + 27 < -20$ $-20 < p + 27 < 50$

Daniel Egeler in front of his elementary school

Apply

Write an equation or inequality for each problem. Solve and check.

1. The first printed copy of the Bible was produced in 1440, seventy-seven years before the Protestant Reformation began. In what year did the Reformation begin?

2. About 130 million Americans were using the Internet in 2000. If 46% (0.46) of the population were using the Internet, what was the approximate population of the United States in 2000? (Round your answer to the nearest million.)

3. Maria is an occupational therapist who sees from 20 to 35 patients each week. What is the average number of patients Maria sees each day if she does not work on the weekends?

4. The perimeter of a square is 36 inches. What is the area? Remember that $P = 4s$ and $A = s^2$.

5. A museum of African art gives a discount to senior citizens who are at least 65 years old and to students who are under 25 years old. Sean noticed that five years from now, his grandfather will be eligible for the discount. By that time, Sean will no longer be eligible for the student discount. What are the possible ages for Sean and his grandfather?

6. Dr. Egeler checked the airline ticket prices to Dar es Salaam, Tanzania, from New York. If he allows $100 per day for housing, food, and miscellaneous expenses, which tickets could he purchase and still be within his $5000 budget for a 14-day trip?

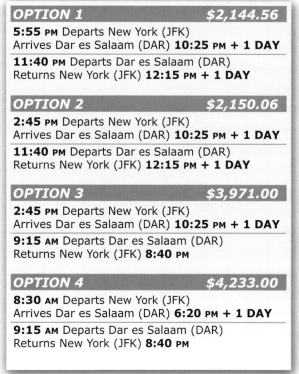

OPTION 1	$2,144.56
5:55 PM Departs New York (JFK) Arrives Dar es Salaam (DAR) **10:25 PM + 1 DAY**	
11:40 PM Departs Dar es Salaam (DAR) Returns New York (JFK) **12:15 PM + 1 DAY**	

OPTION 2	$2,150.06
2:45 PM Departs New York (JFK) Arrives Dar es Salaam (DAR) **10:25 PM + 1 DAY**	
11:40 PM Departs Dar es Salaam (DAR) Returns New York (JFK) **12:15 PM + 1 DAY**	

OPTION 3	$3,971.00
2:45 PM Departs New York (JFK) Arrives Dar es Salaam (DAR) **10:25 PM + 1 DAY**	
9:15 AM Departs Dar es Salaam (DAR) Returns New York (JFK) **8:40 PM**	

OPTION 4	$4,233.00
8:30 AM Departs New York (JFK) Arrives Dar es Salaam (DAR) **6:20 PM + 1 DAY**	
9:15 AM Departs Dar es Salaam (DAR) Returns New York (JFK) **8:40 PM**	

Entire student body of Victoria Primary School, Tanzania (Daniel is on the left.)

Absolute Value Inequalities/Study Guide

Construct Meaning

A glass blower must keep the temperature of his furnace close to 2000°F. If the furnace varies more than 100° hotter or colder than 2000°F, the glass will not harden correctly or will not be moldable. If x represents the actual temperature of the furnace, use an absolute value inequality to determine the range of acceptable temperatures.

$$|x - 2000°| \leq 100°$$

Hebron glass blower

The glass blower does not care if the difference is positive or negative, as long as its absolute value is no greater than 100 degrees. This can be interpreted as a compound inequality.

	$|x - 2000°| \leq 100°$	
	$-100 \leq x - 2000° \leq 100°$	
Solve.	$-100 \leq x - 2000$	$x - 2000 \leq 100$
	$-100 + 2000 \leq x - 2000 + 2000$	$x - 2000 + 2000 \leq 100 + 2000$
	$1900 \leq x$	$x \leq 2100$
	$1900° \leq x \leq 2100°$	

The glass blower must keep the furnace temperature from 1900°F to 2100° F.

Check your answer.	$-100 \leq x - 2000 \leq 100$
First check the endpoints.	$-100 \leq 1900 - 2000$ $\quad$ $2100 - 2000 \leq 100$
	$-100 \leq -100$ $\quad$ $100 \leq 100$
Check one other point, $x = 1950$.	$-100 \leq 1950 - 2000 \leq 100$
	$-100 \leq -50 \leq 100$

think.

What two values of the expression $x - 15$ make the inequality $|x - 15| < 82$ an equality?
$$|?| = 82$$
$x - 15$ could equal 82 or –82.

Check Understanding

a. The value of $x - 15$ in the absolute value inequality $|x - 15| < 82$ must be between what two numbers?

Rewrite each absolute value inequality as a compound inequality and then solve for the variable. Check your work.

b. $|x - 75| \leq 215$ $\qquad$ **c.** $|x + 0.2| \leq 0.2$

d. $|x + \frac{2}{3}| < \frac{1}{3}$ $\qquad$ **e.** $|x - 685| < 906$

1. Draw and label a number line to graph $-6 < x \leq 5$. *Lesson 6.1*

Solve for the variable and check your answer.

2. $4r - 15 = 5$ *Lesson 6.2*

3. $19 = 4 + \frac{s}{3}$ *Lesson 6.2*

4. $\frac{c}{2} + 16 = -4$ *Lesson 6.3*

5. $15d + 33 = 3$ *Lesson 6.3*

6. Write an inequality that represents the following. When Gracia gets a raise of $1.75 per hour, her wage will be greater than $9.50. Let w equal her current hourly wage. Could she currently be making $6.50 per hour? *Lesson 6.4*

7. Solve the inequality $4k + 2 \geq 6$. Graph your solution on a number line. Check your answer. *Lesson 6.5*

8. Solve the compound inequality $-18 < 6x < 36$. Graph your solution and check your answer. *Lesson 6.6*

9. Solve the compound inequality $3 + y < -15$ or $3 + y > 21$. Graph your solution and check your answer. *Lesson 6.6*

Write the inequality described by the graph. *Lesson 6.6*

10.

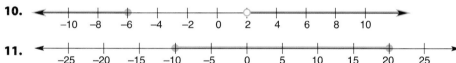

11.

12. Mary's youngest child is two years old and her oldest is thirteen years old. Write an inequality to show the range of their ages twelve years from now. Solve the inequality. *Lesson 6.7*

13. Rewrite the absolute value inequality $|x - 15| < 45$ as a compound inequality. Solve for the variable. *Lesson 6.8*

Chapter 6 Check-Up

Figuring for the Future

Draw and label a number line with an appropriate scale.
Graph each inequality.

1. $a \leq -5200$

2. Redwood trees more than 400 years old

3. $x \leq -\frac{3}{4}$ or $x \geq \frac{1}{2}$

4. The minimum score on a test is 200 and the maximum is 1600.

5. The price varied from \$2.35 to \$4.50.

Write an inequality to describe what is represented on each graph.

6.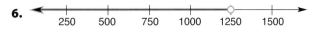

7.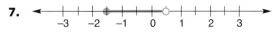

8.

9.

Solve each equation for the given variable. Check your answer.

10. $2y - 9 = 17$ **11.** $\frac{b}{2} + 4 = 9$ **12.** $13 = 4x - 3$

13. $-18 = 3n - 6$ **14.** $\frac{t}{10} + 5 = -15$ **15.** $9a + 102 = -15$

Write an inequality to represent each of the following.

16. Three times the sum of a number and five is less than 20.

17. The square of a number is greater than or equal to 100.

18. The product of six and a number is less than 36.

For each inequality, determine if the value given for the variable is a solution.
Write *yes* or *no*.

19. $64 \leq 4n$ **20.** $-5 < x < 25$ **21.** $-5 \leq y - 2$
   $n = 10$ $x = -20$ $y = 0$

22. $5f > -20$ **23.** $h + 3 \leq -2$ **24.** $200b < 5000$
   $f = -3$ $h = -6$ $b = 25$

Solve each inequality. Graph your solution. Check your answer.

25. $-14 \le \frac{d}{4} \le 15$ **26.** $5.75 < c - 0.25 < 11.75$ **27.** $k + 17 \le -30$ or $k + 17 \ge 34$

Write an equation, inequality, or compound inequality to represent each problem. Solve. Check your answer.

28. Sharon wants to save at least $500 before leaving for college. If she can save $25 per month, how many months before she leaves should she start saving?

29. If Deirdre is wearing 3-inch-high platform shoes, she is still less than five feet tall. How tall is Deirdre?

30. Quinn attended Dayspring Christian College from 1996 to 2000. His brother Ian also attended the same college for four years. If Ian is three years younger than Quinn, what years did Ian attend?

31. Drake purchased four identical fishing rods and one $80 reel for his sportfishing business. If he spent a total of $540, how much was each rod?

32. Rewrite $|x + 7.8| < 10.2$ as a compound inequality and solve for the variable.

33. Is $x = -35$ a solution for the inequality $|10x| \le 340$?

Chapter Theme:
Business

7 Chapter

Ratio, Proportion, and Percent

Ratio

Construct Meaning

Whale-watching is a billion-dollar business. On a whale-watching cruise near Seattle, Washington, you may observe orca whales in their natural habitats. One pod of orcas can have up to twenty members, and the ratio of males to females may be 2 to 3.

A **ratio** compares two quantities and can be written three ways. a to b $\dfrac{a}{b}$ $a{:}b$

An orca's body can be 20 feet long with a flipper that is 4 feet long. Find the ratio of the flipper length to the body length.

$$\dfrac{\text{flipper length}}{\text{body length}} \qquad \text{Write the ratio in words.}$$

$$\dfrac{4 \text{ feet}}{20 \text{ feet}} \qquad \text{Substitute the numbers.}$$

$$\dfrac{4 \text{ feet} \div 4}{20 \text{ feet} \div 4} = \dfrac{1 \text{ foot}}{5 \text{ feet}} \qquad \text{Simplify.}$$

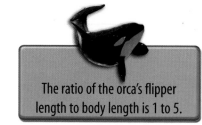

The ratio of the orca's flipper length to body length is 1 to 5.

TO DETERMINE IF RATIOS ARE EQUIVALENT:

Simplify and compare.

One orca has a 5-foot flipper length and is 25 feet long. Another has a 3.3-foot flipper length and is 19.8 feet long. Are the flipper-to-body-length ratios equivalent?

Write each ratio in words.	Simplify the numbers.
Orca 1 $\dfrac{\text{flipper length}}{\text{body length}}$	$\dfrac{5 \text{ ft} \div 5 = 1 \text{ ft}}{25 \text{ ft} \div 5 = 5 \text{ ft}}$
Orca 2 $\dfrac{\text{flipper length}}{\text{body length}}$	$\dfrac{3.3 \text{ ft} \div 3.3 = 1 \text{ ft}}{19.8 \text{ ft} \div 3.3 = 6 \text{ ft}}$

1 to 5 and 1 to 6 are not equivalent ratios.

or

Use cross products. A **cross product** for two ratios in a proportion is the product of one numerator and the other denominator. If two ratios are equivalent their cross products are equivalent.

If $\dfrac{a}{b} = \dfrac{c}{d}$ then $ad = bc$.

$b \cdot \dfrac{a}{b} = \dfrac{c}{d} \cdot b$ Multiply both sides by b.

$d \cdot a = \dfrac{cb}{d} \cdot d$ Multiply both sides by d.

$a \cdot d = c \cdot b$

Are the male-to-female ratios of Pod 1 and Pod 2 equivalent?

Pod 1

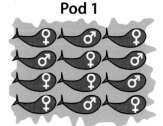

Pod 2

♀ female
♂ male

Pod 1   **Pod 2**
$\dfrac{\text{male}}{\text{female}}$ $\dfrac{5}{7} \overset{?}{=} \dfrac{7}{8}$ $\dfrac{\text{male}}{\text{female}}$

$40 \neq 49$

The ratios are not equivalent.

Check Understanding

a. Copy and complete the chart with equivalent ratios.

$\frac{5}{7}$	$\frac{10}{\square}$	$\frac{\square}{\square}$	$\frac{\square}{\square}$	$\frac{\square}{\square}$

Use the model at the right.
Write each ratio in simplest form.

b. Shaded parts to non-shaded parts
c. Non-shaded parts to total parts
d. Shaded parts to total parts

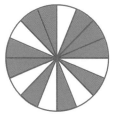

Animal Tracks

In the Yukon Territory there are twice as many moose as there are people. The ratio is 2:1.

Practice

Simplify each ratio.

1. $\frac{12 \text{ feet}}{20 \text{ feet}}$

2. $\frac{64 \text{ males}}{16 \text{ females}}$

3. 80 trucks:10 cars

4. 180 whales to 15 pods

5. $\frac{10 \text{ inches}}{18 \text{ inches}}$

6. 12 rats:24 mice

Find the cross products.

7. $\frac{2}{4} = \frac{10}{20}$

8. $\frac{8}{20} = \frac{24}{60}$

9. $\frac{13}{3} = \frac{26}{6}$

10. $\frac{7}{6} = \frac{21}{18}$

Write = or ≠ to indicate if the ratios are equivalent.

11. $\frac{10}{12} \bigcirc \frac{2}{3}$

12. $\frac{14}{2} \bigcirc \frac{9}{3}$

13. $\frac{3}{5} \bigcirc \frac{9}{15}$

14. $\frac{12}{7} \bigcirc \frac{60}{35}$

Apply

15. The eastern quadrant of a state park has two black bears for every 20 square miles. The western quadrant has three black bears for every 150 square miles. Which quadrant has the greater bear-to-square-mile ratio?

16. A Pileated Woodpecker pair built a nest with a width of $3\frac{1}{2}$ inches and a depth of 21 inches. Another pair built a nest with a width of 3 inches and a depth of 18 inches. Is the width-to-depth ratio equivalent for the nests?

17. The table shows the win/loss record of four of the teams at Trinity Christian School. Which team had the best record?

Team	Win	Loss
Baseball	18	7
Soccer	10	4
Basketball	5	7
Football	9	3

18. Wolf packs in the Northern Yukon Territory have territories of various sizes. Pack A has a territory of 900 km^2 and of that, 600 km^2 are mountainous. Pack B has a territory of 700 km^2 with 500 km^2 being mountainous. Do both territories have the same ratio of mountains to total range? Write each ratio in simplest form and compare.

Rate

Construct Meaning

A business called Burt's Bees sells honey and beeswax-based products such as lip balm, cosmetics, and baby care items. It began as a small home-based business and has grown to produce million-dollar profits.

A Burt's Bees sales representative plans to visit ten stores in two hours.

Think ÷ 2

$$\frac{10 \text{ stores}}{2 \text{ hours}}$$

A **rate** is a ratio comparing two amounts having different units of measure.

$$\frac{5 \text{ stores}}{1 \text{ hour}}$$

A **unit rate** is a rate having 1 as the denominator.

BURT'S BEES PRODUCTS	
Carrot Complexion Soap	$6.50/bar
Lip Balm	$1.95/tin

A **unit price** is a unit rate that shows the cost of one item.

Find a unit rate or a unit price.

Amida earns $66 for 8 hours of work. How much does she earn per hour?

$$\frac{\text{Amount paid}}{\text{Hours worked}}$$ Write the rate in words.

$$\frac{\$66}{8 \text{ hours}}$$ Substitute the numbers.

$$\frac{66 \div 8}{8 \div 8} = \frac{\$8.25}{1 \text{ hour}}$$ Divide the numerator and the denominator by the denominator.

 Amida earns $8.25 per hour.

Compare unit rates.

Burt's Bees' factory can produce 400 soap bars in 3 hours and 15 lip balms in 1 minute. Which product is produced at a faster rate?
Rate comparisons must have the same units.

	soap bars	lip balms
Change hours to minutes. 3 · 60 minutes = 180 minutes Substitute.	$\frac{400 \text{ items}}{3 \text{ hr}}$ $\frac{400 \text{ items}}{180 \text{ min}}$	$\frac{15 \text{ items}}{1 \text{ min}}$
Divide the numerator and the denominator by the denominator.	$\frac{400 \text{ items} \div 180}{180 \text{ min} \div 180}$ 2.22 items/min	15 items/min

Lip balms are produced at a faster rate.

Compare unit prices.

One type of facial cleanser costs $8.50 for 5 ounces. Another type costs $7.75 for 4 ounces. Which is the better buy?

$$\frac{\$8.50}{5 \text{ oz}} \xleftarrow{\text{dollars}} \xrightarrow{} \frac{\$7.75}{4 \text{ oz}}$$ Write the rates.

$$\frac{8.50 \div 5}{5 \div 5} \qquad \frac{7.75 \div 4}{4 \div 4}$$ Find the unit price for each item.

$$\frac{\$1.70}{1 \text{ ounce}} \quad \text{The better buy!} \quad \frac{\$1.94}{1 \text{ ounce}}$$

> **Estimate to compare.**
>
> $$\frac{\$8.50}{5} \approx \frac{\$9.00}{5} = \boxed{\$1.80}$$ Mentally round the price to the nearest whole dollar and divide.
>
> $$\frac{\$7.75}{4} \approx \frac{\$8.00}{4} = \$2.00$$

Check Understanding

a. Which is the better buy, $3.50 for 3 ounces or $4.00 for 4 ounces?

b. Do you receive more for your money if you buy a two-pound bag of granola priced at $6.00 or 14 ounces for $2.80?

Practice

Find the unit rate.

1. $42 for 3 hours of work

2. 150 miles on 4 gallons of gasoline

3. 30 sit-ups in two minutes

4. 200 meters run in 25 seconds

Find the unit price. Round your answer to the nearest cent.

5. $1.83 for 3 ounces

6. $4.99 for $1\frac{1}{2}$ pounds of hamburger

7. $25 for 12 loaves of bread

8. $19.30 for 5 gallons of grape juice

Apply

9.

Product	Unit Price
Orange Essence Cleanser	$28/lb
Citrus Facial Scrub	$3/oz

Which is the better buy?

10. Sheila and Laverne went shopping and purchased separate brands of hand lotion. Sheila paid $7.98 for 8 ounces and Laverne paid $8.35 for 10 ounces. Estimate who found the better buy.

11. The production lines at the Glo Toothpaste factory had different production rates. Line 1 produced 2520 tubes in 3 hours and Line 2 produced 2925 tubes in 225 minutes. Which line had the faster production rate?

12. Marty drove 1200 miles and used 40 gallons of gasoline in his car. Josephine drove 1150 miles and used 35 gallons of gasoline. Whose car gets better gas mileage?

Proportion

Construct Meaning

Makusu Manufacturing Company is an international business based in Japan. The company makes functional ceramics called capacitors and resistors, which are used as electrical components in cell phones and power transistors.

If a ceramic component requires a glossy glaze, the ratio of aluminum to silica in the glaze needs to be 9:1. If Mr. Makusu mixed a glaze with a ratio of 36:4, does the mixture have the correct proportions?

Resistors

$\frac{a}{b} = \frac{c}{d}$ A **proportion** is an equation that shows that two ratios are equal.

$\frac{9}{1} \diagdown \frac{36}{4}$ $36 = 36$ Use cross products to determine if the two ratios are proportional. If the cross products are equal, the ratios are proportional.

Mr. Makusu's glaze is proportionate.

Different sized capacitors may require proportional length-to-width measurements.

0.3 mm 2 mm
0.6 mm   4 mm

1.6 mm 4 mm
3.2 mm   8 mm

3 mm
5 mm

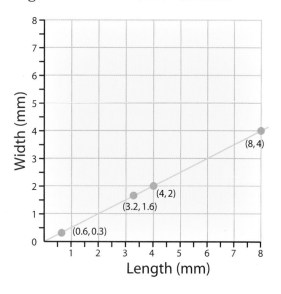

Are the capacitors proportional?
- Plot the measurements (l, w) on a coordinate grid as if each ratio is an ordered pair.
- Ratios that are proportionate can be plotted on a straight line.
- Plot the final ratio (5:3) on the grid. Is it proportional to the other ratios?

A recipe for a ceramic glaze calls for 3 grams of zinc oxide to make 363 grams of glaze. If the lab used 25 grams of zinc oxide, how many total grams of glaze were made?

| Solve using a proportion. | OR | Solve by finding the unit rate. |

Solve using a proportion.

Write the ratio in words.	$\dfrac{\text{grams of glaze}}{\text{grams of zinc oxide}}$
Write the ratios as a proportion. Let x equal the unknown factor.	$\dfrac{363 \text{ g of glaze}}{3 \text{ g of zinc oxide}} = \dfrac{x}{25 \text{ g of zinc oxide}}$
Write the cross products.	$363 \cdot 25 = 3x$ $9075 = 3x$
Use inverse operations.	$\dfrac{9075}{3} = \dfrac{3x}{3}$ $3025 \text{ g} = x$

3025 grams of glaze were made.

Solve by finding the unit rate.

Divide by 3.	$\dfrac{363 \text{ g of glaze} \div 3}{3 \text{ g of zinc oxide} \div 3}$
The unit rate is 121 grams of glaze for every 1 gram of zinc oxide.	$\dfrac{121 \text{ g of glaze}}{1 \text{ g of zinc oxide}}$
Multiply the unit rate by 25 g since there are 25 g of zinc oxide.	$\dfrac{121}{1} \cdot 25 \text{ g} = 3025 \text{ g}$

3025 grams of glaze were made.

Check Understanding

a. Consider a capacitor that is 6 millimeters in length and 3 millimeters wide. Is it proportional to the ratios shown on the coordinate grid?

b. Solve the proportion $\frac{36}{4} = \frac{n}{8}$. Is it easier to solve this problem using cross products or mental multiplication?

Practice

Write the cross products and $=$ or $\neq$ to determine if the ratios form a proportion.

1. $\frac{8}{10} \bigcirc \frac{20}{25}$ **2.** $\frac{5}{16} \bigcirc \frac{1}{3.2}$ **3.** $\frac{28}{12} \bigcirc \frac{35}{14}$ **4.** $\frac{0.8}{0.3} \bigcirc \frac{0.4}{0.15}$

Solve each proportion.

5. $\frac{7}{2} = \frac{n}{12}$ **6.** $\frac{414}{24} = \frac{a}{2}$ **7.** $\frac{1.6}{4.2} = \frac{2.4}{x}$ **8.** $\frac{3}{4} = \frac{b}{10}$

9. $\frac{t}{3} = \frac{7}{12}$ **10.** $\frac{5}{n} = \frac{10}{2}$ **11.** $\frac{34}{14} = \frac{n}{7}$ **12.** $\frac{9}{100} = \frac{1.23}{x}$

Apply

13. Tave's Frame Shop sells prints of *The Starry Night* by Van Gogh in various sizes. Determine which two prints are proportionate and identify one other proportionate print size.

8"

10"

5"

7"

13"

16.25"

14. A recipe for a natural ceramic tile cleaner calls for $\frac{1}{4}$ cup of vinegar to one gallon of water. Annie wants to use only $\frac{1}{4}$ gallon of water. How much vinegar should she use?

15. A manufacturer estimated that if each product required five capacitors, then 740 capacitors would be needed to make 148 products. If it was later determined that they actually only needed four capacitors for each product, how many more products could be produced?

Capacitors

16. HCl + NaOH ➔ H₂O + NaCl
acid   base   water   salt

Appropriate amounts of an acid and a base yield neutral water and salt. If a ratio of 9 milliliters of an acid to 10 milliliters of a base yields a neutral solution, would 4 milliliters of acid and 5 milliliters of base yield a neutral solution? Write a proportion to help determine your answer.

Construct Meaning

Jorgé owns a taco stand in Mexico City, Mexico. It costs Jorgé 3 pesos to make one fish taco, which he sells for 6 pesos. If 9.5 pesos are equivalent to 1 US dollar, how much profit does Jorgé make in US dollars when he sells one fish taco?

Think:

To find the profit, subtract the cost to make one taco from the sales price of one taco.   6 pesos – 3 pesos = 3 pesos

$\dfrac{\text{peso}}{\text{dollar}}$	Identify the needed ratio using words.
$\dfrac{9.5 \text{ pesos}}{1 \text{ dollar}}$	Write the ratio.
$\dfrac{9.5 \text{ pesos}}{\$1} = \dfrac{3 \text{ pesos}}{\$d}$	Set up the proportion. Identify the term you want to find as d. Place d in the denominator to match the units of the other ratio.
$9.5 \text{ pesos} \cdot d = \$1 \cdot 3 \text{ pesos}$	Use cross products.
$\dfrac{9.5 \text{ pesos} \cdot d}{9.5 \text{ pesos}} = \dfrac{\$1 \cdot 3 \text{ pesos}}{9.5 \text{ pesos}}$	Use the inverse operation. Observe the units. Make sure the operation results in the correct unit.
$d = \$0.32$	Jorgé makes \$0.32 profit on each taco he sells.

$\dfrac{\text{peso}}{\text{peso}} = 1$ just as $\dfrac{4}{4} = 1$

Apply

1. A twenty-week subscription to the *Daily Messenger* newspaper costs \$45. At this rate, how much will be paid for subscribing for one year?

2. Mr. Kuhlman and Miss Healey are the sole investors for WebImage, Inc. Mr. Kuhlman invested \$4000 and Miss Healey invested \$6000. The income for the month of March is \$3200. What is each person's share of the income if the profit is divided in proportion to his or her investment?

3. The manger-to-employee ratio at Wild Adventures Amusement Park is 2 to 9. If 108 employees are working at Wild Adventures on Saturday afternoon, how many managers must be working as well?

4. In Japan, Mr. Yoshiba stayed in a hotel room for 19,200 yen. If 128 yen are equivalent to 1 US dollar and the hotel room cost \$50 US per night, how many nights did Mr. Yoshiba stay at the hotel?

5. A city code requires that there are seven trees planted for every acre of developed land. How many trees must be planted on a 14-acre parcel of land designated to be used for office buildings?

6. Clear Voice Electronics is conducting a quality-control test in their manufacturing plant. Out of the 50 cell phones randomly selected for testing, four were defective. Based on the test results, how many cell phones might be defective in a shipment of 125 cell phones?

7. A 12-ounce box of rabbit food can feed Hairball and Hannibal for 4 days. If Phoebe purchased a 30-ounce bag of rabbit food, how many days will the food last? How many ounces of food do Hairball and Hannibal eat in one day?

8. Colleen purchased a 12-ounce bag of chips for $3.50. Louise purchased 16 ounces of chips for $4.10. Who found the better buy?

9. Meshia did 51 sit-ups in 3 minutes. Maris did 36 sit-ups in 2 minutes. Who did their sit-ups at a faster rate? Write each person's unit rate.

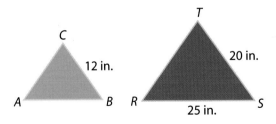

10. $\triangle ABC$ and $\triangle RST$ are similar triangles. Corresponding sides of similar triangles are proportionate to each other. Determine the length of $\overline{AB}$.

11. The triangles made by the person and her shadow and by the tree and its shadow are similar triangles with proportional sides. Determine the height of the tree.

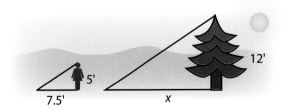

Fractions, Decimals, Percents

Construct Meaning

Many ambitious young adults have started their own businesses, such as lawn care services, recycling, bicycle repair, or web page design. Keisha, Rai, and Sal have decided to form a partnership in a web page design business. Keisha has 52% ownership, Rai has 24% ownership, and Sal has 24% ownership.

A percent may be written as a decimal or a fraction.

Percent	Decimal	Fraction
52%	0.52	$\frac{52}{100}$
24%	0.24	$\frac{24}{100}$
147%	1.47	$\frac{147}{100}$
0.7%	0.007	$\frac{7}{1000}$

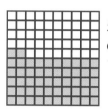

52 out of 100

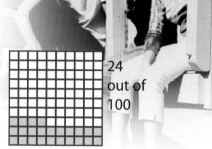

24 out of 100

Express a fraction as a percent.

Write $\frac{2}{5}$ as a percent by solving a proportion. Because percent means per 100, you can write a proportion with 100 as one of the denominators.

$\frac{2}{5} = \frac{n}{100}$

$2 \cdot 100 = 5 \cdot n$ Use cross products.

$\frac{200}{5} = \frac{5n}{5}$ Use inverse operations.

$40 = n$

$\frac{40}{100} = 40\%$ Write the %.

OR

Write $\frac{2}{5}$ as a decimal by dividing the numerator by the denominator. Change the decimal to a percent.

$$\begin{array}{r} 0.4 \\ 5\overline{)2.0} \\ 0 \\ \hline 20 \\ 20 \\ \hline 0 \end{array}$$

$0.4 \cdot 100 = 40$ Multiply by 100.

40%   Write the %.

Express a percent as a fraction.

Write 0.6% as a fraction.

$\frac{0.6}{100}$ Rewrite with a denominator of 100.

$\frac{0.6 \times 10}{100 \times 10}$ Multiply if neccessary to make the numerator a whole number.

$\frac{6}{1000} = \frac{3}{500}$ Simplify if necessary.

Note that 0.6% is less than 1%.

Percent

Multiply by 100 and write the %.

Divide by 100 and remove the %.

Write 100 as the denominator and remove the %.

Write as a fraction and simplify.

Decimal   **Fraction**

Divide the numerator by the denominator.

Express a decimal as a percent.

Write 1.62 as a percent.

$1.62 \cdot 100 = 162$ Multiply by 100.

162%   Write the %.

Note that 162% is greater than 100%.

Express a percent as a decimal.

Write 25% as a decimal.

0.25   Divide by 100 and remove the %.

 think 25% is $\frac{25}{100}$, which is twenty-five hundredths or 0.25.

Check Understanding

a. How is a percent that is greater than 100% like an improper fraction?

b. Write 0.5%, 5%, and $\frac{1}{20}$% in decimal form.

0.01

c. In your own words, explain a method to express a fraction as a percent.

Practice

Write >, < or = .

1. $\frac{1}{4}$ ⊘ 1%

2. 0.34% ⊗ 1%

3. $\frac{235}{100}$ ⊘ 100%

4. 0.0025 ⊘ 1% = 0.01

$\frac{1}{100}$

5. $\frac{1}{5}$ ⊜ 20%

6. 1.05 ⊘ 100%

7. 7% ⊘ 0.007

8. 35% ⊜ $\frac{7}{20}$ ×5 = $\frac{35}{100}$

$\frac{105}{100}$

Write each fraction as a percent.

9. $\frac{3}{5}$ *60%*

10. $\frac{400}{100}$ *400%*

11. $\frac{\frac{1}{2}}{100}$ *0.5%*

12. $\frac{70}{20}$ ×5 = $\frac{350}{100}$ *350%*

13. $\frac{0.4}{1000}$ *0.04%*

Write each decimal as a percent.

14. 0.2 *20%*

15. 0.042 *4.2%*

16. 7.8 ○ *780%*

17. 0.005 ○ *.5%*

18. 0.00015 *0.015%*

Write each percent as a decimal.

19. 175% *1.75%*

20. 0.3% *60%*

21. $5\frac{1}{2}$%

22. 45%

23. $\frac{1}{3}$%

Apply

24. Out of 50 teenagers surveyed, 14 of them ran a lawn-care business during their summer vacation. Determine the percent of the teens that had a lawn-care business.

25. In the town of Belfired, 13 out of 42 businesses carry groceries. What percent of the businesses did <u>not</u> sell groceries?

26. Web Design Company's profit margin doubled during its second year of operation. By the fifth year the profit margin had doubled again. By what percent had their profit margin increased since the end of the first year?

Construct Meaning

The automobile industry is continually looking for useful innovations. The production of gas-electric hybrid vehicles has been steadily gaining popularity. The gas mileage for one hybrid model is 140% of the gasoline-powered model with city gas mileage of 33 mpg. How many miles per gallon does the hybrid model get?

Write an equation.

What is 140% of 33 mpg?

part = percent · whole   Write a word equation.

x = 140% · 33 mpg   Find the part. Let x = part.
x = 1.4 · 33 mpg   Write the percent as a decimal. 140% = 1.4
x = 46.2 mpg   Solve. The hybrid car gets **46.2 mpg.**

Write a proportion.

How can a proportion be made from the word equation?

part = percent · whole   Use the word equation.

$\dfrac{\text{part}}{\text{whole}}$ = percent   Divide both sides by the whole.

$\dfrac{\text{part}}{\text{whole}} = \dfrac{n}{100}$ The percent can be expressed as a number n divided by 100.

> This proportion can be used to solve percent problems by substituting the appropriate numbers.

Find the part.

Write an equation.
What is 60% of 3200?

part | percent | whole

x = 60% · 3200   Substitute.

x = 0.60 · 3200   Write the percent as a decimal.

x = 1920   Solve.

or

Use a proportion.
What is 60% of 3200?

part   percent   whole

$\dfrac{\text{part}}{\text{whole}} = \dfrac{n}{100}$ Identify each part of the question.

$\dfrac{x}{3200} = \dfrac{60}{100}$ Substitute the numbers. Let x = part.

$x \cdot 100 = 3200 \cdot 60$ Use cross products.

$100x = 192{,}000$

$\dfrac{100x}{100} = \dfrac{192{,}000}{100}$ Use inverse operations.

$x = 1920$

> 60% of 3200 is 1920.

Check Understanding

a. When using a proportion to solve a percent problem, one of the fractions may be an improper fraction. Which fraction would this be and what does it mean?

b. Identify each part of the question, "What is 42% of 4600?" by labeling the part, percent, whole, the operation sign, and = .

c. Substitute each part of the question, "What is 18% of 56?" into the proportion $\frac{\text{part}}{\text{whole}} = \frac{n}{100}$.

Practice

Solve by writing an equation.

1. What is 12% of 98?

2. What is 250% of 150?

3. What is 50.5% of 60?

4. What is 0.8% of 20?

Solve by using a proportion.

5. What is 7% of 1120?

6. What is 80% of 3620?

7. What is 135% of 46?

8. What is 0.75% of 40?

Apply

9. 70% of Mrs. Frield's class indicated that they regularly recycle plastic, glass, and paper. If there are 20 students in Mrs. Frield's class, how many students regularly recycle?

10. The price of a hybrid model car is 30% more than the regular model. If the regular model costs $16,990, how much does the hybrid model cost?

11. In 2001, Gran Dealers saw a 180% increase in sales of their hybrid sedans. If the sales were 8000 sedans in 2000, what were the sedan sales in 2001? Round to the nearest whole number.

Review

Draw a line graph to illustrate each inequality.

1. $n \geq -10$

2. $-5 \leq m \leq 5$

3. $15 < p < 20$

4. $q < 2$ or $q > 7$

Concept Car

Find the Percent or the Whole

Construct Meaning

Cobalt is a precious metal produced by mining businesses worldwide. It is used in aircraft engines and steel-belted radial tires. In 1996, Zambia produced about 8000 metric tons (t) of approximately 25,000 metric tons of cobalt mined by the world's top ten producers. Zambia's part can be expressed as a percent of the total production. Given any two values in the percent equation, the missing value can be calculated.

Cobaltocalcite

Find the percent.

Write an equation.
What percent of 200 is 90?

percent | whole | part

$$p \cdot 200 = 90$$

$$\frac{p \cdot 200}{200} = \frac{90}{200} \quad \text{Use inverse operations.}$$

$$p = \frac{90}{200}$$

$$p = 0.45$$

$$p = 45\% \quad \text{Change the decimal to a percent.}$$

or

Use a proportion.
What percent of 200 is 90?

percent | whole | part

$$\frac{\text{part}}{\text{whole}} = \frac{n}{100} \quad \text{Identify each part of the question.}$$

$$\frac{90}{200} = \frac{n}{100} \quad \text{Substitute the numbers.}$$

$$90 \cdot 100 = 200 \cdot n \quad \text{Use cross products.}$$

$$9000 = 200n$$

$$\frac{9000}{200} = \frac{200n}{200} \quad \text{Use inverse operations.}$$

$$45 = n$$

think $\frac{n}{100} = \frac{45}{100} = 45\%$ Write the %.

$$\boxed{45\% \text{ of } 200 \text{ is } 90.}$$

Find the whole.

Write an equation.
75% of what number is 600?

percent | whole | part

$$75\% \cdot w = 600$$

$$0.75 \cdot w = 600 \quad \text{Change the percent to a decimal.}$$

$$\frac{0.75w}{0.75} = \frac{600}{0.75} \quad \text{Use inverse operations.}$$

$$w = 800$$

or

Use a proportion.
75% of what number is 600?

percent | whole | part

$$\frac{\text{part}}{\text{whole}} = \frac{n}{100} \quad \text{Identify each part of the question.}$$

$$\frac{600}{w} = \frac{75}{100} \quad \text{Substitute the numbers. Let } w = \text{whole.}$$

$$600 \cdot 100 = 75 \cdot w \quad \text{Use cross products.}$$

$$60{,}000 = 75w$$

$$\frac{60000}{75} = \frac{75w}{75} \quad \text{Use inverse operations.}$$

$$800 = w$$

$$\boxed{75\% \text{ of } 800 \text{ is } 600.}$$

Check Understanding

a. State what needs to be found in each question:
whole, *percent*, or *part*.
What is 45% of 65?
45 is what percent of 65?
45 is 65% of what number?

b. Discuss whether you prefer to find the percent by writing an equation or using a proportion.

c. What percent of 25,000 metric tons is 8,000 metric tons?

Practice

Solve by writing an equation.

1. What is 70% of 14?

2. What percent of 72 is 24?

3. What is $5\frac{1}{2}$% of 200?

4. What percent of 60 is 180?

5. 80% of what number is 20?

6. 36% of what number is 72?

Solve by using a proportion.

7. What is 9% of 16.2?

8. What is 35% of 15,000?

9. 60% of what number is 54?

10. 30 is 150% of what number?

11. 15 is what percent of 20,000?

12. What percent of 45 is 157.5?

Apply

13. In 1992, Peru produced about 27,000 kilograms of gold out of about 1,800,000 kilograms from the top ten producing countries. What percent of the gold was produced by Peru?

14. The middle school students sold candy bars for $1.50 each. The school received 35% of the total sales of the candy bars. If the students raised $378, how many candy bars were sold?

15. Mr. Hofer receives a $1\frac{1}{2}$% commission on every car he sells. Today Mr. Hofer received $375 for a car he sold. What was the price of the car?

16. Coach Stokes, the girls soccer coach at Carmel Christian School, has a win/loss record of 102/25 since he began coaching. What percent of the total games were won? Round to the nearest tenth of a percent.

Review

1. $4y - 6 = 6$

2. $\frac{r}{5} + 10 = -15$

3. $-9 = 3n + 6$

4. $16x - 20 = -4$

Taxes and Discounts

Construct Meaning

Vending machines can be found almost anywhere and may sell everything from snacks and candy to ice cream and hot beverages. A person who owns a vending machine business can earn a 100% to 200% return on the money invested within the first year of business.

SALES TAX

Mr. Kareem is purchasing a gumball vending machine for $250 plus 6.5% sales tax. What is the total of Mr. Kareem's bill?

What is 6.5% of $250?

Change the percent
to a decimal and multiply. $x = 0.065 \cdot \$250$

$x = \$16.25$

Add the amount $\$250 + \$16.25 = \$266.25$
of the tax to the price.

Mr. Kareem's bill is $266.25.

> Estimate using mental math.
> What is 6.5% of $250?
> Round 6.5% to 7%.
>
> First find 1% of $250. $1\% = \frac{1}{100}$
> $\frac{1}{100} \cdot 250 = \$2.50$
> Next find 7% of $250.
> If 1% is $2.50 then 7% is $2.50 \cdot 7$.
>
> $\$2.50 \cdot 7 = \boxed{\$17.50}$
>
> $\$250 + \$17.50 = \$267.50$

DISCOUNTS

Julian purchased a used soft drink vending machine for 30% off its regular price of $1012. What was the amount of the discount?

What is 30% of $1012?

Change the percent
to a decimal and multiply. $x = 0.30 \cdot \$1012$

$x = \$303.60$

The discount was $303.60.

> Estimate using mental math.
> What is 30% of $1012?
>
> Round $1012 to $1000, the greatest place value.
>
> First find 10% of $1000. $10\% = \frac{1}{10}$
> $\frac{1}{10} \cdot \$1000 = \$100$
> Think: If 10% is $100, then 30% is $100 \cdot 3$.
> $\$100 \cdot 3 = \boxed{\$300}$

TIPS

The VanHume family ate at a restaurant and spent a total of $62.80. How much should the VanHumes give for the 15% tip?

What is 15% of $62.80?

Change the percent
to a decimal and multiply. $x = 0.15 \cdot \$62.80$

$x = \$9.42$

The VanHumes should give $9.42 for the tip.

> Estimate using mental math.
> What is 15% of $62.80?
> Round $62.80 to $63.00.
> 15% is 10% + 5%.
>
> Think: What is 10% of $63?
> $\frac{1}{10} \cdot \$63 = \$6.30$
>
> Think: What is 5% of $6.30?
> 5% is half of 10%. $\$6.30 \div 2 = \$3.15$
>
> $\$6.30 + \$3.15 = \boxed{\$9.45}$

Check Understanding

a. What will you pay for a $40 item that is discounted 10%?

b. Name several situations where you might calculate percent mentally.

c. Explain how to mentally calculate 12% of 25.

Practice

Estimate using mental math.

1. 10% of 40

2. 20% of 83

3. 15% of 30

4. 3% of 12

5. 6% of 304

6. 60% of 190

Find the amount of the sales tax. Round up to the next cent if necessary.

7. Vending machine **$1200**
Sales tax **6.5%**

8. Pair of jeans **$35**
Sales tax **7%**

9. Two candy bars **$1.10**
Sales tax **5.4%**

Find the final cost. Round up to the next cent if necessary.

10. Shirt **$14.50**
Discount **20% off**

11. Bottle of shampoo **$3.79**
Sales tax **7.3%**

12. Television **$259**
Discount **25% off**

Apply

13. Karla purchased a sweater for 25% off its regular price of $32. Leah purchased a sweater for 30% off its regular price of $40. Whose sweater cost less?

14. Mrs. Francis gave a 20% tip for the excellent service at Giuseppe's Deli. If her bill was $9.20, estimate her total bill including the tip.

Business Connection

In the United States, $64,000 is spent every minute on vending machine items.

15. Sean bought a printer for $310.25, a memory card for $70, and a cable for $19.99. If the sales tax is 6%, estimate Sean's total bill.

16. Jordan took $54 to the sale at Stan's Sporting Goods Store. Which three items can he purchase if there is no sales tax?

SALE
ALL ITEMS 20% OFF

ORIGINAL PRICE
Basketball $20.00
Baseball mitt $26.25
Football $27.50
Soccer ball $21.00

7.9 Percent Increase and Decrease

Construct Meaning

A packaging company located in Iceland exports the country's products and manufactures paper products for schools, homes, and businesses. If Iceland Packaging had 140 employees in 2000 and 175 employees in 2002, what was the percent increase of the number of employees?

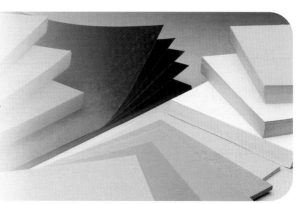

Percent increase is a percent change that describes an increase in quantity.
Percent decrease is a percent change that describes a decrease in quantity.

To determine percent increase or percent decrease, first find the amount of change. In this case, subtract the number of employees in 2000 from the number in 2002 to determine the amount of change.

175 employees – 140 employees = 35 employees

Percent change may be percent increase or percent decrease.

A proportion may be used to find percent changes.

$$\frac{\text{percent change}}{100} = \frac{\text{amount of change}}{\text{original amount}}$$

Use the proportion to determine the percent increase in the number of employees at Iceland Packaging. Let n = percent increase.

Substitute the numbers. $\frac{n}{100} = \frac{35}{140}$

Use cross products. $140n = 100 \cdot 35$

Use inverse operations. $\frac{140n}{140} = \frac{3500}{140}$

$n = 25$

Write the percent. $\frac{n}{100} = \frac{25}{100} = 25\%$

The percent increase was 25%.

Use the proportion to find the number of tourists taking a shore excursion in Iceland during August. There was a 20% decrease in business from July, when 240 people took the tour. Let x represent the amount of change.

Substitute the numbers. $\frac{20}{100} = \frac{x}{240}$

Use cross products. $20 \cdot 240 = 100x$

Use inverse operations. $\frac{4800}{100} = \frac{100x}{100}$

$48 = x$ **There were 48 fewer tourists in August.**

To find the number of tourists in August, subtract the amount of change from the number of tourists in July.

240 – 48 = 192 **THERE WERE 192 TOURISTS IN AUGUST.**

Check Understanding

a. The number of customers that visited Perry's Bakery doubled in one year. The shop manager put a sign in the window that stated, "We now serve 200% more customers." Is the statement true or false? Explain.

b. Brooke decreased the amount of time she spent practicing the piano from one hour to 45 minutes. Mentally determine the percent decrease.

 c. If Iceland Packaging hired 12 more employees, which is a 20% increase in the number of employees, what was the original number of employees?

Practice

Determine the percent increase or decrease.

1. Original price *$40*
Sale price *$28*

2. Original weight *102 lb*
New weight *127.5 lb*

3. Original number of students *215*
Current number of students *258*

Determine the new amount.

4. $45 is increased by 15% **5.** 120 is decreased by 40% **6.** 5 lb is increased by 112%

Determine the original amount.

7. Amount of decrease *$10*
Percent change *10%*

8. Amount of increase *540*
Percent change *80%*

9. Sale price *$35*
Discount *30%*

Apply

 **10.** The population of Monterey Heights decreased from 16,750 to 15,745 in one year. Determine the percent decrease.

11. Mr. Divatz's car has decreased in value by 20% of its original price of $13,500. How much is Mr. Divatz's car worth?

12. Because of the success of the local rugby team, the number of people registered in the fan club increased by 200 people, which is 80% of the original number of fans. How many people are now registered in the fan club?

13. Mr. Bakke recorded the time it took the students to run around the perimeter of the school at the beginning of the year and at the end of the year. Between Gina and Andrea, who had the greater percent of improvement? What was that student's percent of improvement?

Name	Fall Quarter	Spring Quarter
Gina	1 min 30 sec	1 min 15 sec
Andrea	1 min 40 sec	1 min 25 sec

14. Todd bought a pack of basketball cards that contained a rookie card of a player who later became famous. He paid $0.03 for the rookie card, and fifteen years later, the card was worth $1200. Determine the percent increase of the card's value.

Max's ANTIQUE MALL

Max's Antique Mall sells all types of antiques. Antique dealers need to be knowledgeable about the value of old-fashioned items. Signatures are a very important part of determining value. Value is also determined by beauty, rarity, and age.

1. Max is selling an antique pocket watch for $550. It has been sitting in his shop for over a year, and he has decided to sell it at a 25% discount. How much is the pocket watch after the discount?

2. Some of the paintings in the Antique Mall's collection are original paintings. One is for sale for $10,000 plus 7% sales tax. How much would it cost to purchase the painting?

3. The 18th century helmet that the Antique Mall displays is not for sale. If its original price was $25 and its value has increased to $1200, what is the percent increase in the helmet's value?

4. Luella has $680 that she has saved in order to purchase a special antique. She is trying to decide whether she can afford to purchase an $800 pocket watch at 25% off plus 7% sales tax or a painting for $650 plus 7% sales tax. Which item can Luella purchase with $680?

5. Marcella purchased a pocket watch for $96, which is 25% off the regular price of the watch. What was the original price of the pocket watch?

6. Northwood Academy plans to purchase a print of a Winslow Homer painting for $39. They will receive a 15% educational discount. Estimate the amount of the discount.

7. Max often purchases and refinishes furniture to sell for a higher price. If he purchased a dresser for $50 and sold it for $105, by what percent did he mark up or increase the price?

8. Mrs. Lisbet's antique chair was worth $5,000 before she had it refinished. She did not realize that by refinishing the chair the value actually decreased to $1000. Calculate the percent decrease in the value of the chair.

9. Mr. Hovenden purchased a set of six china cups and saucers for $420. They were originally priced at $525. What percent was the discount?

10. Hahn is purchasing an antique motorbike by making payments to Max's Antique Mall. To date he has paid $630, which is 30% of the total price. How much does he still owe?

11. Mr. and Mrs. Nichols collect antiques and have an annual budget of $5000 to spend on them. They have chosen five items from Max's Antique Mall to purchase. Calculate their total bill. Remember to subtract the discounts and add the sales tax. Are the Nichols within their budget?

COST	ITEM
$560	China (15% off, discounted at register)
$600	China (30% off, discounted at register)
$1060	Table
$380	Pocket watch (25% off, discounted at register)
$2400	Paintings
	Sales tax (7%)

12. A cup and saucer of Irish Belleek China was sold for 60% of its value of $195. Estimate the purchase price of the china.

13. Max sells antiques for other people for a fee of 10% of the sales price. If he just sold an item for $286, use mental math to determine his fee.

Construct Meaning

A **topographic map** is a map that shows the shape of the earth's surface with contour lines. It also shows symbols that represent roads, buildings, streams, forests, and other features. Note the features on the topographical map of the Mount Shasta area.

A **contour line** is a line that connects points of equal elevation. Contour lines never cross, and they show the general shape of the land. What is indicated when a contour line forms an enclosed circular shape?

Contour lines that are very close together represent steep slopes. Contour lines that are widely spaced represent relatively level slopes. The elevation difference represented by the distance between each line is the **contour interval**.

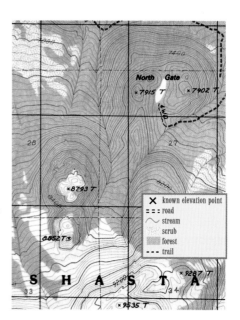

Latitude and Longitude

Latitude and longitude form the most common grid system used for navigation. **Latitude** is angular distance north and south of the equator.

Longitude is angular distance measured east and west of the prime meridian. The **prime meridian** is the imaginary line that runs from the North to the South Pole passing through Greenwich, England.

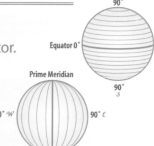

A degree is the common measurement of angular distance. A full circle of arc measures 360°. A degree of arc is divided into 60 smaller units called minutes. One minute of arc can be further divided into 60 seconds.

At the earth's surface, one degree is a distance of about 70 miles. What distance is represented by one minute?   1 degree ≈ 70 mi

$$1 \text{ minute} \approx \tfrac{1}{60} \cdot 70 \text{ mi} \approx 1.2 \text{ mi}$$

What distance is represented by one second?

$$1 \text{ second} \approx \tfrac{1}{60} \cdot 1.2 \text{ mi} \approx 0.02 \text{ mi}$$

> The latitude of the North Gate Peaks is 41 degrees, 27 minutes, 48 seconds north (41° 27' 48" N). Standing at this location, about how far are you from the equator?

Check Understanding

Use the topographic map shown above to answer the following.
   a. Is the elevation on the map increasing to the north or south?
   b. What is the highest elevation labeled on the map?
   c. Which direction, north or south, are the streams flowing?

Simplify the ratio. *Lesson 7.1*

1. $\dfrac{12 \text{ boys}}{8 \text{ girls}}$

2. $\dfrac{13 \text{ feet}}{26 \text{ feet}}$

Find the cross products. *Lesson 7.1*

3. $\dfrac{4}{5} = \dfrac{20}{25}$

4. $\dfrac{4.2}{8.6} = \dfrac{50.4}{103.2}$

Find the unit rate or the unit price. *Lesson 7.2*

5. $1.95 for 5 packs of gum

6. 300 miles on 10 gallons of gasoline

Solve each proportion. *Lesson 7.3*

7. $\dfrac{3}{8} = \dfrac{k}{32}$

8. $\dfrac{a}{6} = \dfrac{15}{4}$

Solve. *Lesson 7.4*

9. If nine pieces of mini-chocolates have 210 calories, how many calories are in 15 pieces of mini-chocolates?

Write each percent as a decimal and as a fraction in simplest form. *Lesson 7.5*

10. 29%

11. 0.6%

12. 40.7%

13. $12\frac{1}{2}\%$

Write each fraction or decimal as a percent. *Lesson 7.5*

14. $\dfrac{114}{100}$

15. $\dfrac{13}{20}$

16. 0.054

17. 2.5

18. What is 24% of 800? *Lesson 7.6*

19. What percent of 320 is 50? *Lesson 7.7*

20. 18% of what number is 27? *Lesson 7.7*

21. Marilyn bought a sweater with a price tag of $30 and a sales tax of $7\frac{1}{2}\%$. How much did she pay for the sweater? *Lesson 7.8*

22. Since the new elementary school has opened on Imperial Avenue, the speed limit has been reduced from 40 miles per hour to 25 miles per hour. Find the percent decrease. *Lesson 7.9*

23. Between 1988 and 1998 Rwanda's cereal crop production decreased by 85,775 metric tons, which is a 29% decrease. How much did Rwanda produce in 1988? Round to the nearest whole number. *Lesson 7.9*

Promoting Proportions

1. Flying Disc Manufacturing is holding a contest for its customers. The first-prize winners will receive a compact disc player. The posted odds of winning the first prize are 3 in 2700. Write this ratio as a fraction in simplest form.

Find the cross products.

2. $\frac{4}{10} = \frac{12}{30}$ **3.** $\frac{2}{7} = \frac{5.2}{18.2}$ **4.** $\frac{8}{18} = \frac{32}{72}$

Write as a unit rate or a unit price.

5. $25.80 for 20 gallons of gasoline

6. 68 sit-ups in 5 minutes

Solve each proportion.

7. $\frac{4}{5} = \frac{28}{w}$ **8.** $\frac{c}{12} = \frac{15}{18}$ **9.** $\frac{620}{320} = \frac{a}{440}$

Write each percent as a decimal and as a fraction in simplest form.

10. 7%   **11.** 251%   **12.** 0.05%

Write each fraction or decimal as a percent.

13. $\frac{31}{50}$ **14.** 0.09   **15.** 0.561

Solve.

16. What is 12% of 400?

17. What percent of 4500 is 990?

18. 32% of what is 250?

19. 112% of what is 89.6?

20. A state law requires that a licensed daycare site have one caretaker for every four infants. If there are 12 infants at Toddler Daycare, how many caretakers are needed?

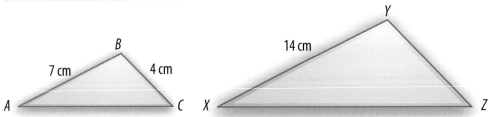

21. $\triangle ABC$ and $\triangle XYZ$ are similar triangles. Corresponding sides of similar triangles are proportionate to each other. Determine the length of $\overline{YZ}$.

22. In 1995 Denmark produced 1,804,000 cubic meters of rough wood and exported 14.8% of it. How many cubic meters did Denmark export?

23. Wesley completed 12 out of the 20 passes that he attempted in the last football game of the season. What was his percent of completion?

24. Between 1995 and 1997, 100,500 metric tons of marine fish were produced by the fishing industry in Yemen. This was 150% of the 1985–1987 figures. How many metric tons of marine fish were produced between 1985–1987?

25. The Olson household reduced the amount of electricity they consumed per month from 800 kilowatt-hours to 650 kilowatt-hours. Find the percent decrease.

26. Great Photos is having a sale on all models of their digital cameras. What is the sale price of a $650 camera if it is discounted 20%?

27. The Garcias, a family of four, paid $6.00 per person to eat dinner at the China Palace. Use mental math to determine the amount of the 15% tip they left.

28. Mark bought two pairs of shoes at the "Buy-one-get-one-half-off" sale at Sole Shoes. Each pair of shoes was originally priced at $55. What was Mark's total bill including the 6.5% sales tax? Round to the nearest cent.

29. In one year Turkey produced 1,569,000 metric tons of mollusks and crustaceans for consumption and 668,000 metric tons of freshwater fish. What percent is 668,000 metric tons of 1,569,000 metric tons? Round to the nearest percent.

30. Watch Plus is selling a watch for $84.49, which is 70% of the original price of the watch. What was the original price of the watch?

Scallops and clam shells

Chapter Theme:
Olympics

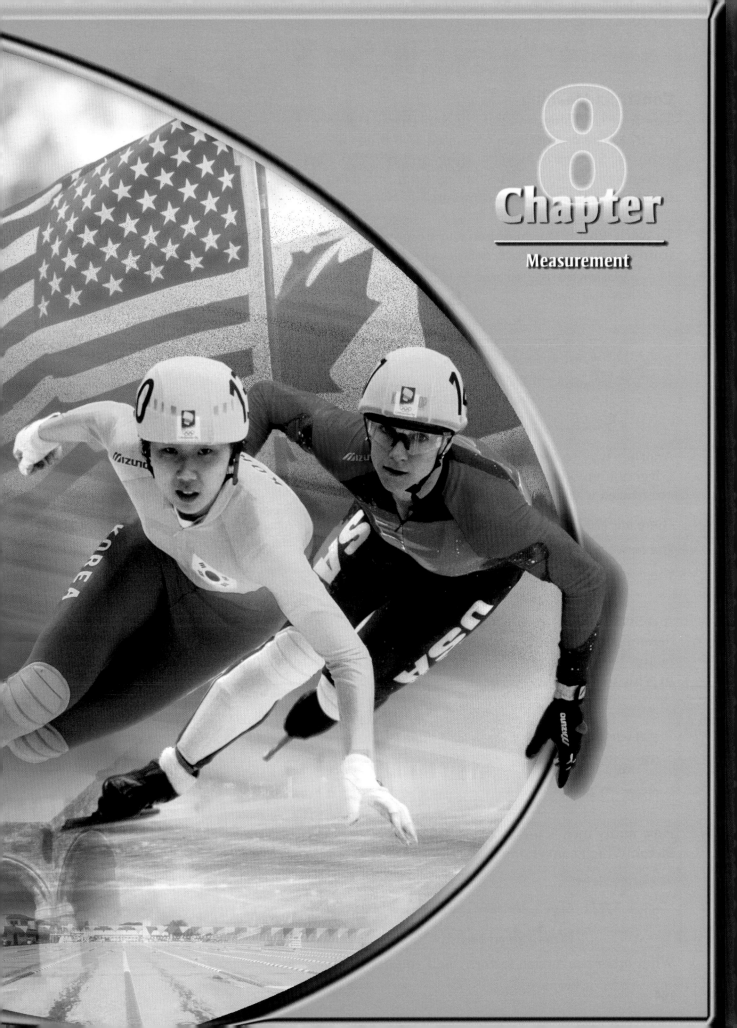

8 Chapter

Measurement

Customary Units of Length

Construct Meaning

The first triathlon was held in San Diego, California, in 1974. The competition consisted of 6 miles of running, 5 miles of bicycle riding, and two 250-yard sections of swimming. How many total miles did the finishers of the triathlon complete?

To work within the customary system, you often need to change units. To convert from one unit to another, decide whether to multiply or divide the equivalent unit.

To convert to a larger unit, divide.

$$\div 12 \quad \div 3 \quad \div 1760$$

in. ft yd mi

$$\times 12 \quad \times 3 \quad \times 1760$$

To convert to a smaller unit, multiply.

Swimming: 250 yd · 2 = 500 yd

Convert yards to miles. ⟶ 500 yd ÷ 1760 yd/mi = 0.28 mi

Triathlon total distance = 6 mi + 5 mi + 0.28 mi = 11.28 mi

Each triathlon finisher completed 11.28 miles.

Another way to convert measures is to multiply by a **conversion factor**, which is a fraction equal to 1, in which the numerator and denominator are equivalent quantities with different units.

Customary Units of Length
12 inches (in.) = 1 foot (ft)
36 inches = 1 yard (yd)
3 feet = 1 yard
5280 feet = 1 mile (mi)
1760 yards = 1 mile

There are 1760 yards in one mile.

The conversion factor for yards to miles is $\frac{1 \text{ mi}}{1760 \text{ yd}}$.

The conversion factor for miles to yards is $\frac{1760 \text{ yd}}{1 \text{ mi}}$.

A conversion factor is a fraction equal to 1 because its numerator and denominator are equivalent. Therefore, multiplying a measure by a conversion factor does not change its value. The conversion factor simply converts the units in which the measurement is expressed.

TO CONVERT FROM YARDS TO MILES

$500 \text{ yd} \cdot \frac{1 \text{ mi}}{1760 \text{ yd}}$ Multiply by the appropriate conversion factor.

$\frac{500 \text{ yd} \cdot 1 \text{ mi}}{1760 \text{ yd}}$ Observe the units.

$\frac{500 \text{ mi}}{1760} = 0.28 \text{ mi}$ Round the answer to the nearest hundredth.
There is 0.28 mile in 500 yards.

> When choosing a conversion factor, the unit you want to convert must be in the denominator.

How many inches are in 2 miles? You may need to use more than one conversion factor. Which conversion factors are needed?

Convert miles to feet.

$2 \text{ mi} \cdot \frac{5280 \text{ ft}}{1 \text{ mi}} \cdot \frac{12 \text{ in.}}{1 \text{ ft}} = \frac{2 \text{ mi} \cdot 5280 \text{ ft} \cdot 12 \text{ in.}}{1 \text{ mi} \cdot 1 \text{ ft}} = \frac{2 \cdot 5280 \cdot 12 \text{ in.}}{1} = 126{,}720 \text{ in.}$ There are 126,720 inches in 2 miles.

Convert feet to inches.

What other conversion factors could you use to convert from miles to inches?

Check Understanding
Convert to the given unit.

a. 252 ft = ☐ yd

b. 6 mi = ☐ yd

c. 156 mi = ☐ ft

d. $3\frac{1}{2}$ mi = ☐ ft

e. 5 yd 2 ft = ☐ ft

f. 7920 ft = ☐ mi

Practice
Write the conversion factor needed to change the following.

1. inches to feet

2. yards to miles

3. yards to feet

4. miles to feet

Complete.

5. 53 in. = ☐ ft ☐ in.

6. 11 yd 8 in. = ☐ in.

7. 5 mi = ☐ yd

8. 10,560 ft = ☐ mi

9. $3\frac{1}{3}$ yd = ☐ ft

10. $7\frac{1}{2}$ ft = ☐ in.

11. 104 yd 1 ft 11 in. = ☐ in.

12. $2\frac{1}{2}$ mi = ☐ ft

13. 92 ft = ☐ yd ☐ ft

Solve. Rename units as needed.

14.　18 yd
　　　− 16 yd 2 ft

15.　12 ft 9 in.
　　　+ 3 ft 4 in.

16.　31 yd 2 ft　7 in.
　　　− 14 yd 2 ft 10 in.

17.　8 ft 9 in.
　　　×　　6

18. How many feet are in 42 yards?

19. How many inches are in 40 yards?

20. How many miles are in 58,080 feet?

21. How many yards are in 30 inches?

Apply

22. A decorative rope is used to enclose the Olympic stand during award ceremonies. If the rectangular area is 26 yards by 14 yards 8 inches, how long is the rope in feet and inches?

23. Colin has a walking pace of about 20 inches. If he were to walk $2\frac{1}{2}$ miles, about how many paces would that be?

24. If one US dollar (USD) = 8.2773 Chinese yuan renminbi (CNY), how many US dollars are needed to purchase a sweater that costs 330 CNY? Show your work using a conversion factor.

Review
Multiply or divide. Express the answer as a power of ten.

1. 100 · 1000

2. 1000 ÷ 100

3. 0.01 · 10,000

Express the answer in scientific notation.

4. 0.05 · 1000

5. 7000 ÷ 10

6. 30 ÷ 0.001

7. 20 · 40

Construct Meaning

The 1500-meter freestyle is the Summer Olympic Games' longest swimming event. During the Winter Games, the 50-kilometer cross-country skiing race is the event of greatest distance. How many meters is 50 kilometers? What part of a kilometer is 1500 meters?

The **meter** is the basic unit of length in the metric system.

1 millimeter	1 centimeter	1 decimeter	*Meter*	1 dekameter	1 hectometer	1 kilometer
= 0.001 meter	= 0.01 meter	= 0.1 meter		= 10 meters	= 100 meters	= 1000 meters
1 m = 1000 mm	1 m = 100 cm	1 m = 10 dm		1 m = 0.1 dkm	1 m = 0.01 hm	1 m = 0.001 km

Because the metric system is based on 10, you can convert from one unit to another by multiplying or dividing by a power of 10.

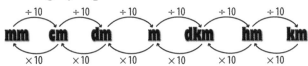

$\div 10 \qquad \div 10 \qquad \div 10 \qquad \div 10 \qquad \div 10 \qquad \div 10$

mm   cm   dm   m   dkm   hm   km

$\times 10 \qquad \times 10 \qquad \times 10 \qquad \times 10 \qquad \times 10 \qquad \times 10$

You can also use a conversion factor to convert metric units.

- A 50-kilometer cross-country race is equal to how many meters?
  Since there are 1000 meters in 1 kilometer, use $\frac{1000 \text{ m}}{1 \text{ km}}$.
  $50 \text{ km} \cdot \frac{1000 \text{ m}}{1 \text{ km}} = \frac{50 \text{ km} \cdot 1000 \text{ m}}{1 \text{ km}} = 50 \cdot 1000 \text{ m} = 50{,}000 \text{ m}$

- A 1500-meter freestyle swimmer travels how many kilometers?
  $1500 \text{ m} \cdot \frac{1 \text{ km}}{1000 \text{ m}} = \frac{1500 \text{ m} \cdot 1 \text{ km}}{1000 \text{ m}} = \frac{1500 \text{ km}}{1000} = 1.5 \text{ km}$

- 40 centimeters is what part of a meter?
  $40 \text{ cm} \cdot \frac{1 \text{ m}}{100 \text{ cm}} = \frac{40 \text{ cm} \cdot 1 \text{ m}}{100 \text{ cm}} = \frac{40 \text{ m}}{100} = 0.4 \text{ m}$

Use mental math.

think One centimeter is one-hundredth of a meter. Dividing 40 by 100 will move the decimal point two places to the left. 40 cm = 0.40 m

Check Understanding

Convert using mental math.

a. 0.1 m = ☐ cm   **b.** 100 m = ☐ hm   **c.** 12 cm = ☐ m

Use a conversion factor to convert.

d. 270 cm = ☐ dm   **e.** 0.4 cm = ☐ mm   **f.** 3.6 m = ☐ cm

g. Which measurement is more precise (exact), 4.125 mm or 4.13 mm?

Practice

Copy and complete the table.

	mm	cm	dm	m	dkm	hm	km
1.				443			
2.							825.7
3.	6910						
4.		53					

Compare. Write >, < or =.

5. 8.4 dm ◯ 840 cm

6. 0.6 cm ◯ 60 mm

7. 4230 mm ◯ 42.3 m

8. 0.7 m ◯ 7 cm

Choose the more reasonable measure.

9. Air mileage from New York City to Buenos Aires is 84.82 kilometers or 8482 kilometers.

10. In freestyle aerials, skiers soar 15–20 meters or 150–200 meters in the air while completing a series of acrobatic maneuvers.

11. The length of a piece of ruled notebook paper is 26.6 centimeters or 266 centimeters.

Convert using mental math.

12. 2 mm = ☐ cm

13. 30 mm = ☐ dm

14. 400 m = ☐ km

15. 36 cm = ☐ m

16. 3 km = ☐ m

17. 2.5 cm = ☐ mm

Convert to the given units.

18. 2.2 hm = ☐ m

19. 3.45 cm = ☐ mm

20. 60 cm = ☐ m

21. A 5.6-kilometer run is equal to how many meters?

Apply

22. On a map of Québec, Canada, 1 centimeter = 15 kilometers. If Trois-Rivières and Québec City are 8.3 centimeters apart on the map, what is the actual distance in kilometers?

23. At 11 years of age, Andrew Pinetti swam the 2.4 kilometers from Alcatraz to San Francisco in 31 minutes. How many kilometers per minute (rounded to the nearest hundredth) did Andrew swim? How many meters per minute is this?

24. The average distance from the earth to the sun is 149,600,000 kilometers. Write this distance in scientific notation.

Review

Change to standard form or scientific notation as appropriate.

1. 51,300

2. 7.4×10^4

3. 5.63×10^7

4. 4900

5. 6.32×10^3

6. 6,250,000

7. 9.5×10^5

8. 2,300,000,000

Compare Customary and Metric Units

Construct Meaning

In 1975, the US Metric Conversion Act was signed, declaring a national policy of encouraging the voluntary use of the metric system, or International System of Units (SI). Today the metric system exists side by side with the US Customary system.

It is important to know how to operate within each system and helpful to develop a sense of the size of metric units to make reasonable approximations.

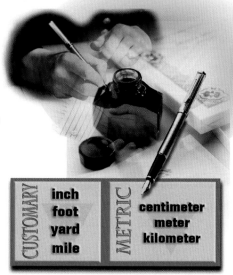

Some useful figures for comparing length in customary and metric systems include:

An inch is about 2.5 centimeters.
A foot is about 30 centimeters.
A meter is slightly longer than a yard (39.37 inches).
A kilometer is about 0.6 of a mile.
A mile is about 1.6 kilometers.

Use mental math to solve.

About how many centimeters equal 10 inches?

About how many miles are equal to 100 kilometers?

Is a distance of three yards more or less than three meters?

Is 45 inches longer or shorter than 45 centimeters?

Is the thickness of a magazine more likely to measure 1 inch or 1 centimeter?

Choosing a <u>convenient</u> unit of measure is also important. It is reasonable to select a unit that gives as small a whole number as possible.

Which is more sensible? Why?
- To measure the length of a city block in meters or kilometers
- To measure your height in centimeters or meters
- To find the length of a mountain hike in miles or yards

Check Understanding

Complete.
  a. The customary unit associated with the meter is the ☐.
  b. The metric unit associated with the mile is the ☐.
  c. A customary unit associated with the centimeter is the ☐.
  d. A metric unit that would be convenient for measuring the length of an ice rink is the ☐.
  e. A customary unit that would be convenient for measuring the height of a tree is the ☐.

Practice

Write the appropriate unit of measure for use in the customary system and in the metric system.

	CUSTOMARY	METRIC
1. The length of a marathon		
2. The width of a gold medal		
3. The length of one lap around the track		
4. The length of a landing mat for gymnastics		
5. The blade of an ice skate		
6. The length of a four-person bobsled		
7. The diameter of the shot used in the shot put		

Choose the more reasonable measure.

8. Height of the Statue of Liberty	91.5 in.	91.5 m
9. Length of your stride	0.5 m	$\frac{1}{2}$ ft
10. Height of Niagara Falls	176 km	176 ft
11. Width of an open newspaper	64 cm	64 in.
12. Length of an average newborn baby	20 in.	20 cm
13. Appalachian Trail from Maine to Georgia	2160 mi	2160 m
14. Height of a door	2 ft	2 m

Niagara Falls

Apply

15. If a road sign states "Exit 42, 3 miles," about how many kilometers is this?

16. Your family is on vacation in Mexico. The map you are using shows metric measurements with a key of 1 centimeter = 50 kilometers. The highway distance between Monterrey and Mexico City on the map is 18 centimeters. About how many miles is this?

17. The winning distance for the men's high jump was 2.39 meters. For women the winning attempt was 2.05 meters. Which jump was closer to 2 yards?

18. Would a 400-meter race be closer to 440 yards or 380 yards?

19. Nancy's bean plants have grown to a height of 10 centimeters by the fifth day. About how many inches is this?

Review

Convert fractions to decimals and decimals to fractions.

1. $\frac{17}{20}$ **2.** 0.125   **3.** $\frac{7}{16}$ **4.** $\frac{3}{50}$ **5.** 0.900

6. $\frac{5}{32}$ **7.** $\frac{21}{25}$ **8.** 0.875   **9.** 0.4   **10.** $\frac{3}{125}$

Customary Capacity and Weight

Construct Meaning

Seth's class is preparing hygiene boxes for the Mariner's Shelter. Each box will contain a bar of soap, one deodorant stick, a toothbrush, and a tube of toothpaste. A washcloth, hand towel, and bath towel will add $1\frac{1}{2}$ pounds to each box. How much will each box weigh in pounds and ounces?

The class goal is 24 boxes. What will be the total weight if the goal is met? To solve, use the equivalencies of capacity and weight in the customary system.

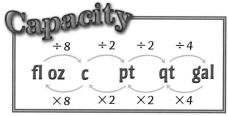

Find the weight of one filled box.

Box	⟶	4 oz
Soap	⟶	5 oz
Deodorant	⟶	2.75 oz
Toothbrush	⟶	1 oz
Toothpaste	⟶	3.25 oz

16 ounces = 1 lb

Add the 1.5 lb towel set. ⟶ + 1.5 lb

2.5 lb or 2 lb 8 oz

Customary Units of Weight

16 ounces (oz) = 1 pound (lb)
2000 pounds = 1 ton (T)

Determine the weight of 24 completed boxes.

24×2.5 lb = 60 pounds

How many gallons are in 30 quarts? Solve by using conversion factors.

$30 \text{ qt} \cdot \dfrac{1 \text{ gal}}{4 \text{ qt}}$ — Use the conversion factor to convert quarts to gallons. Multiply by the conversion factor with quarts in the denominator.

$\dfrac{30 \cancel{\text{ qt}} \cdot 1 \text{ gal}}{4 \cancel{\text{ qt}}}$ — Observe the units.

7.5 gal — Simplify.

There are 7.5 gallons in 30 quarts.

Customary Units of Capacity

3 teaspoons (tsp) = 1 tablespoon (tbsp)
2 tablespoons = 1 fluid ounce (fl oz)
8 fluid ounces = 1 cup (c)
2 cups = 1 pint (pt)
2 pints = 1 quart (qt)
4 quarts = 1 gallon (gal)

How many pints are in 2.5 gallons?

$2.5 \text{ gal} \cdot \dfrac{4 \text{ qt}}{1 \text{ gal}} \cdot \dfrac{2 \text{ pt}}{1 \text{ qt}} \cdot \dfrac{2.5 \cancel{\text{ gal}} \cdot 4 \cancel{\text{ qt}} \cdot 2 \text{ pt}}{1 \cancel{\text{ gal}} \cdot 1 \cancel{\text{ qt}}} = 20 \text{ pt}$

There are 20 pints in 2.5 gallons.

Check Understanding

a. What conversion factor is needed to convert cups to pints?

b. How many conversion factors are needed to convert ounces to tons? List them.

c. 18,000 T = ☐ lb   **d.** 9 qt = ☐ c   **e.** 12 lb 15 oz − 9 lb 8 oz = ☐ lb ☐ oz

Practice

Complete.

1. 7 lb = ☐ oz   **2.** $2\frac{1}{4}$ lb = ☐ oz   **3.** 35 qt = ☐ gal ☐ qt

4. $\frac{1}{4}$ c = ☐ fl oz   **5.** $\frac{1}{2}$ pt = ☐ c   **6.** $6\frac{1}{4}$ gal = ☐ qt

7. $\frac{1}{2}$ gal = ☐ qt   **8.** 259 oz = ☐ lb ☐ oz

Write the conversion factor(s) to change the following.

9. Cups to gallons   **10.** Pounds to ounces   **11.** Tons to pounds

Solve.

12. How many fluid ounces are in 2 cups?   **13.** How many cups are in one gallon?

14. How many gallons are in 4 pints?   **15.** How many pounds are in 12 tons?

16. How many pints are in 32 fluid ounces?   **17.** How many fluid ounces are in $\frac{1}{2}$ gallon?

Solve. Rename units as needed.

18.   18 lb 9 oz   **19.**   16 gal 1 qt   **20.**   5 T   450 lb   **21.**   3 qt 1 pt
    + 7 lb 8 oz   − 9 gal 3 qt   − 2 T 1800 lb   + 1 qt 1 pt

Apply

22. At the Chop Shop, pork loin roast costs $3.84 per pound. What will Allen pay for a cut that weighs $3\frac{3}{4}$ pounds?

23. Abby and Keith's twin daughters weighed a total of 13 pounds 3 ounces at birth. If Allison weighed $6\frac{1}{2}$ pounds, what did Alexandra weigh? The twins' older sister Anna weighed $25\frac{1}{4}$ pounds at the time. How much heavier was Anna than the smaller twin?

24. There are 280 guests expected at Jackie and Mike's wedding. It is estimated that each guest will drink two 5-fluid ounce cups of fruit punch. How many gallons of punch should be made?

25. Fred is carrying a load of quadruple sculls to the Summer Olympic Games. Each scull weighs 105 pounds. Fred's truck weighs 35,000 pounds when empty. How many sculls are in the trailer if the loaded truck weighs 36,890 pounds? What is the value of the cargo if each scull costs $13,600?

Metric Capacity and Mass

Construct Meaning

Knowing the mass of a horse is important for calculating balanced rations and giving medications. A horse owner can use a formula to estimate a horse's mass in metric units.

girth

Length

$$\text{Mass} = \frac{(\text{girth})^2 \cdot (\text{length})}{11{,}000}$$

If a horse has a girth of 178 cm and a length of 165 cm, what is its estimated mass?

$$\frac{178^2 \cdot 165}{11{,}000} = \frac{31{,}684 \cdot 165}{11{,}000} = \frac{5{,}227{,}860}{11{,}000} = 475 \text{ kg}$$

The **gram** is the basic unit for measuring **mass**, the amount of matter in an object. A dime has a mass of about 2 grams, and your textbook is about 1 kilogram. The **liter** is the basic unit for measuring **capacity**, the volume of an object expressed in liquid measurement. What everyday objects have a capacity measured in liters?

Metric Units of Mass
1000 milligrams (mg) = 1 gram (g)
1000 grams = 1 kilogram (kg)
1000 kilograms = 1 metric ton (t)

÷1000 ÷1000 ÷1000

mg   **g**   **kg**   **t**
milligram   gram   kilogram   metric ton

×1000 ×1000 ×1000

Metric Units of Capacity
1000 milliliters (mL) = 1 liter (L)

÷1000

mL   **L**
milliliter   liter

×1000

83 mL = ☐ L   83 ÷ 1000 = 0.083   83 mL = 0.083 L

720 g = ☐ mg   720 · 1000 = 720 000.   720 g = 720,000 mg

Dividing or multiplying by 1000 moves the decimal point three places to the left or three places to the right.

Patty's mother takes a 250 milligram calcium supplement every morning with breakfast. Use the appropriate conversion factor to convert this amount to grams.

$250 \text{ mg} \cdot \dfrac{1 \text{ g}}{1000 \text{ mg}}$ Multiply by a conversion factor.

$\dfrac{250 \text{ mg} \cdot 1 \text{ g}}{1000 \text{ mg}}$ Observe the units.

$\dfrac{250 \text{ g}}{1000} = 0.25 \text{ g}$ Simplify.

The calcium supplement is 0.25 gram.

Check Understanding

Convert to the given units.

a. 225 mL = ☐ L **b.** 6.4 kg = ☐ g **c.** 0.009 t = ☐ kg **d.** 0.73 L = ☐ mL

Practice

Convert to the given units.

1. 0.05 L = ☐ mL **2.** 950 mL = ☐ L **3.** 3 t = ☐ kg
4. 0.01 kg = ☐ g **5.** 4.2 kg = ☐ mg **6.** 841 mg = ☐ g

Write the letter of the most reasonable measurement.

7. Box of cereal
  a. 1.5 kg
  b. 510 g
  c. 51 g

8. Bottle of lemon extract
  a. 0.057 mL
  b. 5 L
  c. 57 mL

9. Mass of a hummingbird
  a. 0.014 g
  b. 0.014 kg
  c. 0.01 mg

10. Can of tomato juice
  a. 10 mL
  b. 1 L
  c. 100 mL

Compare. Write >, < or = .

11. 23 t ○ 230,000 kg **12.** 0.5 kg ○ 500 g **13.** 250 mL ○ 2.5 L

Apply

14. Which brand of calcium supplements is the better buy? Explain your answer.

| Brand A | $9.00 for 200 tablets | Three tablets provide 1.2 g of calcium. |
| Brand B | $4.50 for 100 tablets | Each tablet provides 250 mg of calcium. |

15. Chemical Trucking arrived at a farm having 100 acres of turf grass. The truck contained 1 metric ton of chemical. The driver used a table to determine how much chemical to deliver to the farm. What percentage of the contents of the truck did he deliver to that farm?

Chemical Application Table
8.5g/1000 sq ft grass

16. A Belgian mare needs between 1 and 1.5 kilograms of roughage daily per 100 kilograms of body weight. Will 0.4 metric ton of roughage be adequate for one month for a 777-kilogram horse? Explain your answer.

17. A horse having a 536 kilogram mass is given 0.75 kilogram of supplemental food per 100 kilograms of mass. The daily ration should be split into three equal feedings. How many grams of supplement would be given each time?

18. The Franklin's swimming pool has 0.4 the capacity of the Cotogno's pool. The Cotogno's pool holds 90,000 L of water. How much less water does the Franklin's pool hold?

Compare Customary and Metric Units

Construct Meaning

Meagahn McDonald is a registered nurse working in the Portland, Oregon, area. She grew up on the West Coast attending Christian schools. In her career Mrs. McDonald uses math every day. She uses it to calculate medication doses, count heart and respiratory rates, measure and track intake and output, convert Celsius to Fahrenheit, and convert metric to customary units. In her daily life she uses math when shopping, cooking, balancing her checkbook, and creating a budget.

Can you compare measures of capacity and mass in two different systems of measurement? Learn these approximations and you will be able to mentally estimate a quantity in either the customary or metric system.

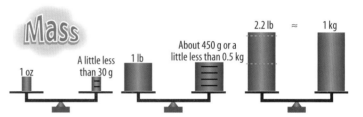

Some useful comparisons of capacity and mass include:

A fluid ounce is about 30 milliliters.

A quart is a little less than a liter.

A pound is a little less than one-half kilogram.

A kilogram is about 2.2 pounds.

Use mental math to solve.

About how many liters equal one gallon?
About how many pounds equal 50 kilograms?
Is 2 liters more or less than one-half gallon?
Would a bottle of cough syrup be more likely to contain 240 milliliters or 240 fluid ounces?

Check Understanding

a. Of the liquid measures pint, quart, liter, and cup, the ⬚ is the greatest.
b. Use a conversion factor to convert 10 pounds to kilograms.
c. The quart is associated with the metric unit ⬚.
d. Of the units of mass, kilogram, ounce, gram, and pound, the ⬚ is the least.
e. The metric unit often used to measure non-liquid medications is the ⬚.
f. Which is larger, a metric ton (t = 1000 kg) or a customary ton (T = 2000 lbs)?

Practice

Write *true* or *false*.

1. 3 qt < 3 L

2. 5 lb < 2 kg

3. 1 c < 1 L

4. $\frac{1}{2}$ kg is about 1 lb.

5. 4 fl oz is about 120 mL.

6. 1 oz < 30 g

7. 1 c is about 50 mL.

8. 1 t < 1 T

Solve.

9. If 1 lb is about 450 g, $\frac{1}{2}$ lb is approximately ☐ g.

10. If 1 kg is greater than 2 lb, is 5 kg greater or less than 10 lb?

11. Would a 2-liter pitcher hold a half-gallon of apple juice?

12. If a kitten has a mass of 0.5 kg, would this be greater or less than one pound?

13. If 1 fl oz is about 30 mL, would 1 pint be more or less than 500 mL?

14. If the weight of an automobile is given as 3000 lb, is this greater or less than 1300 kg?

Apply

Compare the customary and metric units to determine the better buy.

15. $\frac{1}{2}$ gal ice cream $3.99
or
2 L ice cream $3.99

16. 1 lb $3.20
or
$\frac{1}{2}$ kg $3.20

17. Crackers   10 oz $2.79
or
Crackers   200 g $2.79

18. Ketchup   36 oz $2.39
or
Ketchup   680 g $2.39

Review

Solve.

1. 21.472 − 9.7

2. 3.42 + 15.095

3. 0.085 · 69

4. 0.43 · 0.08

5. 3.55 ÷ 15

6. 6.0031 − 0.8582

7. 0.3726 ÷ 0.018

8. 5.6139 + 11.26 + 0.7

Conversion Factors with Rates

Construct Meaning

The winning cyclist in the 240-kilometer men's Olympic road race completed the course in just over 5 hours. What was his average speed in kilometers per hour? Use the formula: rate (or speed) = distance/time. Substitute the values into the formula.

$$r = \frac{d}{t} = \frac{240 \text{ km}}{5 \text{ hr}} = \frac{48 \text{ km}}{1 \text{ hr}} = 48 \text{ km/hr}$$

Find his speed in kilometers per minute.
Use a conversion factor to change one rate to another.

Convert
hr to min

$$\frac{48 \text{ km}}{1 \text{ hr}} \cdot \frac{1 \text{ hr}}{60 \text{ min}} = \frac{48 \text{ km}}{60 \text{ min}} = 0.8 \text{ km/min}$$

To convert a unit in the *denominator* of a rate, choose a conversion factor with that unit in the *numerator*.

Use multiple conversion factors to calculate this speed in meters per second.

Convert   Convert
km to m   min to sec

$$\frac{0.8 \text{ km}}{1 \text{ min}} \cdot \frac{1000 \text{ m}}{1 \text{ km}} \cdot \frac{1 \text{ min}}{60 \text{ sec}} = \frac{0.8 \cdot 1000 \text{ m}}{60 \text{ sec}} = 13.\overline{3} \text{ m/sec}$$

---

175 km/hr is equivalent to about 110 mph. Convert 175 kilometers per hour to meters per second. Use multiple conversion factors. Round your answer to the nearest tenth.

Convert   Convert   Convert
km to m   hr to min   min to sec

$$\frac{175 \text{ km}}{1 \text{ hr}} \cdot \frac{1000 \text{ m}}{1 \text{ km}} \cdot \frac{1 \text{ hr}}{60 \text{ min}} \cdot \frac{1 \text{ min}}{60 \text{ sec}} = \frac{175 \cdot 1000 \text{ m}}{60 \cdot 60 \text{ sec}} = 48.6 \text{ m/sec}$$

Restaurants must calculate food costs in order to establish menu prices. For use in sauces each day Lucio's Restaurant prepares 45 pounds of tomatoes at a cost of $0.79 a pound. What is the cost per serving for the tomatoes if Lucio's serves the sauces to about 600 customers daily?

From the information in the problem, determine what rates will produce an answer with the correct units in the numerator and denominator.

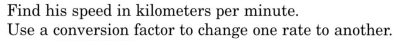

$$\frac{45 \text{ lb}}{1 \text{ day}} \cdot \frac{\$0.79}{1 \text{ lb}} \cdot \frac{1 \text{ day}}{600 \text{ servings}} = \frac{45 \cdot \$0.79}{600 \text{ servings}} \approx \$0.06 \text{ per serving}$$

Check Understanding
Convert each unit rate to an equivalent unit rate.
  a. 90 kilometers per hour to kilometers per minute
  b. 4 fluid ounces per hour to quarts per day
  c. $6.88 per pound to cents per ounce
  d. 4.8 meters per minute to centimeters per second

Practice
Convert.

1. 75 mi/hr to mi/min

2. $7.20/yd to $/ft

3. $4.64/lb to cents/oz

4. 6 m/sec to km/hr

5. Top speed for a peregrine falcon exceeds 200 miles per hour. How many feet can the falcon fly per second?

6. The black mamba snake has a maximum speed of about 550 meters per minute. Convert this to kilometers per hour.

7. The largest blue whale ever measured weighed 380,000 pounds and was about 90 feet long. What was her average weight in pounds per foot of length? (Round your answer to the nearest whole number.)

8. At a speed equivalent to 109 kilometers per hour, the cosmopolitan sailfish is the fastest fish in the sea. At this rate, how many meters could the sailfish swim in one minute? (Round your answer to the nearest whole number.)

Apply
Solve.

9. If Tuff Tread Tire Company manufactures 1440 tires in an 8-hour shift, how many tires are produced every 15 minutes?

10. The SR-71 Blackbird reconnaissance plane can fly at about 2160 mph—three times the speed of sound. How many miles per second can the SR-71 fly?

11. The cost of drapery material was $52.15 for $3\frac{1}{2}$ yards. How much did the fabric cost per yard? How much per foot? (Round your answers to the nearest cent.)

12. Mr. Maxwell's salary is $46,500 per year. How much income does he receive each payday if he is paid twice a month?

Problem Solving

A *stadium* was originally a Greek unit of measure equal to about 200 yards. At the first Olympic festival in 776 B.C. the only athletic event was the stadium foot race, a 200-yard dash.

Olympic Stadium, Athens, Greece

Apply

1. The stadium foot race continued to be the single athletic event of the Olympic festivals until 724 B.C., when a two-stadia race was added to the Olympic competition. If the festivals were held every four years, how many were held with just a single athletic event?

WORLD TRACK AND FIELD RECORDS

Event	Name	Country	Year	Record
100-Meter Dash	Tim Montgomery	USA	2002	9.78 sec
1000-Meter Run	Noah Ngeny	Kenya	1999	2 min 11.96 sec
Mile Run	Hicham El Guerrouj	MAR	1999	3 min 43.13 sec
Men's High Jump	Javier Sotomayor	Cuba	1993	8 ft $\frac{1}{2}$ in.
Women's High Jump	Stefka Kostadinova	Bulgaria	1987	6 ft 10 $\frac{1}{4}$ in.
Men's Long Jump	Mike Powell	USA	1999	29 ft 4 $\frac{1}{2}$ in.
Women's Long Jump	Galina Chistyakova	URS	1988	24 ft 8 $\frac{1}{4}$ in.

The table above lists the world records through November, 2002. Use the table to answer the following questions.

2. In the high jump, about how many meters did Stefka Kostadinova jump? In the long jump, about how many meters did Mike Powell jump?

3. In 1985 the Russian high jumper Rudolf Paklin set a world record of 7 feet 10 $\frac{3}{4}$ inches. How much higher did Javier Sotomayor jump in 1993?

4. How many kilometers did Noah Ngeny run in his event? About how many kilometers farther did Hicham El Guerrouj run in his event?

5. Determine Hicham's average speed in miles per hour and Noah's approximate average speed in miles per hour. (Hint: Consider the steps needed to convert the listed times.) Use a calculator.

WORLD TRACK AND FIELD RECORDS				
Country	Gold	Silver	Bronze	**Points**
Germany	12	16	7	75
United States	10	13	11	☐
Norway	11	7	6	53

6. Referring to the table, determine how points are assessed and calculate the number of points won by Team USA at the 2002 Winter Olympics.

7. What was the combined number of medals won by the top two European countries competing at the 2002 Winter Olympics?

WORLD TRACK AND FIELD RECORDS		
Class	**Winner**	**Time**
Women	Team USA	3:29.95
Men	Team USA	3:03.71

The table shows the winners of a relay event in the 1994 World Junior Track and Field competition. Each race was run by four team members who ran 400 meters each. The total times given are in minutes, seconds, and hundredths of seconds.

8. What was the average time (to the nearest hundredth of a second) run by each member of the men's team?

9. In the US Junior Olympics held in 2000, the bantam girls team ran the 1600-meter relay in 4:19.00. How much longer did it take them to complete this event than the women's World Junior Championship team?

Transformed Lives

Meagahn McDonald expresses the impact that Christian school education had on her life:

"My Christian school teachers emphasized that Jesus Christ needed to be the center of my life. By integrating biblical principles into their classes, they taught me that God cares about every detail of my life. He is not just interested in being involved in my 'church life,' but He cares about every aspect, no matter how large or small. Whether it be a math problem I struggled with, or a major life decision, I learned that God is available and interested. This lesson has helped me greatly in my nursing career. There are so many times I come to the end of my abilities when caring for my patients—I don't know what more I can do for them to make them more comfortable or to improve their condition. So I pray sometimes silently and sometimes with the patients to ask for God's help and to seek His healing and comfort. I have received many answers to my prayers, and I have seen situations change as God has answered."

Temperature/Study Guide

Construct Meaning

Before the 2002 Winter Olympic Games in Salt Lake City, Utah, the Olympic torch was taken on a cross-country tour of the United States.

Use a formula to convert the daytime temperatures of the cities through which the torch traveled.

Formulas to Convert Temperature

<table>
<tr><td>

Convert Fahrenheit to Celsius

$$C = \frac{5}{9}(F - 32)$$

Example: $95°F = \Box °C$

$$C = \frac{5}{9}(95 - 32)$$

$$C = \frac{5}{9}\left(\frac{63}{1}\right)$$

$$C = 35°$$

</td><td>

Convert Celsius to Fahrenheit

$$F = \frac{9}{5}C + 32$$

Example: $45°C = \Box °F$

$$F = \frac{9}{5} \cdot 45 + 32$$

$$F = \frac{9}{5} \cdot \frac{45}{1} + 32$$

$$F = 81 + 32$$

$$F = 113°$$

</td></tr>
</table>

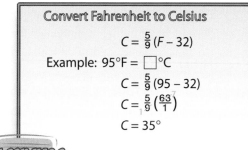

You can use a calculator to convert temperatures.

Enter degrees Fahrenheit.

① Subtract 32.
② Multiply by 5.
③ Divide by 9.

The calculator displays the Celsius temperature.

Enter degrees Celsius.

① Multiply by 9.
② Divide by 5.
③ Add 32.

The calculator displays the Fahrenheit temperature.

Check Understanding

 **USING A CALCULATOR** Convert the temperature of each host city.

a. Washington, D.C. $5°C = \Box °F$

b. Kansas City, MO $35.6°F = \Box °C$

c. Oklahoma City, OK $46.4°F = \Box °C$

d. Tucson, AZ $11°C = \Box °F$

e. Los Angeles, CA $20°C = \Box °F$

f. Olympia, WA $48.2°F = \Box °C$

Practice

Convert each temperature.

1. Atlanta, GA $44.6°F = \Box °C$

2. New Orleans, LA $53.6°F = \Box °C$

3. San Antonio, TX $14°C = \Box °F$

4. Louisville, KY $2°C = \Box °F$

5. Compare the Fahrenheit temperature halfway between boiling and freezing to the Celsius temperature halfway between boiling and freezing. Are these two temperatures equivalent? Is this temperature commonly found on the earth's surface?

Chapter 8 Study Guide

Solve. *Lesson 8.1*

1. 15 yd
  − 9 yd 2 ft

2. 7 ft 8 in.
  ×   4

3. 23 yd 2 ft 6 in.
  + 17 yd 2 ft 9 in.

Compare. Write >, < or = . *Lesson 8.2*

4. 3200 mm ○ 32 cm

5. 4100 m ○ 4.1 km

6. 1.7 m ○ 1700 cm

Choose the more reasonable measure. *Lesson 8.3*

7. The height of an adult male: 70 in. or 70 cm

8. Length of a puppy: 12 cm or 12 in.

9. Height of some Himalayan peaks: 8 km or 8 mi

Solve. *Lesson 8.4*

10. 6 lb 12 oz
  ×   4

11. 12 gal 1 qt
  − 3 gal 3 qt

12.   9 qt 2 c 5 fl oz
  + 4 qt 1 c 7 fl oz

Compare. Write >, < or = . *Lesson 8.5*

13. 1.5 kg ○ 150 g

14. 81 g ○ 8100 mg

Choose the more reasonable measure. *Lesson 8.6*

15. Weight of a bowling ball: 6 kg or 6 lb

16. Capacity of a juice pitcher: 2 L or 20 c

Convert each rate. *Lesson 8.7*

17. 18 kilometers per hour to meters per minute

18. $2.45 for 7 liters to cents per liter

19. 630 miles per hour to feet per minute

20. Geoff determined that he ran an average of 12 km/hr. About how many miles per hour did he run? *Lesson 8.8*

Convert to the given units. *Lesson 8.9*

21. 70°C = □ °F

22. 59°F = □ °C

Meagahn McDonald advises every young adult: "Make the most of every day that you have. Enjoy life and the blessings that God has given you, but do not be frivolous with your time and resources. Use what you have now to make a difference in the lives of people around you. You do not need to wait until you are older and grown up for God to use you. I Timothy 4:12 says: 'Don't let anyone look down on you because you are young, but set an example for the believers in speech, in life, in love, in faith and in purity.' (NIV) God has a unique purpose and specific plan for each of your lives. Pray and ask Him for guidance, and He will not disappoint you. He will lead you to a career or type of work that will enable you to use the gifts that He has placed within you."

Go for the Gold

Choose the more reasonable measure.

1. Mass of an automobile: 7000 kg or 700 kg

2. Volume of a bucket of water: 12 qt or 12 c

3. Chicago, Illinois, to Toronto, Ontario:
   850 km or 85 km

4. Weight of a tennis ball: 3 oz or 12 oz

5. Cup of hot tea: 15°C or 50°C

6. Height of the Statue of Liberty:
   300 yd or 300 ft

Solve. Rename units as needed.

7. $\begin{array}{r} 20 \text{ ft } 3 \text{ in.} \\ -9 \text{ ft } 8 \text{ in.} \\ \hline \end{array}$

8. $\begin{array}{r} 3 \text{ T } 875 \text{ lb} \\ \times 4 \\ \hline \end{array}$

9. $\begin{array}{r} 42 \text{ gal } 3 \text{ qt } 1 \text{ pt } 1 \text{ c} \\ +18 \text{ gal } 2 \text{ qt} 1 \text{ c} \\ \hline \end{array}$

10. $\begin{array}{r} 5 \text{ qt } 7 \text{ fl oz} \\ \times 9 \\ \hline \end{array}$

Compute.

11. 1000 mm = ____ m

12. 10 m = ____ dkm

13. 1 m = ____ cm

14. 1 km = ____ m

15. 16 cm = ____ m

16. 540 cm = ____ mm

17. 94 mg = ____ g

18. 4352.8 mL = ____ L

19. 76.5 kg = ____ t

20. 4 m 62 cm = ____ cm

21. $3\frac{1}{3}$ yd = ____ ft

22. $2\frac{1}{2}$ pt = ____ c

Convert each rate.

23. $5.74 for 14 pounds to cents per ounce

24. 289 miles in 5 hours to miles per hour

25. 2784 liters per day to liters per hour

26. $77.20 for 8 hours work to an hourly rate

27. 690 assembled per hour to the rate per minute

Compare customary and metric units.

28. A.J. is allowed to take 20 kilograms of luggage on the airline flight. Is this closer to 40 pounds or 10 pounds?

29. A car's gas tank has a capacity of 15 gallons. Is this closer to 16 liters or 60 liters?

30. A tower is 250 feet high. Is this closer to 80 meters or 180 meters?

Solve.

31. Pam shipped six identical packages on the air express service. Each weighed 28 ounces. What was the total weight in pounds?

32. A common gross maximum weight for a freight truck is 15,400 kilograms. If the weight is evenly distributed over the three axles, how many metric tons does each axle carry? Round to the nearest ton.

33. When the Geiger family left home, the odometer in their car read 52,548 miles. When they arrived in Thunder Bay, Ontario, it read 53,504 miles. They had used $43\frac{1}{2}$ gallons of gas. How many miles per gallon did they get on the trip?

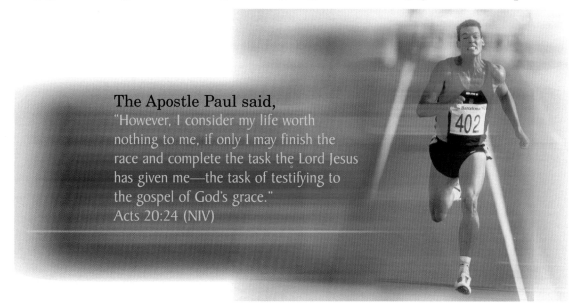

The Apostle Paul said,
"However, I consider my life worth nothing to me, if only I may finish the race and complete the task the Lord Jesus has given me—the task of testifying to the gospel of God's grace."
Acts 20:24 (NIV)

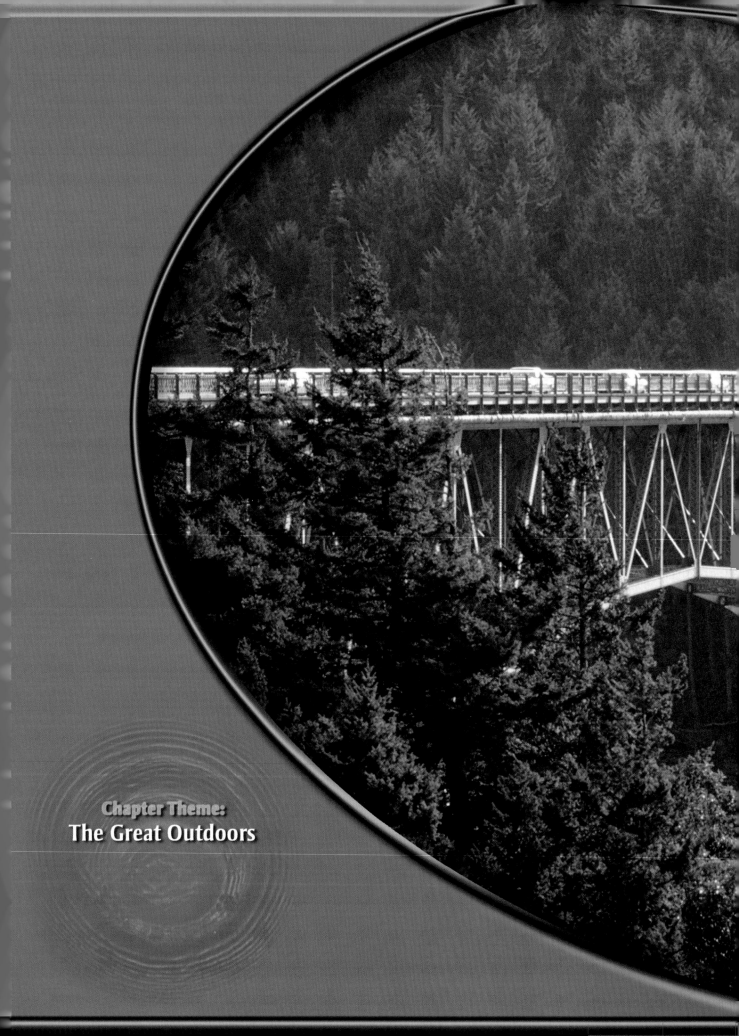

Chapter Theme:
The Great Outdoors

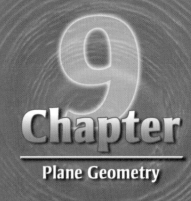

9 Chapter

Plane Geometry

Construct Meaning

Words are one means of communicating knowledge. Good writers have a powerful command of language, which allows them to express ideas clearly and beautifully. Every new word you learn increases your vocabulary and your ability to communicate well.

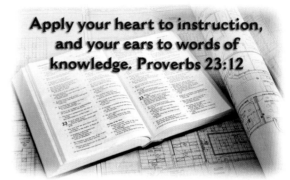

Apply your heart to instruction, and your ears to words of knowledge. Proverbs 23:12

Plane geometry deals with two-dimensional figures.

A **point** is a specific location in space. A collection of all points extending without end in two dimensions in every direction is called a **plane**.

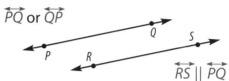

A **line** is a straight path of points that extends without end in opposite directions. A line is defined by any two of its points. Two lines are **parallel** if they lie in the same plane and have no points in common.

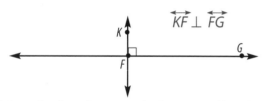

Intersecting lines share one point in common. Lines that intersect at **right angles** (90°) are **perpendicular**.

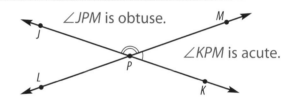

Intersecting lines that are not perpendicular form angles that are either **acute** (less than 90°) or **obtuse** (greater than 90° but less than 180°).

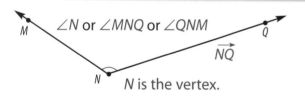

A **ray** is part of a line that begins at a point and extends without end in one direction. Two rays that originate at the same point form an **angle**. The common endpoint is the **vertex** of the angle.

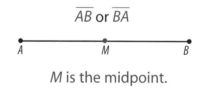

A **line segment** is the part of a line that lies between two endpoints. The point halfway between the endpoints of a line segment is its **midpoint**. The midpoint **bisects** the line segment, dividing it into two congruent parts.

A **perpendicular bisector** is a line that intersects a line segment at a right angle and divides it into two congruent segments.

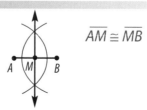

Line segments or angles having equal measures are **congruent**.

Check Understanding

a. Give all possible names for the rays in the drawing.

b. Name the vertex.

c. Which of the following name the angle correctly?

∠*BAE*   ∠*D*   ∠*ACE*   ∠*EAD*

∠*ABD*   ∠*CAB*   ∠*A*   ∠*BCA*

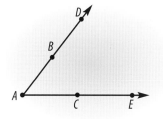

d. Which is larger, ∠*BAC* or ∠*DAE*?

e. In the figure at the right, is $\overrightarrow{QS}$ the same as $\overrightarrow{QR}$?

f. Is $\overrightarrow{QR}$ the same as $\overrightarrow{QR}$?

g. Is $\overline{QR}$ the same as $\overline{RQ}$?

Practice

In the drawing, three equally spaced parallel, vertical lines intersect a horizontal line and line segment at 90° angles. Write the names of the figures that match each description.

1. Lines containing point *D*

2. Line segments with endpoint *B*

3. Rays beginning at point *C*

4. Angles with vertex *G*

5. Parallel lines

6. Perpendicular lines

7. Line segments with labeled midpoints

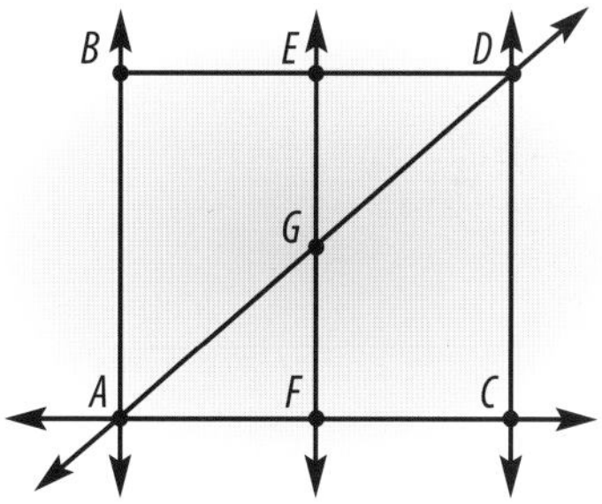

8. In this figure, how many angles share *A* as a common vertex?

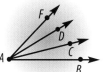

9. If $\overleftrightarrow{XY} \perp \overleftrightarrow{AZ}$ and $\overleftrightarrow{BC} \perp \overleftrightarrow{AZ}$, what is the relationship between $\overleftrightarrow{XY}$ and $\overleftrightarrow{BC}$?

10. Robbie says two intersecting lines create one angle. Angela says two. Who is right?

11. If $\overline{FG}$ is 67 cm long and *H* is the midpoint of $\overline{FG}$, what is the length of $\overline{GH}$?

Apply

12. Draw and label ∠*EFG*.

13. Draw and label $\overrightarrow{AD}$.

14. Draw $\overleftrightarrow{AC}$. Then use a compass to construct $\overline{AB} \perp \overleftrightarrow{AC}$.

15. Draw four different arrangements of three lines such that they have 0, 1, 2, or 3 intersections.

187

Construct Meaning

Just as words are the building blocks of literature, geometry is one of the building blocks of visual art. Angles can be used to create perspective or to fit pieces together. All expert artists must begin by learning the basics.

vanishing point

When the sum of the measures of two angles equals 90°, the angles are **complementary**.

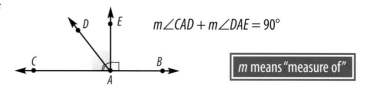

$m\angle CAD + m\angle DAE = 90°$

m means "measure of"

An angle that measures 180° is a **straight angle**. $m\angle GEH = 180°$

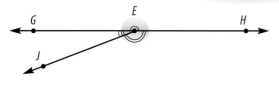

$m\angle JEG + m\angle JEH = 180°$

Two adjacent angles that form a straight line are a **linear pair**.

When the sum of the measures of two angles equals 180°, the angles are **supplementary**.

Two intersecting lines form two pairs of congruent **vertical angles**.

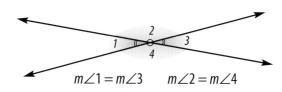

$m\angle 1 = m\angle 3 \qquad m\angle 2 = m\angle 4$

A **transversal** is a line that intersects two or more lines.

A transversal that intersects two parallel lines forms pairs of congruent **corresponding angles** in matching positions.

$$m\angle 1 = m\angle 5 \qquad m\angle 3 = m\angle 7$$
$$m\angle 2 = m\angle 6 \qquad m\angle 4 = m\angle 8$$

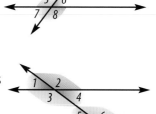

A transversal that intersects two lines forms angles both between and outside the lines. Congruent **alternate interior angles** are pairs of angles formed between parallel lines on either side of a transversal, one angle at each intersection.

$$m\angle 3 = m\angle 6 \qquad m\angle 4 = m\angle 5$$

Congruent **alternate exterior angles** are formed outside parallel lines on either side of a transversal, one angle at each intersection.

$$m\angle 1 = m\angle 8 \qquad m\angle 2 = m\angle 7$$

Check Understanding

In the drawing, identify two angles or two pairs of angles that match the terms.

a. Acute
b. Obtuse
c. Right
d. Straight
e. Linear pair
f. Supplementary
g. Corresponding
h. Alternate interior
i. Alternate exterior

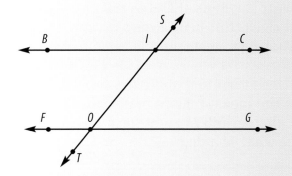

Practice

Match the given angles with a term at the right. Use <u>all</u> letters a through h.

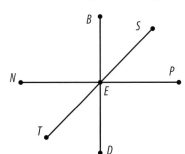

1. ∠*BET* and ∠*SED*
2. ∠*BED* and ∠*PEN*
3. ∠*NET* and ∠*PET*
4. ∠*NED* and ∠*PED*
5. ∠*BEN* and ∠*BES*
6. ∠*SEP* and ∠*NET*
7. ∠*NET* and ∠*TED*
8. ∠*TED* and ∠*SEP*

a. Right
b. Acute
c. Obtuse
d. Complementary
e. Supplementary
f. Vertical
g. Straight
h. None

Answer *true* or *false*.

9. The complement of an acute angle is obtuse.
10. If one angle of a linear pair is acute, the other is obtuse.
11. The sum of the angles formed by any two intersecting lines equals 360°.
12. All linear pairs are supplementary angles.

13. Find the measure of the remaining numbered angles if $m\angle 1 = 75°$.

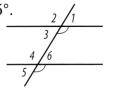

Name the angle pairs from the drawing at right.
14. ∠3 and ∠7
15. ∠1 and ∠6
16. ∠6 and ∠8
17. ∠1 and ∠8
18. ∠1 and ∠3

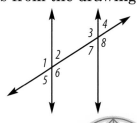

Apply

19. Peter needs to cut two 49" braces as shown from an 8-foot two-by-four. Make a drawing to show how this could be done. What is the geometric relationship between the 45° angles where the two-by-four is cut?

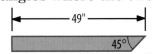

Measuring Angles

Construct Meaning

Creativity begins with the ability to imagine something new. In 1656 Christiaan Huygens, a Dutch scientist, invented the first mechanical clock that kept accurate time by employing the regular oscillating movement of a pendulum.

The hands of a clock turn to display the time. An angle can be thought of as the measurement of a turn. The hands in the clock in the photograph at right form an angle of 150 degrees. But what is a degree?

 1°

One degree (1°) measures a very small turn. One complete turn around a circle measures 360°.

What is the measure of the angle formed between the hour and minute hands at 3:40?

Angles are used by ships and aircraft for navigation. The direction a ship travels is often described by the degree of turn relative to north. The distance a ship travels can be plotted as the length of a line segment on the ray of an angle.

North

East Northeast

76°

263 miles

Many times you can determine the measurement of an angle by its relationship to other known angles.

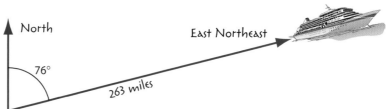

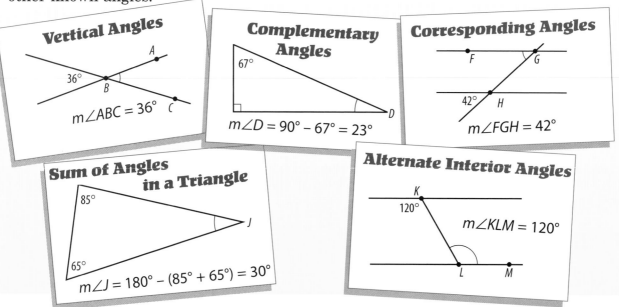

Vertical Angles

A

36°

B

C

$m\angle ABC = 36°$

Complementary Angles

67°

D

$m\angle D = 90° - 67° = 23°$

Corresponding Angles

F

G

42° H

$m\angle FGH = 42°$

Sum of Angles in a Triangle

85°

J

65°

$m\angle J = 180° - (85° + 65°) = 30°$

Alternate Interior Angles

K

120°

$m\angle KLM = 120°$

L M

Check Understanding

a. How many degrees does each interval on the clock face represent?

b. How many degrees are there between consecutive numbers?

c. What is the measurement of the angle between the hands at 4:00?

d. What is the measurement of the angle between the hands at 6:30?

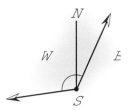

e. Two ships leave a port at the same time, one at a heading of 98° west and the other at a heading of 25° east. What is the measure of the angle between their headings?

f. One angle of a right triangle is 22°. What are the measures of the other two angles?

g. If $m\angle 2 = 125°$ what is the measure of $\angle 6$?

Practice

Trace the clock picture above and draw the hands accurately for each problem. Determine the measure of the angle between the clock hands.

1. At 6:00   **2.** At 10:00   **3.** At 4:30   **4.** At 6:20

Make a drawing using a protractor and ruler.

5. A plane travels 100 miles on a heading 40° west of north. Let $\frac{1}{8}$ inch = 10 miles.

6. A ship travels 450 km on a heading 100° east of north. Let 1 mm = 10 km.

Make a drawing and label the measures of the angles.

7. Two vertical angles each measure 126°. What is the measure of each adjacent angle?

8. Two angles in a triangle measure 24° and 33°. What is the measure of the third interior angle?

A transversal intersects two parallel lines as shown, forming $\angle 1 = 60°$. Give the measure for the following angles:

9. The alternate exterior angle to $\angle 1$

10. An angle supplementary to $\angle 1$

11. What is the measure of $\angle CBD$?

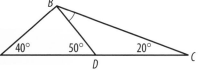

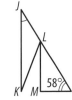

12. If $\overline{JK} \parallel \overline{LM}$ and $\overline{MP} \perp \overline{LM}$ and $m\angle P = 58°$, what is the measure of $\angle J$?

Apply

13. An aircraft carrier is sailing on a heading of 43.5° northeast. Two fighter jets are dispatched on a heading of 82.5° east-northeast. What is the degree of angle between the headings of the fighters and their ship?

Working with Triangles

Construct Meaning

Sometimes we forget to appreciate the importance of familiar things. How often do you think about the air you breathe or about God's faithful love? Triangles play important roles in our world. They are used to strengthen buildings and structures, to survey land, and as elements of artistic design.

Triangles are classified by sides . . .

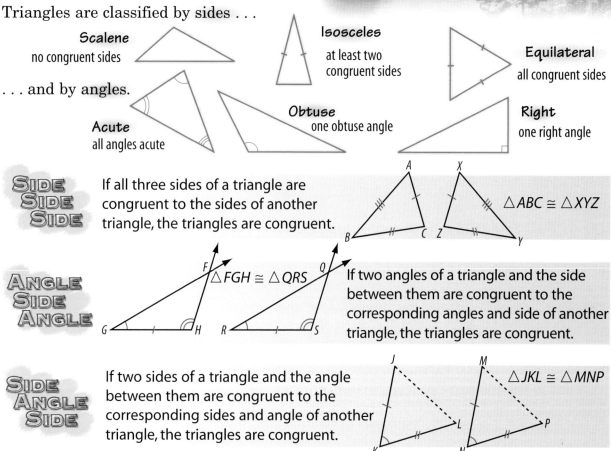

Scalene
no congruent sides

Isosceles
at least two congruent sides

Equilateral
all congruent sides

. . . and by angles.

Acute
all angles acute

Obtuse
one obtuse angle

Right
one right angle

SIDE SIDE SIDE If all three sides of a triangle are congruent to the sides of another triangle, the triangles are congruent.

$\triangle ABC \cong \triangle XYZ$

ANGLE SIDE ANGLE $\triangle FGH \cong \triangle QRS$ If two angles of a triangle and the side between them are congruent to the corresponding angles and side of another triangle, the triangles are congruent.

SIDE ANGLE SIDE If two sides of a triangle and the angle between them are congruent to the corresponding sides and angle of another triangle, the triangles are congruent.

$\triangle JKL \cong \triangle MNP$

Check Understanding

a. Classify the triangles in the quilt pattern block at right.

b. How many large triangles appear congruent?

c. How many small triangles appear congruent?

d. Why is it not possible for a triangle to have more than one right or obtuse angle?

e. If an isosceles triangle has congruent angles measuring 58° each, what is the measure of the third angle?

f. What are the measures of the angles in an isosceles right triangle?

g. Name the triangle with congruent sides and congruent angles.

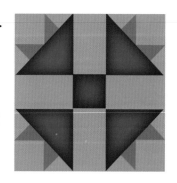

h. M is the midpoint of $\overline{AB}$ and $\overline{CD}$. If you draw $\overline{AC}$ and $\overline{DB}$, will the resulting triangles be congruent? By what rule?

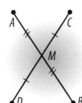

i. In this pair of congruent triangles find the value of a.

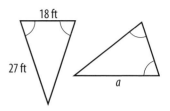

Practice

1. In the quilt block at left, classify the different types of triangles.

2. How many congruent right triangles do you see in the pattern at right?

3. Without measuring, calculate the measure of each angle in one of the green obtuse isosceles triangles at right.

4. Name the right triangle, the isosceles triangle, and the obtuse triangle.

5. Which side of the second congruent triangle is 16 inches?

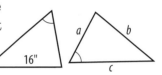

Find the value of x for each pair of congruent triangles.

6.
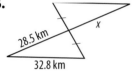

7.

8.
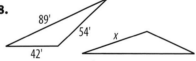

Write which rule shows each pair of triangles to be congruent: SSS, ASA, or SAS.

9.
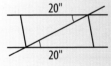

10.
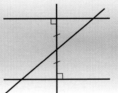

11.
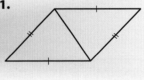

Apply

12. Pat marked two pieces of stiff wire as shown and challenged Chris to take either piece, bend it on the marks, and form a triangle. Chris took the second piece and made a triangle. Then Pat took the first piece and did the same. Were the triangles congruent?

13. The ideal kitchen has cook top, refrigerator, and sink located in such a way that the front center points of each form a triangle whose sides are between 4 and 9 feet and the sum of whose sides is no more than 26 feet. Draw a 3" square representing a kitchen floor plan at a scale of $\frac{1}{4}$" = 1'. Draw your ideal kitchen. Don't forget windows and doors! Measure the distances between sink, cook top, and refrigerator. Do these distances fit within the guidelines?

9.5 Similar Triangles

Construct Meaning

For a school project, Maddy and Bill had to measure the height of the 15-story Franklin Insurance building. "We can do this on a sunny day with my dad's measuring tape," said Bill. Maddy was skeptical.

On Saturday, the students went downtown. On the corner near the insurance building they found a street signpost. Bill reached to the top of the signpost with the measuring tape and Maddy read at the ground. The signpost measured 8 ft 9 in. (8.75 ft). Next, they measured the shadow cast by the signpost on the ground and found it to be exactly 2 feet 6 in. (2.5 ft). Then they measured the length of the building's shadow, which was 48 ft 3 in. (48.25 ft).

The two triangles formed by the objects and their shadows are similar. **Similar triangles** have congruent angles. Their sides are proportionate.

Write the proportion.	$\dfrac{8.75}{2.5} = \dfrac{h}{48.25}$
Cross multiply.	$2.5h = (8.75)(48.25)$
Simplify.	$2.5h = 422.2$
Divide.	$h = \dfrac{422.2}{2.5}$
	$h = 168.9$

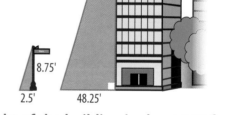

The height of the building is about 169 feet.

Surveyors make measurements using an instrument called a theodolite, a telescope mounted on a tripod. Here is how the height of a radio transmission tower could be measured—even on a cloudy day.

The larger triangle is similar to the smaller triangle within it.

Solve the proportion. $\dfrac{5}{7.1} = \dfrac{h}{107.1}$

$h = 75.4$ ft

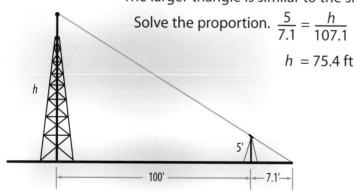

The side opposite the right angle in a right triangle is called the **hypotenuse**. The two sides forming the right angle are called **legs**.

Check Understanding

a. One triangle has sides measuring 5, 4, and 6 inches. Another has sides of 12, 8, and 9 inches. Are the triangles similar?

b. One triangle has sides measuring 3, 4, and 5 cm. The longest side of a similar triangle is 20 cm. What are the lengths of its other two sides?

c. Find the measure of side x.

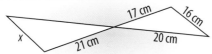

d. Find the measure of side y.

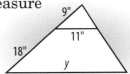

Practice

1. One triangle has sides of 2.4, 3.2, and 3.4 cm. Is it similar to a triangle whose sides are 3.6, 4.8, and 5.1 cm?

2. One triangle has sides measuring $1\frac{1}{2}$, $3\frac{1}{4}$, and $2\frac{3}{8}$ inches. Two sides of a similar triangle measure $4\frac{3}{4}$ and 3 inches. What is the length of its third side?

3. Find the lengths of r and s.

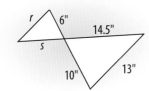

4. Given $m\overline{CD}$ = 11 yd, $m\overline{BF}$ = 14 yd, and $m\overline{AF}$ = 28 yd, what is the length of $\overline{AE}$?

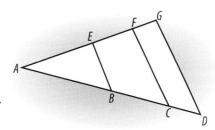

5. Lengths of sides:

△1	9"	21"	27"
△2	12"	28"	36"
△3	18"	45"	54"

Which two triangles are similar?

6. Lengths of sides:

△4	7.5 cm	12.5 cm	9 cm
△5	5 cm	9 cm	6 cm
△6	2.5 cm	4.5 cm	3 cm

Which two triangles are similar?

7. Given $\overline{EB} \parallel \overline{FC} \parallel \overline{GD}$.
$m\overline{AG}$ = 48 mm $m\overline{FC}$ = 25 mm
$m\overline{AD}$ = 64 mm $m\overline{EB}$ = 16 mm
$m\overline{GD}$ = 32 mm
Find the measures of $\overline{BC}$ and $\overline{FG}$.

Apply

8. Mike and Jeff were at the driving range with their dads. After watching for a time, Jeff suggested they guess the height of the safety netting. Jeff guessed 20 feet and Mike guessed 25 feet. Then Jeff got a putting iron and a measuring tape from his dad's truck. Use the diagram to determine the height of the net.

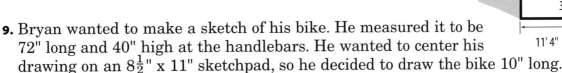

9. Bryan wanted to make a sketch of his bike. He measured it to be 72" long and 40" high at the handlebars. He wanted to center his drawing on an $8\frac{1}{2}$" x 11" sketchpad, so he decided to draw the bike 10" long.
a. Approximately how tall will the sketch be?
b. How far from the bottom should he draw the wheels?

9.6 **Attributes of Quadrilaterals**

Construct Meaning

Out of the ground the LORD God formed every beast of the field and every bird of the air, and brought them to Adam to see what he would call them. Genesis 2:19a

God allowed Adam to name the animals. A name is the first step to making new acquaintances and gaining new knowledge. Naming and comparing the plane figures classified as quadrilaterals leads to greater knowledge of geometric relationships.

Review the name and attributes of each quadrilateral shown on the diagram. What distinguishes a trapezoid from the other quadrilaterals?

Two facts about quadrilaterals to help determine the measures of the sides and angles:

• The sum of the measures of the angles of any quadrilateral is 360°.

• In any parallelogram, opposite sides and opposite angles are congruent.

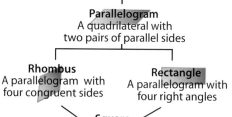

Quadrilateral
A polygon with four sides

Parallelogram
A quadrilateral with two pairs of parallel sides

Trapezoid
A quadrilateral with only one pair of parallel sides called bases

Rhombus
A parallelogram with four congruent sides

Rectangle
A parallelogram with four right angles

Square
A parallelogram with four right angles AND four congruent sides

In parallelogram $ABCD$, $m\angle A = 25°$. Find the measure of each remaining angle.

think ∠A and ∠C are opposite angles. $m\angle C = 25°$.
∠B and ∠D are congruent.
The sum of the four angle measures is 360°.

Write an equation. Let $x = m\angle B = m\angle D$.	$25° + 25° + \boxed{x + x} = 360°$
Simplify.	$50° + \boxed{2x} = 360°$
Use inverse operations.	$50° - 50° + 2x = 360° - 50°$
	$2x = 310°$
	$\frac{2x}{2} = \frac{310°}{2}$
$m\angle B = m\angle D = 155°$	$x = 155°$

In an isosceles trapezoid, the non-parallel sides are congruent and the angles opposite the congruent sides are congruent. What is the measure of ∠W?

think ∠$W \cong \angle V$
$m\angle W + m\angle V = 360° - 2(55°) = 250°$
Since $m\angle W = m\angle V$, each angle measures 125°.

Check Understanding

a. A quadrilateral with opposite sides that are congruent is a ☐.
b. A rhombus with one right angle is a ☐.
c. A quadrilateral with only one pair of parallel bases is a ☐.
d. The measure of every angle in a rectangle is ☐.

Practice

1. Name a figure of each type on the diagram.
   a. Trapezoid
   b. Parallelogram
   c. Rectangle

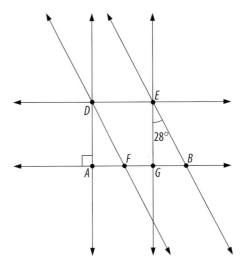

2. Given that $m\angle GEB$ is 28°, find the measure of each angle in $DEBF$.

3. Find the measure of each angle in $DEBA$.

4. $\triangle DAF \cong \triangle EGB$. Identify the measure of each angle in $\triangle DAF$.

Write *true* or *false*.
5. Every square is a rhombus.
6. Every quadrilateral is a trapezoid.
7. A rectangle can be a rhombus.
8. If the measure of one angle in a parallelogram is 40°, it contains an angle of 140°.

Apply

9. Trapezoid $MNOP$ has one pair of parallel sides and two right angles. If $m\angle N = 36°$, what is $m\angle O$?

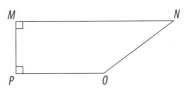

10. A kite has two sets of congruent, adjacent sides. Are any sides parallel? A **diagonal** is a line segment that connects two opposite vertices. The two diagonals on a kite are perpendicular. Name the other quadrilaterals in this lesson that always have perpendicular diagonals.

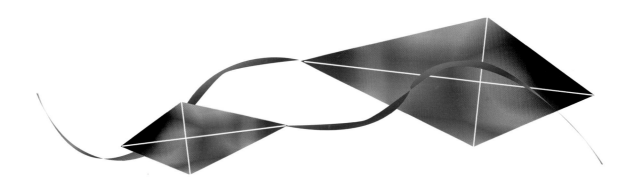

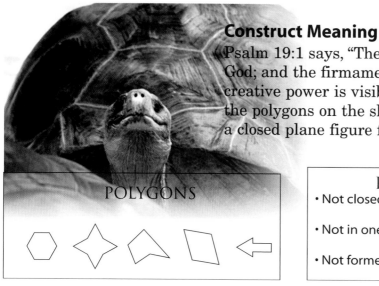

9.7 Polygons

Construct Meaning

Psalm 19:1 says, "The heavens declare the glory of God; and the firmament shows His handiwork." God's creative power is visible in the design that includes the polygons on the shell of a tortoise. A **polygon** is a closed plane figure formed by line segments.

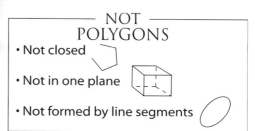

POLYGONS

NOT POLYGONS
• Not closed
• Not in one plane
• Not formed by line segments

Polygons are classified by the number of line segments, or sides.
Review the chart and identify each polygon shown above.

Number of sides	3	4	5	6	7	8	9	10	11	12
Polygon name	Triangle	Quadrilateral	Pentagon	Hexagon	Heptagon	Octagon	Nonagon	Decagon	Hendecagon	Dodecagon

OTHER ATTRIBUTES FOR CLASSIFYING POLYGONS

A **regular polygon** has all sides and all angles congruent.		All polygons are either **convex** or **concave**.	
Examples	Counterexamples	Convex	Concave
		Any line segment with endpoints inside the polygon lies completely within the polygon.	A line segment with endpoints inside the polygon can pass outside the polygon.

ANGLES OF POLYGONS

You know that two triangles may be used to form a rectangle. Because the sum of the angle measures in each triangle is 180°, the sum of the angle measures in the rectangle is 360°.

To determine the sum of the angle measures in any polygon:
• Draw line segments from one vertex to the non-adjacent vertices.
• Count the triangles.
• Multiply the number of triangles by 180°.

(example)   The hexagon with 6 sides divides into 4 triangles.

$$4 \times 180° = 720°$$

For any polygon, the number of triangles formed is two less than the number of sides.

A formula can be used to find the sum of the angle measures in a polygon.
  Sum of the angle measures = (number of sides − 2) · 180°
$$S = (n - 2) \cdot 180°$$

Check Understanding

Examine the counterexamples of regular polygons on page 198.
- **a.** Which polygon is equilateral but not equiangular?
- **b.** Which polygon is equiangular but not equilateral?

Sketch a pentagon and draw diagonals from one vertex.
- **c.** What number of triangles result?
- **d.** What is the sum of the angle measures of a pentagon?
- **e.** Check your answer using the formula $S = (n - 2) \cdot 180°$.

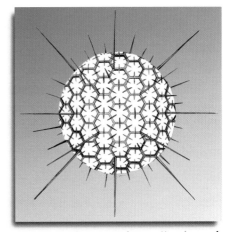

A microalgae is spherically shaped with polygons on its surface.

Practice

Polygon	Number of sides	Sum of angle measures
Triangle	3	180°
Quadrilateral	4	
Pentagon		
Hexagon		
Heptagon		
Octagon		
Nonagon		

1. Complete the table to show the number of sides and the sum of the angle measures for each regular polygon. You may use the drawing method or use $S = (n - 2) \cdot 180°$.

2. How does increasing the sides by one affect the sum of the angle measures?

3. Predict the sum of the angles in a dodecagon. Check your answer using the formula.

4. Identify the polygon having 1440° as the sum of angle measures. If it is a regular polygon, what is the measure of each angle?

Apply

5. A five-petaled flower often has the same central angles as a regular pentagon. The central angle of a regular polygon is formed when two line segments are drawn from its center to two adjacent vertices. What is the measure of a central angle of a regular pentagon?

6. Before hiking around Golden Pond, Lindy studied the map on the sign at the trailhead. The map showed that the trail consisted of twenty connected line segments of the same length that went around the pond. Find the angle measure of each slight turn on the trail.

7. Standing inside a geodesic dome, Lakeesha measured one of the angles between wall segments to be 150° where they joined the floor. If the dome has a regular shape, how many sides does it have?

9.8 Area and Perimeter

Construct Meaning

A horse paddock will be built near the stables on Continental Divide Dude Ranch. There are 200 feet of fencing material available to enclose the area in the shape of a polygon. Which of the shapes shown has a greater area for the horses?

The perimeter of the paddock will be 200 feet. **Perimeter** is the distance around a figure. It is the sum of the side measures.

Square paddock $s = 50'$

Rectangular paddock $h = 25'$
$b = 75'$

Perimeter = 4 · 50' = 200'

Perimeter = (2 · 75') + (2 · 25') = 200'

Perimeter Formulas

Square	$P = 4s$
Rectangle	$P = 2b + 2h$

Area is the number of square units that cover a surface.

Use the formulas to find the area of each paddock.

Area of square paddock
50 ft · 50 ft = 2500 sq ft

Area of rectangular paddock
75 ft · 25 ft = 1875 sq ft

Area Formulas

Square	$A = s^2$
Rectangle	$A = bh$
Parallelogram	$A = bh$
Triangle	$A = \frac{1}{2}bh$

The square paddock has a greater area for the horses.

Consider a parallelogram with a perimeter of 200 feet.

$h = 37.59'$ $40'$ $b = 60'$

The **base** of any quadrilateral is one of the sides from which its height is measured. The **height** is the perpendicular distance from the base to the opposite side.

Perimeter = 2(60') + 2(40') = 200'   Area = 60' · 37.59' = 2255.4 ft^2

Compare the area of the parallelogram to the area of the square and rectangular paddocks having the same perimeter.

The area of a triangle is half the product of the measure of its base and height. Any side of a triangle may be a **base**. The **height** is the perpendicular distance between the base and the opposite vertex.

$A = \frac{1}{2}(3 \text{ cm} \cdot 2 \text{ cm}) = \frac{1}{2}(6 \text{ cm}^2) = 3 \text{ cm}^2$

$h = 2$ cm
$b = 3$ cm

How does the area change when the measures of the base and the height are doubled?

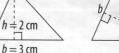
8 in.
3 in.

$A = 8 \text{ in.} \cdot 3 \text{ in.} = 24 \text{ in.}^2$

16 in.
6 in.

$A = 16 \text{ in.} \cdot 6 \text{ in.} = 96 \text{ in.}^2$

When the side lengths are doubled, the area is multiplied by four.

Check Understanding

a. Draw two similar triangles making the base and height measures on one triangle twice the base and height measures on the other. Find the area of each triangle and explain how the areas compare.

Name one or more units appropriate to measure each.

b. Shoreline of a lake   **c.** Land covered by a desert   **d.** Floor to be carpeted

e. A rectangle has a perimeter greater than 100 cm, but its area is less than 1 cm². How is this possible?

f. If the area and base of a rectangle are given, how is the height determined?

Practice

Find the perimeter and area of each figure. Label your answers.

1.

2.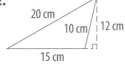

3.

4.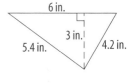

5. 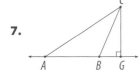 The side of the red square is three times the length of the side of the blue square. The area of the red square is how many times the area of the blue square?

6. The area of a parallelogram is 286 sq cm and its base is 22 cm. What is its height?

7. Determine the area of $\triangle ABC$ if:
$\overline{AB} = 14$ in. $\overline{GC} = 9$ in. $\overline{BG} = 2$ in.

Apply

8. How will the areas compare if Barbara draws a rectangle and later draws a second rectangle having the same height but with the measure of the base doubled?

9. A square room is covered by 16 square yards of carpet. Determine the number of feet of baseboard needed around the carpet. You will need to subtract 3 feet of baseboard to compensate for the door of the room.

10. A five-meter wide portion of a park is covered with 50 square meters of sod. How many meters of fence are sufficient to surround the area?

Trapezoids and Irregular Figures

Construct Meaning

God's creation comes in an amazing variety of shapes. Notice how the visible part of Ayers Rock, located in Australia's Katu Tjuta National Park, resembles a trapezoid. The rock has a height of 348 meters, a perimeter of eight kilometers, and it extends over five and one-half kilometers below the ground.

Area of a Trapezoid

A **trapezoid** is a quadrilateral with only one pair of parallel sides called bases. To understand how to calculate the area of a trapezoid, recall finding the area of a parallelogram.

The drawing shows an isosceles trapezoid.

A parallelogram can be formed with a second congruent trapezoid. The base measure of this parallelogram equals $b_1 + b_2$, and the height equals h. Remember the formula for area of a parallelogram is $A = bh$. For this parallelogram $A = (b_1 + b_2)h$. Therefore, the area of the trapezoid is half of that, or $A = \frac{1}{2}(b_1 + b_2)h$.

Area of a Trapezoid
$$A = \frac{1}{2}h(b_1 + b_2)$$

Substitute the measurements to find the area.
$$A = \frac{1}{2} \cdot 2 \text{ cm}(2 \text{ cm} + 6 \text{ cm}) = \frac{1}{2} \cdot 2 \text{ cm}(8 \text{ cm}) = 1 \text{ cm}(8 \text{ cm}) = 8 \text{ cm}^2$$

Area of Irregular Figures

The area of an irregular figure may be found by dividing it into polygons, using formulas to find the area of each one, then finding the sum of the areas. There may be more than one way to divide the figure.

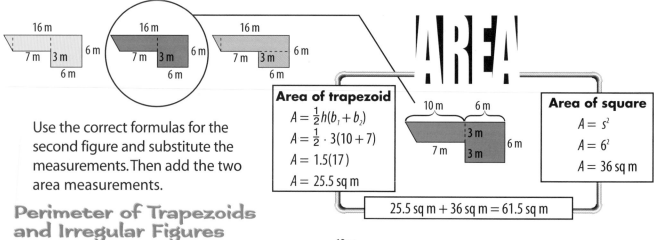

Use the correct formulas for the second figure and substitute the measurements. Then add the two area measurements.

Area of trapezoid
$$A = \frac{1}{2}h(b_1 + b_2)$$
$$A = \frac{1}{2} \cdot 3(10 + 7)$$
$$A = 1.5(17)$$
$$A = 25.5 \text{ sq m}$$

Area of square
$$A = s^2$$
$$A = 6^2$$
$$A = 36 \text{ sq m}$$

$$25.5 \text{ sq m} + 36 \text{ sq m} = 61.5 \text{ sq m}$$

Perimeter of Trapezoids and Irregular Figures

To determine the perimeter, find the sum of the side lengths.

$P = 51 \text{ m}$

Check Understanding

a. In your own words, explain how to find the area of a trapezoid.

b. Use the Distributive Property to rewrite the formula for the area of a trapezoid.

c. Identify the area formulas you would use to determine the area of the figure shown here.

Practice

Find the area of each figure.

1.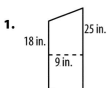

2.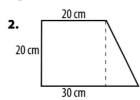

3.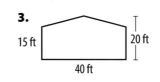

4.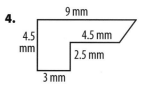

Draw and divide each figure to show how you would find its area. Write each formula needed.

5.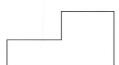

6.

7.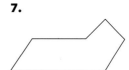

8.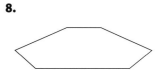

9. A regular hexagon can be divided into six equilateral triangles. One side of the hexagon measures four centimeters, and the distance from its center to the midpoint of any side is approximately 3.5 centimeters. What is the approximate area of the regular hexagon?

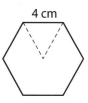

10. The area of the entire square is 36 square units. Find the area of the shaded region.

Apply

11. Often, determining the amount of paint to buy requires finding the area of the object to be painted. Help the stage crew of the school play find the area of the front of the stage prop they built.

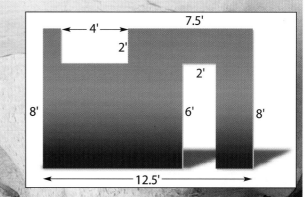

12. A square tablecloth measures 54 inches on a side. It is constructed from four congruent triangles. What is the area of one of the triangles?

9.10 Circles

Construct Meaning

Biking is a healthy and enjoyable way to enjoy God's great outdoors. Notice the geometric terms illustrated on the bicycle wheel.

$\overline{QP}$ is a radius.
$\overline{QM}$ is a chord.
$\overline{MN}$ is a diameter.
$\angle QPN$ is a central angle.

A **circle** is the set of all points in a plane that are **equidistant**, the same distance, from a given point, P, the **center**. The distance from the center to any point on the circle is the **radius**, r. A **chord** is a line segment joining any two points on a circle. The length of a chord that passes through the center is the **diameter**, d. An angle formed by two radii is a **central angle**. The sum of the measures of all central angles in a circle is 360°. Each central angle marks a **sector** of the circle.

The diameter of a circle is twice the radius, $d = 2r$. What is the formula for the radius of a circle in terms of d?

The distance around a circle, or its perimeter, is the **circumference**, C. The ratio of the circumference of a circle to its diameter is always **pi**, or π. This relationship, $\frac{C}{d} = \pi$, yields the formula $C = \pi d$. By substitution, $C = 2\pi r$.

Find the circumference of a 14-mm diameter circle.

$C = \pi d$	Use the formula.
$C \approx \frac{22}{7} (14 \text{ mm})$	Substitute. Use $\frac{22}{7}$ for ease in calculation.
$C \approx 44 \text{ mm}$	Simplify.

The approximate value of π is $\frac{22}{7}$ or 3.14.

Find the radius of a circle with a circumference of 314 inches.

$C = \pi d$	Use the formula.
$314 \text{ in.} \approx 3.14d$	Substitute. Use 3.14 for π.
$\frac{314 \text{ in.}}{3.14} \approx d$	Solve.
$100 \text{ in.} \approx d$	Simplify.

Since $r = \frac{d}{2}$, the radius is approximately 50 inches.

The area, A, of a circle is the number of square units it contains. The formula is $A = \pi r^2$. What is the approximate area of a circle with a radius of 5 cm?

$A = \pi r^2$	Use the formula.
$A \approx 3.14(5 \text{ cm})^2$	Substitute. Use 3.14 for π.
$A \approx 78.5 \text{ cm}^2$	Simplify.

Check Understanding

Match each item with the appropriate figure or quantity from the circle. Use 3.14 for π.

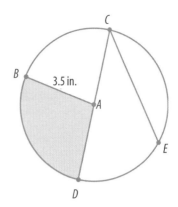

CHOICES

a. Central angle	**7 in.**
b. Chord	**DAB**
c. Diameter length	**38.465 sq in.**
d. Radius	**∠BAC**
e. Sector	**21.98 in.**
f. Center	**CE**
g. Circumference	**A**
h. Area	**AB**

i. When you found the area and circumference of the circle above, did you find an exact or an approximate answer?

Practice

Use the circle for problems 1 through 6. Use π ≈ 3.14.

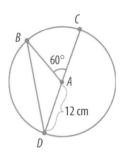

1. What is the area of the circle?

2. What fraction of the circle is sector *BAC*?

3. What is the area of sector *BAC*?

4. Find the measure of ∠*DAB*.

5. Find the approximate circumference of the circle.

6. Classify △*DAB* by angle size and side lengths.

Apply

7. A student drew a cross-section of a sapling to show its new growth. The diameter of the inner core is 1 inch and the diameter of the tree is 1.4 inches. Use π ≈ 3.14 and round your answer to the nearest hundredth.

a. What is the area of the cross-section of the tree?

b. What is the area of the tan inner core?

c. What is the area of the new growth ring?

Tree cross-section

8. Consider a bike wheel with a diameter of 24 inches.

a. Approximately how far does a point on the wheel travel in one revolution (turn) of the wheel? Use π ≈ 3.14. Round your answer to the nearest inch.

b. Approximately how many revolutions are necessary to travel a mile?

9. Determine which of the following covers a greater land area—one spruce tree with a base diameter of 1 meter or three 0.5-meter diameter trees.

Challenge

10. Tara wants to cover one-fourth of a 44-square foot garden with bushes. If her design includes 14 bushes, what size (approximate diameter) bushes should she purchase?

Problem Solving

Construct Meaning

The Redfields are considering several options for replacing the tile floor in their family room. The room measures 15 feet by 21 feet. They compared rates for the same tile from several companies. Which company would be the least expensive?

Alpine Flooring
Tile: $3.50 each
for 12" x 12" tiles
Installation:

Room Size	Price
Less than 300 sq ft	$800
300-500 sq ft	$1000

Floors-R-Us
Tile: $30 per square yard
Installation: $3.50 per square foot

Regis Tile Co.
Tile
(including installation)
$7.50/sq ft

Divide the problem into smaller problems.
Since the price is dependent on the size of the room,
first calculate the area of the room.

Area = bh
A = 15 ft × 21 ft   Use a formula.
A = 315 sq ft   Write the formula and substitute the numbers.

The next step is to calculate the cost based on the rate for each company.

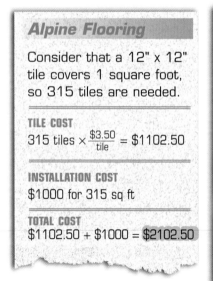

Alpine Flooring

Consider that a 12" x 12" tile covers 1 square foot, so 315 tiles are needed.

TILE COST
315 tiles × $\frac{\$3.50}{\text{tile}}$ = $1102.50

INSTALLATION COST
$1000 for 315 sq ft

TOTAL COST
$1102.50 + $1000 = $2102.50

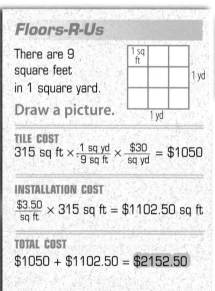

Floors-R-Us

There are 9 square feet in 1 square yard.
Draw a picture.

TILE COST
315 sq ft × $\frac{1 \text{ sq yd}}{9 \text{ sq ft}}$ × $\frac{\$30}{\text{sq yd}}$ = $1050

INSTALLATION COST
$\frac{\$3.50}{\text{sq ft}}$ × 315 sq ft = $1102.50 sq ft

TOTAL COST
$1050 + $1102.50 = $2152.50

Regis Tile Company

TOTAL COST
$\frac{\$7.50}{\text{sq ft}}$ × 315 sq ft = $2362.50 sq ft

Compare the numbers to answer the question.

Alpine Flooring offers the best price.

Apply

1. The perimeter of a rhombus is 36 meters. What is the length of one side?

2. Mrs. Gomez chose vinyl flooring that costs $10 per square yard. Find the cost of her new kitchen floor if the measurements are 15 feet by 18 feet and the installation charge is $300.

3. One of the sides forming the right angle of an isosceles triangle is 10 centimeters long. Find the area of the triangle.

4. The height of a triangle is 32 inches and the base is $1\frac{3}{4}$ times longer. Find the area of the triangle.

5. A triangular garden plot has one 16-foot side. The height perpendicular to that side is 12 feet 6 inches. If each plant requires 36 square inches of space, how many plants can be placed in the plot?

6. How many square feet of marble is cut off if the largest possible circular tabletop is cut from a slab that is 3 feet 6 inches square? Round your answer to the nearest tenth of a square foot.

7. About how many revolutions, or complete turns, will a $3\frac{1}{2}$-foot diameter wheel make in one mile? Round your answer to the nearest ten revolutions.

8. What diameter wheel would make about 960 revolutions in one mile? Give your answer to the nearest inch.

9. One of the angles of a parallelogram in a wheel design measures 112°. Find the measures of the other three angles.

10. A bird leaves a tree flying due east. Another bird leaves the same spot flying 10° west of north. What is the measure of the angle formed by the flights of the two birds?

Review

State your answer using numbers and mathematical symbols or write *never*.

1. When is x greater than $2x$?
2. When is x greater than x^2?
3. When is $|x|$ less than x?
4. When does $x + x = 2$?
5. When is x^2 less than zero?
6. When is $|x|$ greater than x?

Pythagorean Theorem/Study Guide

Construct Meaning

Pythagoras was a Greek philosopher and mathematician who lived in the sixth century B.C. Pythagoras discovered mathematical relationships in nature and in music, such as those between notes in an octave. Observing such design, he believed that the universe was created with harmonious mathematical order.

Pythagoras discovered a relationship between the sides of a right triangle.

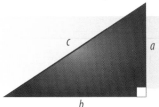

$a^2 + b^2 = c^2$

The Pythagorean Theorem

For any right triangle, the sum of the squares of the lengths of the legs is equal to the square of the length of the hypotenuse.

Nick wanted to build a ramp for skateboard jumping three feet long and one foot high. How long will he need to cut a board for the ramp itself?

Use the formula.

$$a^2 + b^2 = c^2$$
$$1^2 + 3^2 = c^2$$
$$1 + 9 = c^2$$
$$10 = c^2$$
$$\sqrt{10} = \sqrt{c^2}$$
$$\sqrt{10} = c$$
$$3.16 \approx c$$

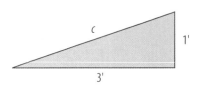

The board will be $3\frac{16}{100}$ feet or about 3 feet 2 inches long.

Check Understanding

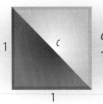

$$a^2 + b^2 = c^2$$
$$1^2 + 1^2 = c^2$$

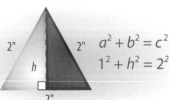

$$a^2 + b^2 = c^2$$
$$1^2 + h^2 = 2^2$$

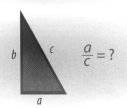

$$\frac{a}{c} = ?$$

a. What are the measures of the angles of the triangles formed by the diagonal of a square?

b. What is the length of a diagonal of a square that is one unit wide?

c. Calculate the area of an equilateral triangle having sides 2 inches long.

d. What are the measures of the angles of the darker triangle?

e. What is the ratio of the length of the shorter leg to the length of the hypotenuse in a 30°-60°-90° right triangle?

Chapter 9 Study Guide

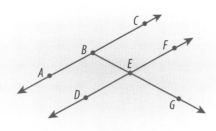

1. Name the following: *Lesson 9.1*

    a. Obtuse angles with vertex E
    b. Line segments on $\overleftrightarrow{BG}$
    c. One pair of intersecting lines
    d. Rays originating at point E

2. Tell the relationship for each pair of angles. *Lesson 9.2*

    a. $\angle 5$ and $\angle 7$ b. $\angle 6$ and $\angle 3$
    c. $\angle 7$ and $\angle 4$ d. $\angle 6$ and $\angle 7$
    e. $\angle 4$ and $\angle 2$ f. $\angle 5$ and $\angle 4$

3. What is the measure of the angle made by clock hands at 2 P.M.? *Lesson 9.3*

4. Classify each triangle completely.
    a. $\triangle BCD$ *Lesson 9.4*
    b. $\triangle ABD$
    c. $\triangle ABC$

5. Find the length of y. *Lesson 9.5*

    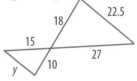

6. Find the measure of $\angle B$ in the trapezoid. *Lesson 9.6*

    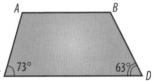

7. What is the sum of the measures of the angles in a stop sign? *Lesson 9.7*

8. Calculate the perimeter and area of the polygon. *Lessons 9.8 and 9.9*

    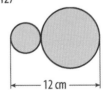

9. Find the area of the trapezoid. *Lesson 9.9*

    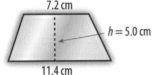

10. The diameter of one circle is half the diameter of a second circle. The sum of their diameters is 12 cm. Find the combined areas of the circles. Use $\pi \approx 3.14$. *Lesson 9.10*

11. You purchase 8" × 8" × 8' landscape timbers to frame a rectangular flower bed. You cut one in half and make the frame as shown. How much space will you have for the flowers? *Lesson 9.11*

    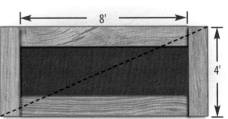

12. To make sure your flower bed frame is perfectly square (all corners are right angles), you measure one of its diagonals as shown. What should its measurement be? *Lesson 9.12*

Chapter 9 Check-Up

A Piece of Pi

Match the angle or pair of angles with the letter of one of the terms below. Answers may be used more than once.

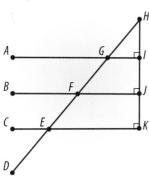

1. ∠AGH
2. ∠IGF and ∠BFG
3. ∠HFJ and ∠HEK
4. ∠FJK
5. ∠BFG and ∠EFJ
6. ∠AGF and ∠CED
7. ∠BFD
8. ∠BFH and ∠GFJ
9. ∠GHI and ∠GFJ
10. ∠HGI and ∠BFD
11. ∠BFD and ∠HFB
12. ∠AGF and ∠KEF

a. Complementary	b. Supplementary	c. Vertical
d. Acute angle	e. Right angle	f. Obtuse angle
g. Alternate exterior	h. Alternate interior	i. Corresponding

Calculate the measurement of the angle.

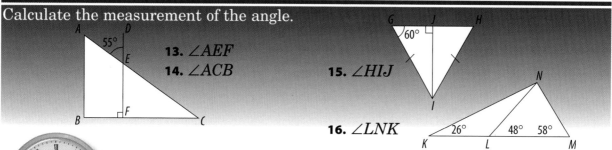

13. ∠AEF
14. ∠ACB

15. ∠HIJ

16. ∠LNK

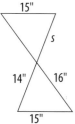

17. What is the measurement of the angle formed between clock hands at 11:40?

Find the value of side *s* or angle *A*.

18.
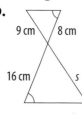

19.
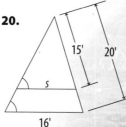

20.

21.

22. By what rule do you know that the triangles are congruent?

23. What name does <u>not</u> apply to this figure?
 a. Quadrilateral
 b. Polygon
 c. Rhombus
 d. Parallelogram

24. Find the sum of the angle measures of an octagon.

25. Name the regular polygon with a central angle of 60°.

Find the area (A) and perimeter (P) of each figure.

26. $A = \square$

27. $P = \square$

13 cm 12 cm 9 cm

28. $A = \square$

29. $P = \square$

30" 18" 24"

30. $A = \square$

31. $P = \square$

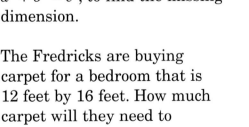
10.4" 6"

32. $A = \square$

33. $P = \square$

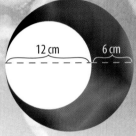
25' 23' 12' 8'

34. In a 6 cm radius circle, what is the length of a chord connecting radii that form a 60° central angle?

35. Using $\pi \approx 3.14$, find the circumference and area of a circle whose diameter is 4 inches.

36. Find the shaded area. Use $\pi \approx 3.14$.

12 cm 6 cm

37. Find the area of the figure.

38. Find the perimeter of the figure. Use the Pythagorean Theorem, $a^2 + b^2 = c^2$, to find the missing dimension.

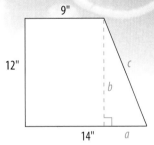
9" 12" c b 14" a

39. The Fredricks are buying carpet for a bedroom that is 12 feet by 16 feet. How much carpet will they need to purchase, to the nearest square yard?

40. The total area of a painting including a two-inch-wide frame is 396 square inches. If the length of the frame is 22 inches, what is the area of the painting?

Chapter Theme:
Endangered Animals

Exploring Rational Numbers

Construct Meaning

God created the entire animal kingdom, but today part of that kingdom has become endangered. Any part-to-whole relationship can be expressed as a ratio. A number that can be written as a ratio of two integers is a rational number.

The combined population of northern right whales and blue whales at the beginning of the 21st century was approximately 22,100. Northern right whales account for a small part of the total.

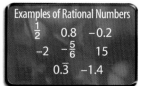

Examples of Rational Numbers
$\frac{1}{2}$ 0.8   −0.2
−2   −$\frac{5}{6}$ 15
0.$\overline{3}$ −1.4

$$\frac{\text{Northern right whale population}}{\text{Combined population}} = \frac{x}{22{,}100}$$

There are ten times as many blue whales as northern right whales. This may be written in more than one way. Each is an equivalent form.

$$\frac{\text{Blue whale population}}{\text{Combined population}} = \frac{10x}{22{,}100} = 10\left(\frac{x}{22{,}100}\right) = \left(\frac{10}{22{,}100}\right)x$$

EQUIVALENT FORMS OF RATIONAL NUMBERS

$\frac{2x}{3} = \left(\frac{2}{3}\right)x$ Think of $\frac{2x}{3}$ as $\frac{2}{3} \cdot \frac{x}{1}$ and rewrite as $\frac{2}{3}(x)$.

$\frac{2x}{3} = 2\left(\frac{x}{3}\right)$ Think of $\frac{2x}{3}$ as $\frac{2}{1} \cdot \frac{x}{3}$ and rewrite as $2\left(\frac{x}{3}\right)$.

$\frac{2x}{3} \neq \frac{2}{3x}$ Think, $\frac{2}{3} \cdot \frac{x}{1}$ is not the same as $\frac{2}{3} \cdot \frac{1}{x}$.

Remember that a whole number or a variable has a denominator of 1.
$2 = \frac{2}{1}$ $x = \frac{x}{1}$

Consider the negative rational number $-\frac{4}{5}$.

$-\frac{4}{5} = \frac{-4}{5} = \frac{4}{-5}$, but $-\frac{4}{5} \neq \frac{-4}{-5}$. Will the quotient of $\frac{-4}{-5}$ be a positive or negative number?

ORDERING RATIONAL NUMBERS

Place the rational numbers in order from least to greatest:

$$\frac{9}{5}, \; -\frac{2}{3}, \; \frac{6}{4}, \; -\frac{1}{4}, \; \frac{7}{15}, \; -\frac{9}{7}$$

Mentally compare each number to a pair of numbers. For example, $\frac{9}{5}$ is between $1\frac{1}{2}$ and 2. $-\frac{2}{3}$ is between −1 and $-\frac{1}{2}$. Consider their placement on a number line.

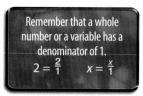

or

Order rational numbers by finding the least common denominator and using the equivalent fractions.

To order $-\frac{13}{15}, -\frac{11}{12}$, and $-\frac{17}{20}$ from greatest to least, use the LCD of 60.

$-\frac{13}{15} = -\frac{52}{60}$ $-\frac{11}{12} = -\frac{55}{60}$ $-\frac{17}{20} = -\frac{51}{60}$

$$-\frac{17}{20} > -\frac{13}{15} > -\frac{11}{12}$$

Check Understanding

For each set of expressions, select the expression that is not equivalent to the others.

a. $\frac{-7x}{-10}$ $\frac{-7x}{10}$ $\frac{7x}{-10}$ $-7\left(\frac{x}{10}\right)$

b. $\frac{4}{5x}$ $\frac{4x}{5}$ $\frac{4}{5}\left(\frac{1}{x}\right)$ $4 \cdot \frac{1}{(5x)}$

c. Explain why $\frac{-20}{15} = \frac{20}{-15}$. Write each fraction as a mixed number.

Practice

Write $<$, $>$ or $=$.

1. $\frac{14}{21} \bigcirc 0.\overline{6}$ 2. $\frac{-4}{10} \bigcirc -0.04$ 3. $-3\frac{1}{4} \bigcirc -3\frac{9}{10}$ 4. $-2.4 \bigcirc -\frac{13}{5}$

5. Draw a number line and label the location of -1, -0.5, 0, 0.5, and 1. Mark the point for each rational number below after estimating its approximate location.
$-\frac{1}{5}, \frac{3}{4}, 0.3, -0.6, -\frac{7}{8}$

6. Order each set of rational numbers from greatest to least.
a. $-\frac{4}{5}, -\frac{2}{3}, -\frac{9}{10}$ b. $\frac{3}{5}, \frac{7}{10}, 0.65$ c. $-0.2, -0.15, -0.8$ d. $-\frac{9}{8}, -\frac{7}{4}, -\frac{7}{5}$

7. Select all the equivalent forms of $\frac{x}{2}$.

$x\left(\frac{1}{2}\right)$ $\frac{-x}{-2}$ $\frac{2x}{4}$ $\frac{-x}{2}$ $\frac{2}{x}$ $2x$ $\frac{1}{2}(x)$

Evaluate each expression if $b = 4$, $x = -2$, and $m = 10$. Write each answer as a fraction and as a decimal.

8. $\frac{6x}{15}$ 9. $\left(\frac{1}{8}\right)b$ 10. $\frac{m}{x} \cdot \left(\frac{1}{b}\right)$ 11. $\frac{9}{3b}$

Apply

12. A commercial airplane may fly at the rate of 0.15 miles per second. State its rate in miles per hour.

13. There are 1000 parking spaces at a car rental agency near a major airport. Sixty-five percent of the spaces are used only for compact cars. On Sunday morning there were 300 compact cars, and all of the other vehicles were mid-sized cars. If the lot is 50% full, how many mid-sized cars are parked in the lot?

14. If four 8-ounce glasses have been filled with milk, what fractional amount of the gallon of milk remains?

Add and Subtract Rational Numbers

Construct Meaning

Habitat destruction is a major threat for endangered species. The Queen Alexandra's birdwing butterfly, found only in Papua New Guinea, is believed to be the largest butterfly in the world. Some females may have a wingspan as large as one foot. Its rainforest habitat is being reduced as oil palm plantations expand. Compare its size to that of the Oregon silverspot butterfly, a threatened species, with a wingspan of 2.2 inches. What would you estimate the difference to be?

This comparison is simply finding the difference between two rational numbers.

| Convert units. | 1 ft – 2.2 in. = 12 in. – 2.2 in = 9.8 in.

The Queen Alexandra's birdwing wingspan is 9.8 in. wider than the Oregon silverspot. Was this close to your estimate?

SUMS AND DIFFERENCES OF NEGATIVE RATIONAL NUMBERS

Find the difference between 12.63 and –15.5.

$$12.63 - (-15.5) = 12.63 + 15.5$$

> Rewrite as an addition problem.

$$= 28.13$$

Add the following fractions: $\frac{1}{2}, -\frac{5}{8}, -\frac{7}{8}, \frac{3}{4}$. Find the least common denominator and use the Commutative and Associative Properties of Addition.

$$\frac{1}{2} + \left(-\frac{5}{8}\right) + \left(-\frac{7}{8}\right) + \frac{3}{4} = \frac{4}{8} + \left(-\frac{5}{8}\right) + \left(-\frac{7}{8}\right) + \frac{6}{8}$$

$$= \frac{4}{8} + \frac{6}{8} + \left(-\frac{5}{8}\right) + \left(-\frac{7}{8}\right)$$

$$= \frac{10}{8} + \left(-\frac{12}{8}\right)$$

$$= -\frac{2}{8}$$

$$= -\frac{1}{4}$$

> When adding numbers with opposite signs, find the difference of their absolute values. The sign of the sum is that of the number having the greater absolute value.

Simplify –96.5 – (72.98 – 45.7). Use the order of operations.

$$-96.5 - (72.98 - 45.7) = -96.5 - (27.28)$$

$$= (-96.5) + (-27.28)$$

$$= -123.78$$

> Do the operations inside the parentheses first.

Simplify $-\frac{4}{5} + \left(5\frac{1}{4} - \frac{2}{5}\right) - 4\frac{1}{20}$.

> Rename the fraction.

$$-\frac{4}{5} + \left(5\frac{1}{4} - \frac{2}{5}\right) - 4\frac{1}{20} = -\frac{16}{20} + \left(5\frac{5}{20} - \frac{8}{20}\right) - 4\frac{1}{20}$$

$$= -\frac{16}{20} + 4\frac{17}{20} - 4\frac{1}{20}$$

$$= \quad ?$$

Check Understanding

Estimate the value of each expression as –1, 0, or 1.

a. $-\frac{1}{2} + \frac{3}{8} + (-1)$ b. $-0.55 + 1.45$ c. $-5 + 6 - \left(\frac{5}{6} + \frac{1}{3}\right)$

d. How can the Associative Property of Addition be applied to a subtraction problem?

e. Explain the difference between the additive inverse of a number and the absolute value of a number.

Practice

Estimate the value of each expression, then find the exact value. Simplify.

1. $\frac{18}{100} - \frac{16}{25}$

2. $8.97 + 10.1 + 30$

3. $-16.52 + 19$

4. $-24.3 - (6.4 - 12.6)$

5. $-\frac{5}{8} + \frac{3}{4} - \left(-\frac{1}{4}\right)$

6. $-15 - \frac{2}{3} + 5$

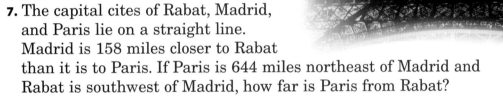

Rabat

Paris

Madrid

Apply

7. The capital cites of Rabat, Madrid, and Paris lie on a straight line. Madrid is 158 miles closer to Rabat than it is to Paris. If Paris is 644 miles northeast of Madrid and Rabat is southwest of Madrid, how far is Paris from Rabat?

8. A cheetah, one of the fastest land animals in the world, can accelerate to a running speed of 93 kilometers per hour in just a few seconds. A pronghorn can reach a maximum speed of 53.8 miles per hour. Compare their speeds. A kilometer is approximately equal to 0.62 mile.

9. A six-sided irregular figure has a perimeter of 6 meters. What is the length of the remaining side if the other sides measure 1.6 m, 1.5 m, 0.8 m, 40 cm, and 30 cm?

10. Brian measured his stride at $17\frac{1}{2}$ inches per step. His backward step measured only 13 inches. If Brian takes one step backward for every two steps forward, how many forward steps must he take to move a distance of 44 yards?

11. Give the range of acceptable measurements for a manufactured component that cannot be more than 0.01 cm larger or smaller than 3.27 cm.

12. The value of Jonah's stock went up $1.30 per share on Monday, but fell $2.25 per share on Tuesday. If his stock was worth $2.45 per share on Monday morning, what was its value at the close of business on Tuesday? What was his gain or loss if Jonah had 200 shares?

Addition and Subtraction Equations

Construct Meaning

Pollution, hunting, and other factors have added Nile crocodiles to the list of endangered species. These wild and extremely dangerous crocodiles are found in Africa. Their diet consists of fish, zebras, hippos, porcupines, and other prey.

The Nile crocodile can grow to a maximum of 20 feet. While this may seem very large, the largest saltwater crocodile ever recorded is 33.1 feet. Write an equation to solve for the difference in size.

If x represents the difference in size, then $33.1 - 20 = x$. Since $x = 13.1$, the saltwater crocodile may be 13.1 feet longer than the Nile crocodile.

To evaluate expressions with negative and positive rational numbers, use the order of operations.

Evaluate. $-4\frac{1}{20} + (-3\frac{1}{5} + a)$ if $a = 2\frac{1}{20}$.

$$-4\frac{1}{20} + \left(-3\frac{1}{5} + 2\frac{1}{20}\right) = -4\frac{1}{20} + \left(-3\frac{4}{20} + 2\frac{1}{20}\right) \quad \text{Rename the fractions.}$$

$$= -4\frac{1}{20} - 1\frac{3}{20} \qquad\qquad \text{Complete the operation inside the parentheses.}$$

$$= -4\frac{1}{20} + \left(-1\frac{3}{20}\right) \qquad \text{Rewrite.}$$

$$= -5\frac{4}{20} \qquad\qquad\qquad \text{Add.}$$

$$= -5\frac{1}{5} \qquad\qquad\qquad \text{Simplify.}$$

To solve algebraic equations having negative and positive numbers, use the rules for solving equations having a variable.

- ☆ Isolate the variable on one side of the equation using inverse operations.
- ☆ If an operation is performed on one side, it must be performed on the other side.

Solve. $\quad x + 2\frac{1}{4} = -8\frac{1}{2}$

$$x + 2\frac{1}{4} - 2\frac{1}{4} = -8\frac{1}{2} - 2\frac{1}{4}$$

Think:
$-8\frac{2}{4} + (-2\frac{1}{4})$
$$x = -8\frac{2}{4} - 2\frac{1}{4}$$
$$x = -10\frac{3}{4}$$

If the same number is subtracted from each side, the two sides remain equal.

Check. $\quad -10\frac{3}{4} + 2\frac{1}{4} = -8\frac{1}{2}$

$$-8\frac{2}{4} = -8\frac{1}{2}$$

$$-8\frac{1}{2} = -8\frac{1}{2} \checkmark$$

Solve. $\quad x - 1\frac{6}{13} = 5\frac{5}{26}$

$$x - 1\frac{6}{13} + 1\frac{6}{13} = 5\frac{5}{26} + 1\frac{6}{13}$$

Think:
$x - 1\frac{6}{13} = x + (-1\frac{6}{13})$
$$x = 5\frac{5}{26} + 1\frac{12}{26}$$
$$x = 6\frac{17}{26}$$

If the same number is added to each side, the two sides remain equal.

Check. $\quad 6\frac{17}{26} - 1\frac{6}{13} = 5\frac{5}{26}$

$$6\frac{17}{26} - 1\frac{12}{26} = 5\frac{5}{26}$$

$$5\frac{5}{26} = 5\frac{5}{26} \checkmark$$

Solve. $\quad 3.27 + x = -1.63$

$$3.27 - 3.27 + x = -1.63 - 3.27$$

Think:
$-1.63 + (-3.27)$

$$x = -4.9$$

Check. $\quad 3.27 + (-4.9) = -1.63$

$$-1.63 = -1.63 \checkmark$$

Solve. $\quad x - 0.57 = -8.$

$$x - 0.57 + 0.57 = -8 + 0.57$$

$$x = -7.43$$

Check. $\quad -7.43 - 0.57 = -8$

$$-8 = -8 \checkmark$$

Check Understanding

What operation would be used to solve each equation?

a. $j - 2\frac{3}{4} = \frac{7}{2}$ **b.** $1\frac{5}{7} + p = \frac{11}{22}$

c. $k - 0.5 = -3.7$ **d.** $m + 7.91 = -3.41$

e. Find a negative rational number between $-1\frac{3}{4}$ and $\frac{1}{2}$.

f. Determine the solutions to $w + 4\frac{3}{5} = -1\frac{1}{4}$ and $w - 4\frac{3}{5} = -1\frac{1}{4}$.

Practice

Evaluate each expression if $a = \frac{3}{4}$, $b = -\frac{1}{8}$, $c = -1.25$, and $d = 4.82$.

1. $a - b$ **2.** $c - d$ **3.** $a + b$ **4.** $d - c$

5. $d - (-2.1)$ **6.** $19\frac{7}{8} - a$ **7.** $-4\frac{3}{4} + (a + b)$ **8.** $13\frac{5}{6} - (a + 1)$

Solve for the given variable. Check your solution.

9. $t + 4\frac{5}{8} = -2\frac{1}{4}$ **10.** $2.8 + x = -7.81$ **11.** $-84 + b = 52\frac{3}{8}$

12. $m - 7.41 = 19.36$ **13.** $5\frac{1}{6} + c = -7$ **14.** $k - 5.7 = -8.4$

Write the letter of the equation that matches each statement.

15. A number decreased by $1\frac{3}{4}$ is 12.

16. Twelve is the sum of a number and $1\frac{3}{4}$.

17. Negative $1\frac{3}{4}$ is the sum of a number and 12.

18. The sum of $1\frac{3}{4}$ and 12 is a number.

19. The difference of 12 and $1\frac{3}{4}$ is a number.

a. $n + 1\frac{3}{4} = 12$

b. $1\frac{3}{4} + 12 = n$

c. $12 - 1\frac{3}{4} = n$

d. $n - 1\frac{3}{4} = 12$

e. $n + 12 = -1\frac{3}{4}$

Apply

20. Write an equation to find the length of the missing side of the figure if the perimeter is $20\frac{3}{4}$ inches. Solve the equation.

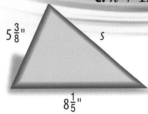

$5\frac{3}{8}''$ s

$8\frac{1}{5}''$

21. A roast decreased in weight by $1\frac{3}{8}$ pounds during the cooking process. It now weighs $3\frac{3}{8}$ pounds. Write an equation to show how much it weighed before the cooking process. Solve the equation.

22. The highest temperature recorded in Africa is 135.9°F. The lowest temperature is −9.4°F. Write a subtraction equation to show how to find the difference t between the extreme temperatures. Solve the equation.

Multiply and Divide Rational Numbers

Construct Meaning

Cheetahs and African wild dogs are remarkable animals of Africa in danger of extinction. The cheetah is the fastest land animal. To catch its prey, the cheetah is capable of an incredible burst of speed that can reach up to 70 miles per hour. However, it is a quick chase because the cheetah can only maintain this speed for a short distance. Although the African wild dog runs at about $\frac{4}{7}$ the speed of the cheetah, it has more endurance and will continue to chase its prey until the prey is exhausted. What is the speed of the African wild dog?

$$70 \cdot \frac{4}{7} = \frac{70}{1} \cdot \frac{4}{7} = 40 \text{ miles per hour}$$

To Multiply or Divide Rational Numbers

Find the product or quotient of the numbers.

Determine whether the answer is positive or negative.

The product or quotient of one negative rational number and one positive rational number is negative.

Multiply $-1\frac{4}{21} \cdot \frac{3}{4}$.

$$-\frac{25}{21} \cdot \frac{3}{4} = -\frac{25}{28}$$

Change mixed numbers to improper fractions and cross-cancel.

Two unlike signs: The answer is negative.

Divide $5\frac{1}{2} \div (-4)$.

$$\frac{11}{2} \div \left(-\frac{4}{1}\right) = \frac{11}{2} \cdot \left(-\frac{1}{4}\right)$$
$$= -\frac{11}{8} \text{ or } -1\frac{3}{8}$$

Change to improper fractions and multiply by the reciprocal.

The product or quotient of two positive rational numbers is positive.

Multiply $7\frac{1}{3} \cdot 1\frac{1}{22}$.

$$\frac{22}{3} \cdot \frac{23}{22} = \frac{23}{3} \text{ or } 7\frac{2}{3}$$

Multiply $(13.1)(2.1)$.

$$(13.1)(2.1) = 27.51$$

Same signs: The answer is positive.

Divide $\frac{25}{28} \div 2\frac{1}{2}$.

$$\frac{25}{28} \div \frac{5}{2} = \frac{25}{28} \cdot \frac{2}{5} = \frac{5}{14}$$

Divide $\frac{13.1}{2}$.

$$13.1 \div 2 = 6.55$$

The product or quotient of two negative rational numbers is positive.

Multiply $\left(-1\frac{1}{3}\right) \cdot \left(-2\frac{3}{5}\right)$.

$$\left(-\frac{4}{3}\right) \cdot \left(-\frac{13}{5}\right) = \frac{52}{15} \text{ or } 3\frac{7}{15}$$

Divide $\left(-1\frac{1}{5}\right) \div \left(-\frac{5}{6}\right)$.

$$\left(-\frac{6}{5}\right) \div \left(-\frac{5}{6}\right) = \left(-\frac{6}{5}\right) \cdot \left(-\frac{6}{5}\right)$$
$$= \frac{36}{25} \text{ or } 1\frac{11}{25}$$

Evaluate $\frac{ab}{c}$ if $a = 2$, $b = -\frac{1}{6}$, and $c = 3\frac{1}{2}$.

$$\frac{(2)\left(-\frac{1}{6}\right)}{\left(3\frac{1}{2}\right)}$$

Write the given values into the expression.

$$\frac{-\frac{1}{3}}{\frac{7}{2}}$$

Complete any operation above or below the fraction bar.

$$-\frac{1}{3} \div \frac{7}{2} = \left(-\frac{1}{3}\right)\left(\frac{2}{7}\right) = -\frac{2}{21}$$ Simplify.

Animal Tracks

Cheetahs only partially retract their claws. This permits the claws to act like cleats when they run.

Check Understanding

State whether each product or quotient is *positive*, *negative*, *zero*, or *undefined*.

a. $-\frac{4}{5} \div \frac{2}{3}$

b. $4\frac{1}{2} \cdot \left(-\frac{4}{9}\right)$

c. $-0.6 \div (-0.2)$

d. $\left(1\frac{3}{4}\right)\left(-\frac{2}{3}\right)\left(\frac{2}{7}\right)$

Is the quotient *greater than*, *equal to*, or *less than* 3?

e. $-3 \div \left(-1\frac{1}{4}\right)$

f. $3 \div \left(-1\frac{1}{4}\right)$

g. $-3 \div (-0.5)$

h. $-3 \div (0.5)$

Practice

Find each product or quotient.

1. $-\frac{3}{4} \cdot \left(-\frac{1}{5}\right)$

2. $(-5.7)(0.3)$

3. $3\frac{5}{9} \div \left(-2\frac{2}{9}\right)$

4. $0 \cdot \left(-3\frac{5}{19}\right)$

5. $\left(-\frac{7}{2}\right)\left(\frac{3}{7}\right)\left(-\frac{2}{3}\right)$

6. $\left(1\frac{1}{4}\right)\left(1\frac{1}{3}\right)\left(-1\frac{4}{5}\right)$

7. $\left(-7\frac{2}{5}\right)\left(-\frac{5}{7}\right)$

8. $-2.175 \div 0$

9. $\left(-\frac{1}{10}\right) \div \left(-\frac{9}{34}\right)$

Use your calculator to solve each problem. Round decimals to the nearest thousandth.

10. $\left(-\frac{1}{4}\right)(0.10)$

11. $\left(1\frac{3}{4}\right)\left(-1\frac{4}{5}\right)(-0.625)$

12. $\frac{-437.925}{108.65}$

Evaluate each expression for $a = -\frac{1}{2}$, $b = \frac{1}{4}$, and $c = -\frac{3}{5}$.

13. $\frac{ca}{b}$

14. $\frac{a}{c}$

15. $\frac{b}{a}$

16. $\frac{b}{ca}$

Apply

17. A bathtub is draining water at a rate of $2\frac{1}{4}$ gallons per minute. Describe the change in the amount of water in the tub after $3\frac{1}{2}$ minutes.

18. The chart shows the 1998 average monthly temperatures for Wolverine Glacier Basin, Africa, in degrees Celsius. Use a calculator to find the average temperature for 1998 in °C. What is the equivalent average temperature in °F? ($F = \frac{9}{5}C + 32$)

JAN	FEB	MAR	APR	MAY	JUNE	JULY	AUG	SEPT	OCT	NOV	DEC
−6.1	−3.5	−4.3	−2.4	0.5	5.3	7.1	5.6	3.0	−3.3	−4.3	−8.7

19. An inspector found pollutants leaking from a tank at a rate of $\frac{7}{10}$ gallon per hour. When he discovered the leak at 3 P.M., 4.2 gallons were already gone. To begin his investigation, the inspector needs to know during which shift the leak began. What time did the leak begin?

Multiplication and Division Equations

Construct Meaning

Scientists have classified over 1.4 million species of plants and animals. Some of the species are in danger of extinction. As of the year 2000, about 3396 animals and plants in North and South America were considered endangered species. This represented approximately 20.6% of all the endangered species worldwide. Approximately how many plants and animals were listed as endangered species?

20.6% of all endangered species is 3396.

$$(0.206)x = 3396 \quad \text{Write an equation to represent the problem.}$$

$$\frac{(0.206)x}{0.206} = \frac{3396}{0.206} \quad \text{Both sides remain equal if they are divided by the same number.}$$

$$x = 16{,}485.44 \qquad \text{Approximately 16,485 species were endangered.}$$

Solve each of the following equations for x.

	$\frac{x}{3} = -1\frac{7}{9}$
Rewrite as an improper fraction.	$\frac{x}{3} = -\frac{16}{9}$
Multiply both sides by 3.	$3 \cdot \frac{x}{3} = -\frac{16}{9} \cdot 3$
Cross-cancel.	$x = -\frac{16}{9} \cdot \frac{\overset{1}{3}}{1}$
	$x = -\frac{16}{3} \text{ or } -5\frac{1}{3}$
Check your solution.	$\frac{-\frac{16}{3}}{3} = -1\frac{7}{9}$
	$-\frac{16}{3} \div 3 = -1\frac{7}{9}$
	$-\frac{16}{3} \cdot \frac{1}{3} = -1\frac{7}{9}$
	$-\frac{16}{9} = -1\frac{7}{9}$ ✔

	$\frac{-2x}{5} = -12\frac{1}{2}$
$\left(-\frac{2}{5}\right)x = -\frac{25}{2}$	Rewrite the equation.
$\frac{\left(-\frac{2}{5}\right)x}{\left(-\frac{2}{5}\right)} = \frac{-\frac{25}{2}}{\left(-\frac{2}{5}\right)}$	Divide both sides by $\left(-\frac{2}{5}\right)$.
$\left(-\frac{5}{2}\right) \cdot \left(-\frac{2}{5}\right)x = -\frac{25}{2} \cdot \left(-\frac{5}{2}\right)$	*think* Dividing by $-\frac{2}{5}$ is the same as
$x = \frac{125}{4} \text{ or } 31\frac{1}{4}$	multiplying by the reciprocal.
$\frac{-2\left(\frac{125}{4}\right)}{5} = -12\frac{1}{2}$	Check your solution.
$-\frac{125}{2} \div 5 = -12\frac{1}{2}$	
$-\frac{125}{2} \cdot \frac{1}{5} = -12\frac{1}{2}$	
$-\frac{25}{2} = -12\frac{1}{2}$ ✔	

The multiplicative inverse can be used to solve equations.

$$\left(-\frac{3}{4}\right)x = 18$$

$$\left(-\frac{4}{3}\right)\left(-\frac{3}{4}\right)x = \overset{6}{18}\left(-\frac{4}{3}\right)_1$$

$$x = -24$$

Using the **multiplicative inverse**, which is the reciprocal, is the same as using the inverse operation of dividing by a fraction.

Check Understanding

Is the solution 4 or −4?

a. $\left(-\frac{7}{4}\right)x = -7$ **b.** $\frac{x}{4} = -1$ **c.** $-\frac{7x}{4} = -1\frac{3}{4}$

d. $\left(\frac{3}{4}\right)x = -3$ **e.** $\left(-\frac{1}{4}\right)x = -1$ **f.** $0.25x = -1$

Explain the steps needed to solve each equation and write whether each solution is *negative* or *positive*.

g. $\frac{2x}{3} = -\frac{2}{7}$ **h.** $\left(-\frac{3}{8}\right)y = -12$ **i.** $(-1.2)x = 4.4$

Practice

Copy and complete the table.

	$-\frac{1}{2}$	$-1\frac{6}{7}$	4	$-2\frac{3}{10}$	$13\frac{1}{2}$	-3
Additive Inverse	1.	2.	3.	4.	5.	6.
Multiplicative Inverse	7.	8.	9.	10.	11.	12.

Solve for x.

13. $\left(\frac{4}{7}\right)x = -\frac{3}{14}$

14. $\frac{x}{-12} = 1\frac{1}{2}$

15. $\left(-3\frac{1}{3}\right)x = -\frac{5}{6}$

16. $\frac{11x}{45} = -\frac{22}{9}$

17. $\frac{-13x}{7} = -1\frac{5}{21}$

18. $\frac{x}{5} = -\frac{4}{7}$

19. $7.2x = -14.4$

20. $\frac{7x}{10} = -14$

21. $\frac{2x}{-3} = -\frac{8}{9}$

Apply

22. Shannon's father has decided to build an aquarium for the den. It will be a rectangular tank $96\frac{1}{2}$ inches long, $18\frac{1}{4}$ inches wide, and $24\frac{1}{2}$ inches high. What is the maximum number of goldfish Shannon should buy for the tank if each goldfish requires 3000 cubic inches of water? Set up the equation and solve. (Volume of rectangular solid = length × width × height)

23. The bricklayer's formula, $N = 7LH$, gives the approximate number of bricks in a wall that measures L feet by H feet. A bricklayer purchases 7000 bricks for a wall 8 feet in height. The architect then decides to decrease the length of the wall by 1 foot. How many bricks will be left over?

24. A zookeeper is designing a habitat for an endangered giant panda. The constraints of the zoo require the habitat to be a rectangular area with a length of 40 feet. If the zookeeper is trying to build an area of 2300 square feet, how wide should it be? What is the total length of fence needed to surround the area?

Challenge

25. A student completed a calculation and obtained an answer of $-22\frac{1}{2}$. On the last step, the student multiplied by $-3\frac{1}{3}$ when a division of $-3\frac{1}{3}$ should have been done. What is the correct answer?

Two-Step Equations/Study Guide

Construct Meaning

Lemurs are very social animals with long noses, long limbs, and flexible fingers. They belong to the primate category and live in Madagascar. Many of the lemur species are in danger of extinction. Programs have been developed by organizations to restock the endangered lemur population. This involves genetically managing a captive lemur population and releasing a limited number of lemurs into the wild each year.

In 1998, an organization released four black and white ruffed lemurs into the wild. The year before, only three-fifths of the black and white ruffed lemurs released into the wild by this organization survived. By the end of 1998, there were seven healthy black and white ruffed lemurs in Madagascar that had entered the wild through the restocking program. How many black and white ruffed lemurs were initially released into the wild in 1997?

1997: NUMBER OF LEMURS RELEASED AND LIVING	+	1998: NUMBER OF LEMURS RELEASED	=	TOTAL LIVING LEMURS AT END OF 1998	
Number of lemurs <u>initially</u> released in 1997. $\frac{3}{5}x$	+	4	=	7	Write the equation.
$\frac{3}{5}x$	+	$4 - 4$	=	$7 - 4$	Subtract 4 from both sides.
		$\frac{3}{5}x$	=	3	Simplify.
		$\left(\frac{5}{3}\right)\frac{3}{5}x$	=	$3\left(\frac{5}{3}\right)$	Multiply both sides by the multiplicative inverse.
Five lemurs were initially released into the wild in 1997.		x	=	5	Simplify and check your answer.

Check Understanding

Write an algebraic equation for the following statements and list the steps to solve the equation.

a. Three-fourths of a number increased by 7 is $9\frac{1}{2}$.

b. Eighteen decreased by two-thirds of a number is $3\frac{3}{4}$.

Solve for x.

c. $\left(-\frac{2}{3}\right)x + 6 = 18$ **d.** $\frac{2}{9}x - 2 = 4\frac{4}{9}$ **e.** $\left(-\frac{3}{4}\right)x - 1\frac{1}{2} = 4$

f. In 1998, there were 52 species of lemurs. If 34 of these were not endangered species, what percentage of the total species of lemurs was on the endangered species list? Write an equation and solve. Round your answer to the nearest tenth.

Study Guide

1. Which of the following are equivalent forms of $\frac{-3x}{5} - 1\frac{1}{2}$? *Lesson 10.1*

a. $\left(-\frac{3}{5}\right)x - 1\frac{1}{2}$ **b.** $\frac{-3x}{-5} - 1\frac{1}{2}$ **c.** $\left(-\frac{3}{5}\right)x - \frac{3}{2}$ **d.** $\frac{-3x}{5} + \left(-\frac{3}{2}\right)$ **e.** $\frac{3x}{-5} - 1\frac{1}{2}$

2. Order the rational numbers from least to greatest. *Lesson 10.1*

$\frac{4}{9}, -\frac{2}{3}, 1\frac{1}{6}, 0, -\frac{5}{6}, 1\frac{1}{3}, -1\frac{1}{9}$

3. If Donna has traveled 131 miles in 120 minutes on her motorcycle, what is her average speed in miles per hour? *Lesson 10.1*

Indicate whether each answer will be *positive*, *negative*, or *zero*. *Lesson 10.2*

4. $-5 + 2 + 3\frac{1}{2} - 4$ **5.** $-0.79 + 2.5 + (-0.79)$ **6.** $-\frac{1}{3} - \frac{1}{3}$

Simplify. *Lesson 10.2*

7. $-\frac{4}{5} - \left(-3\frac{1}{3}\right)$ **8.** $-\frac{5}{7} + \left(-1\frac{1}{2}\right)$ **9.** $5\frac{1}{2} - 6\frac{2}{3}$

Write the equation for each statement and solve. *Lesson 10.3*

10. Seventeen is the sum of a number and negative $4\frac{3}{8}$.

11. Negative $4\frac{3}{8}$ is the sum of a number and 17.

Solve for each variable. Check your solution. *Lesson 10.3*

12. $k - 7\frac{1}{8} = 12\frac{3}{4}$ **13.** $3\frac{1}{9} + m = -17\frac{1}{3}$ **14.** $-1\frac{3}{8} + p = -9\frac{2}{3}$

Simplify. *Lesson 10.4*

15. $\left(-7\frac{1}{5}\right)\left(5\frac{5}{8}\right)$ **16.** $\left(-7\frac{1}{5}\right) \div 5\frac{5}{8}$ **17.** $\left(-5\frac{5}{8}\right) \div \left(-7\frac{1}{5}\right)$

18. Evaluate $\frac{ab}{c}$ if $a = -\frac{1}{4}$, $b = \frac{2}{3}$, and $c = \frac{5}{8}$. *Lesson 10.4*

19. A milkshake recipe requires $\frac{3}{4}$ cup milk, $1\frac{1}{2}$ cups of strawberry ice cream, and $\frac{1}{8}$ teaspoon vanilla. Silvia plans to make a milkshake for each of her 12 friends. How much of each ingredient does she need? *Lesson 10.5*

Solve for x. *Lesson 10.5*

20. $\frac{2x}{-3} = 19\frac{1}{2}$ **21.** $\left(3\frac{1}{2}\right)x = \frac{1}{3}$ **22.** $-3x = -13.5$

23. The opposite of two-tenths of a number is 84. Write an equation and solve to find the number. *Lesson 10.5*

24. Solve for x. $\left(-\frac{3}{4}\right)x + 9\frac{1}{8} = 12$ *Lesson 10.6*

Thinking Rationally

1. Order the set of rational numbers from least to greatest.
$$\left\{-0.3, \tfrac{3}{7}, -\tfrac{1}{3}, 0, 0.4\right\}$$

Write *true* or *false*.

2. All integers are rational numbers.

3. All rational numbers are integers.

4. The sum of a number and its additive inverse is 1.

5. The product of a number and its multiplicative inverse is 1.

6. The sum of two negative rational numbers is negative.

7. The product of two negative rational numbers is positive.

8. The sum of a negative number and a positive number is always negative.

9. The product of a negative number and a positive number is always negative.

10. What is the area of the shaded region in the given figure? What is the perimeter of the shaded region?

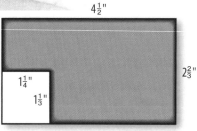

Simplify.

11. $-4\tfrac{1}{3} + 3\tfrac{1}{4}$

12. $-10\tfrac{3}{4} + 2.25$

13. $-5 + 2 + 3\tfrac{1}{2} - 4\tfrac{3}{4}$

14. $-\tfrac{1}{7} - \tfrac{1}{7}$

15. $41 - \left(-7\tfrac{1}{2}\right)$

16. $-1\tfrac{1}{2} - 17\tfrac{3}{4}$

Solve for the variable. Check your solution.

17. $k + 7\tfrac{1}{4} = 19\tfrac{1}{2}$

18. $-3\tfrac{3}{8} + m = -12\tfrac{11}{16}$

19. $j - 4\tfrac{1}{3} = 16\tfrac{5}{6}$

20. A runner has run $\tfrac{1}{3}$ mile and will stop when he has run $1\tfrac{1}{2}$ miles. How much farther does the runner have to go? Write an addition equation and solve.

21. A student says that $\left(-4\frac{1}{5}\right)\left(-1\frac{3}{7}\right) = 4\frac{3}{35}$. What mistake is the student making, and what is the correct answer?

Simplify.

22. $\left(-\frac{5}{9}\right)\left(12\frac{3}{5}\right)$ **23.** $\left(\frac{5}{9}\right) \div \left(-\frac{5}{9}\right)$ **24.** $\left(-\frac{5}{9}\right)\left(-12\frac{3}{5}\right)$

25. After driving 190 miles, $\frac{5}{9}$ of the trip is completed. How long is the total trip? How many miles are left to travel?

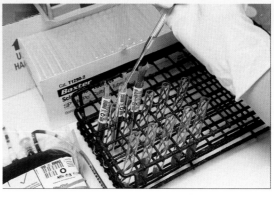

26. How many sample vials can a medical assistant fill from a full 10-mL test tube if $\frac{2}{5}$ mL is put in each vial?

27. As part of her daily workout, Alyssa decides to swim and walk a total of $\frac{9}{10}$ kilometer per day. If one lap in the swimming pool is 100 meters, how far must she walk after swimming eight laps? Write an addition equation and solve.

Solve for the variable.

28. $\frac{-7k}{9} = 7\frac{2}{3}$ **29.** $k \div (-9) = \frac{2}{3}$

30. Evaluate $\frac{a+b}{c+d}$ if $a = \frac{1}{2}$, $b = \frac{1}{4}$, $c = \frac{2}{3}$, and $d = -\frac{1}{2}$.

Solve for the variable.

31. $\frac{5}{6}x - 4 = 5$ **32.** $\frac{x}{5} - 12 = 7$

Write the equivalent algebraic equation for each statement and solve.

33. The sum of seventeen and the opposite of one-fifth of a number is twenty and one-half.

34. Seventeen increased by one-fifth of a number is twenty and one-half.

Chapter Theme:
Games

11 Chapter

Probability

Fundamental Counting Principle

Construct Meaning

Computer game designers have many options for designing a "look" for a computer character. Tina has four choices of hair color and three choices of eyewear for her design. Use the table to determine how many ways the design for the character can be put together if Tina chooses one from each of the two categories.

Construct a tree diagram. A **tree diagram** uses lines as branches to represent all possible outcomes of a given situation.

Hair color	Eyewear
Brown	Glasses
Black	Sunglasses
Blond	Goggles
Red	

Brown — Glasses, Sunglasses, Goggles
Black — Glasses, Sunglasses, Goggles
Blond — Glasses, Sunglasses, Goggles
Red — Glasses, Sunglasses, Goggles

A tree diagram shows the number of outcomes and lists the outcomes.

12 outcomes

Construct a sample space. A **sample space** is a table or list that shows all possible outcomes of a given situation.

Brown, glasses	Black, glasses	Blond, glasses	Red, glasses
Brown, sunglasses	Black, sunglasses	Blond, sunglasses	Red, sunglasses
Brown, goggles	Black, goggles	Blond, goggles	Red, goggles

Use the Fundamental Counting Principle. The **Fundamental Counting Principle** states that the total number of possible outcomes is the product of the number of items in each category. It can be used to count the possible outcomes when <u>one</u> choice from each category is selected.

Number of possible outcomes = 4(hair color) × 3(eyewear) = 12 possible outcomes

Use the Fundamental Counting Principle to determine how many arrangements are possible for a license plate containing two letters followed by two digits. Each letter can be any letter from A to Z; each digit is any number from 0 to 9.

There are 26 possibilities for each letter and 10 possibilities for each digit.

26 × 26 × 10 × 10 = 67,600 possible outcomes
1st letter   2nd letter   1st digit   2nd digit

How would the number of possible outcomes change if there were three digits followed by three letters on the license plate?

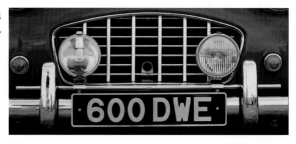

Check Understanding

Consider using this spinner and tossing a penny.

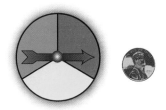

  a. Make a tree diagram of the possible outcomes.

  b. Construct a sample space of the possible outcomes.

  c. Use the Fundamental Counting Principle to determine the total number of possible outcomes. Does this agree with the number of possible outcomes in a. and b.?

  d. What are some limitations of using a tree diagram? a sample space? the Fundamental Counting Principle?

Practice

Use the menu for problems 1 through 3. For each dinner, pick one item from each category.

Entrée	Vegetable	Salad Dressing	Beverage	Dessert
Chicken	Corn	French	Milk	Yogurt
Ravioli	Beans	Creamy Italian	Fruit Juice	Strawberries
Clam Chowder	Fried Okra	Oil & Vinegar	Iced Tea	Melon
Tacos	Squash	Ranch	Lemonade	Blueberry Pie
Fajitas	Peas		Caesar	Apple Pie
Chili			Blue Cheese	Cheesecake
Hamburger				

1. Determine the number of different dinners that are possible.

2. How many different dinners are possible that have ravioli for the entrée?

3. How many different dinners are possible that have milk for the beverage and chicken for the entrée?

4. An automobile dealer offers 5 different accessory packages, 16 exterior paint colors, and 8 interior colors for a particular truck model. Determine the number of possible outcomes available for that truck model.

5. Sarai has five different routes that she can take between her home and her office. If she uses one route to go to work in the morning and a different route to return home, how many ways can she make the round trip? (Hint: The return route will have one less choice than the morning route.)

6. In Ohio, a standard license plate has three letters followed by three digits. The first letter cannot be I or O, and the last digit cannot be a zero. Determine the number of possible license plates.

7. Telephone area codes consist of three digits. The first digit can be any number 2 through 9. Before 1989, the middle digit was either 1 or 0, but now the middle digit can be any number except 9. The last digit can be any number 0 through 9.
  a. Determine the number of possible area codes before 1989.
  b. Determine the present number of possible area codes.

Permutations

Construct Meaning

Doreen has four Scrabble® tiles remaining on her rack. In how many ways can she arrange the four tiles, regardless if a word is formed or not?

How many choices does Doreen have for the first position? Once the first position is filled, how many choices does Doreen have for the second position? Once the first two positions are filled, how many choices does Doreen have for the third position? There is only one tile left for the fourth position.

$$4 \times 3 \times 2 \times 1 = 24$$

position 1   position 2   position 3   position 4

> The mathematical expression $4 \times 3 \times 2 \times 1$ can be written in factorial notation as 4!

A **factorial** of a number n is the product of all the whole numbers from 1 to n, starting with n. It is written as $n!$ and read as n factorial. $6 \times 5 \times 4 \times 3 \times 2 \times 1 = 6!$

A **permutation** is an arrangement of items in which order matters. The number of arrangements of n distinct, or different, items chosen from a group of n items is $n!$

Scott has seven different letter tiles on his rack. Determine how many ways he can arrange his tiles. Since there are 7 distinct items, use 7! to find the number of arrangements. $7! = 7 \times 6 \times 5 \times 4 \times 3 \times 2 \times 1 = 5040$

The $n!$ formula can be used for determining the number of permutations only when each item in the set is distinct and all the items are used in every arrangement.

example Dan knew his friend's three-digit house number contained the digits 6, 9, and 4, but he could not remember the order. In this case, each digit is distinct since it can be used only once. Use $n!$ to determine the number of possible house numbers or permutations.

$$3! = 3 \times 2 \times 1 = 6 \text{ possible house numbers}$$

example How many arrangements are possible for awarding first, second, and third place to twelve entries in an art contest? Is order important? Yes, but all of the entries are not involved in the winning arrangement. In this case, use the Fundamental Counting Principle.

$$12 \times 11 \times 10 = 1320 \text{ possible winner arrangements}$$

Check Understanding

a. What is the difference between the two examples at the end of the previous page?

b. How many ways can the five Monopoly® pieces be arranged in a row?

c. How many arrangements can be made for an identification code consisting of any two letters except I and O, followed by a single digit?

Apply

1. Maxine, Hakim, and Leonard are all sitting in the back seat of a car.
   a. How many ways can they be seated in the back seat?
   b. Make a list of all the possible arrangements.

2. There are five people in the Grenne family.
   a. How many ways can they be arranged in a row for a family portrait?
   b. How many ways can they be arranged in a row if the father is on the far right?

3. If there are nine players on Vineta's softball team, how many different arrangements are there for the first three batters?

4. Daley is arranging her stacks of Monopoly® money. She has stacks of $500, $100, $50, $20, $10, $5, and $1 bills. How many ways can she arrange the stacks?

5. Jeff is conducting an experiment to see if people can tell the difference between three brands of cranberry juice. He will give the three samples to each participant in random order. In how many different orders can the samples be presented?

6. Each teacher at Century Christian School has a three-digit phone extension number. How many different extension numbers can be made if the first digit cannot be a zero?

7. Mrs. Reed, the librarian, can display five mystery novels in a row in a display case. How many different arrangements could she make if she has ten novels to choose from?

8. Four students running for class president will be making speeches at an assembly.
   a. In how many different orders can the students give their speeches?
   b. Describe a way in which you could randomly assign the order of the speeches.

11.3 Combinations

Construct Meaning

At Alejandro's Pizza, customers can choose two different toppings for their pizza without extra charge. How many different pizzas can be made by choosing any two of the five toppings?

TOPPINGS
- **Mushrooms**
- **Black olives**
- **Extra cheese**
- **Peppers**
- **Onions**

think A mushroom and olive pizza is the same as an olive and mushroom pizza. The order in which the toppings are chosen is not important.

An arrangement of items in which order does not matter is a **combination**. Contrast this with permutations where order does matter, such as the numbers on a license plate.

MB	MC	MP	MO
BM	BC	BP	BO
CM	CB	CP	CO
PM	PB	PC	PO
OM	OB	OC	OP

Melissa made a **sample space** to determine the possible pizzas with two toppings. Letters represent each topping. The sample space shows all 20 permutations, arrangements in which order matters. Since order does not matter in this case, Melissa eliminated all the duplicates. Ten **combinations** remained.

Lorenzo made an **organized** list to find all possible combinations for two toppings.

	Select the first topping and list combinations with each other topping.	MB	MC	MP	MO
	Select the second topping and list combinations that do not include the first.	BC	BP	BO	
	Select the third topping and list combinations that do not include the first or second.	CP	CO		
	Repeat until no toppings remain.	PO			

> There are ten possible combinations.

Joshua used a **mathematical expression** to determine the number of combinations. To eliminate any duplicates, he found the number of permutations, then divided by the number of ways each smaller group could be arranged.

$$\frac{\text{Number of permutations of entire group}}{\text{Number of permutations of each smaller group}} = \frac{5 \text{ choices for first item} \times 4 \text{ for second}}{2! \text{ ways to arrange 2 items}} = \frac{5 \cdot 4}{2 \cdot 1} = 10 \text{ combinations}$$

How is Joshua's method related to Melissa's method?

Check Understanding

a. A chess tournament at Trinity Christian School has six participants: Paula, Ray, Sam, Vera, Tim, and Geraldo. How many games will be played if every person plays each other one time? List the possible combinations.

b. Discuss the advantages and disadvantages for each method of determining combinations.

234

Apply

1. At the Wheatridge Creamery, customers can choose three out of four toppings for a sundae: whipped cream, cherries, nuts, and sprinkles. Why is this <u>not</u> a permutation problem? List the possible combinations to determine how many different three-topping sundaes could be made.

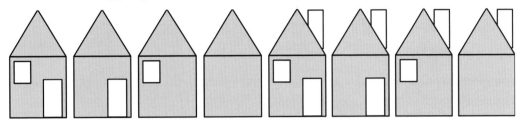

2. For each house drawing, the possible features are door, window, and chimney. There is only one possible position for each feature.
   a. How many different drawings can be made with two features? all three features? none of the features? only one feature?
   b. Do these drawings represent combinations or permutations? Explain.

3. Mrs. Field has eight reference books to arrange between two bookends on her desk. How many ways can the books be arranged?

4. The transportation department predicts that about 800,000 cars will be registered in a certain state by the year 2012. Their license plates are made using any two letters followed by any three digits from 0 to 9. Will there be enough possible arrangements? Explain.

5. Three class representatives will be chosen from a class of 24 students. Will the three elected representatives be a permutation or a combination? Use a mathematical expression to determine how many arrangements are possible.

6. Wesley's suitcase lock has three rotating cylinders, each having ten different digits. Does the set of three numbers used to open the lock represent a combination or a permutation? Use a mathematical expression to determine how many different sets of three digits are possible for this type of lock.

7. Nancy has three extra tickets to the Calvary Christian Academy winter festival. Determine how many different sets of three friends she could take if she chooses from a group of five friends: Ann, Bea, Cora, Dee, and Eva. List them.

Probability

Construct Meaning

If your Monopoly® game token is on the GO space, what is the probability that on your next move you will land on the Chance space, seven spaces from GO? The chart shows the 36 possible combinations when rolling two regular number cubes. There are 6 ways to roll a sum of 7. You have a 6 out of 36 probability of rolling a sum of 7.

	(6,1)									
	(5,1)	(5,2)	(6,2)							
	(4,1)	(4,2)	(4,3)	(5,3)	(6,3)					
	(3,1)	(3,2)	(3,3)	(3,4)	(4,4)	(5,4)	(6,4)			
	(2,1)	(2,2)	(2,3)	(2,4)	(2,5)	(3,5)	(4,5)	(5,5)	(6,5)	
(1,1)	(1,2)	(1,3)	(1,4)	(1,5)	(1,6)	(2,6)	(3,6)	(4,6)	(5,6)	(6,6)
sum 2	3	4	5	6	7	8	9	10	11	12

$$P(7) = \frac{6}{36} = \frac{1}{6}$$

This **theoretical probability** is the ratio of the number of favorable outcomes to the number of possible outcomes.

$$\text{Theoretical probability} = \frac{\text{Number of favorable outcomes}}{\text{Number of possible outcomes}}$$

What is the theoretical probability of rolling a sum greater than 12?

$$P(>12) = \frac{0 \text{ favorable outcomes}}{36 \text{ possible outcomes}} = 0$$ The probability is zero. This event is <u>not possible</u>.

What is the theoretical probability of rolling a sum less than or equal to 12?

$$P(\leq12) = \frac{36 \text{ favorable outcomes}}{36 \text{ possible outcomes}} = 1$$ The probability is 1. This event is <u>certain</u> because all possible sums are less than or equal to 12.

What is the theoretical probability of rolling a sum that is prime? The sums 2, 3, 5, 7, and 11 are prime. A 2 can be rolled one way, a 3 in two ways, a 5 in four ways, a 7 in six ways, and an 11 in two ways.

$$P(\text{prime}) = \frac{\overbrace{1+2+4+6+2}^{\text{Total number of favorable outcomes}}}{36} = \frac{15}{36} = \frac{5}{12}$$

Probability can be used to predict the number of times an event may occur. Using theoretical probability, what would be the predicted number of times a sum of 7 would be rolled in 24 rolls?

Theoretical probability for a sum of 7 $\dfrac{1}{6} = \dfrac{n \text{ predicted outcomes}}{24 \text{ possible outcomes}}$ Write a proportion.

$6n = 24$ Use cross products.

$n = 4$ times

Experimental probability is the ratio of the number of times an event actually occurs to the total number of trials during an experiment.

$$\text{Experimental probability} = \frac{\text{Number of times an event occurred}}{\text{Total number of trials}}$$

Two number cubes are rolled 24 times. The resulting sums are recorded on a **line plot**, a graph that uses an x above a number on a number line to represent each favorable outcome. Using this data, determine the experimental probability for rolling a sum of 7.

$$\text{Experimental probability} = \frac{\text{Sum of 7 occurred 2 times}}{24 \text{ trials}} = \frac{2}{24} = \frac{1}{12}$$

Did the number of times a 7 was rolled match the predicted outcome calculated previously? Why is the experimental probability $\left(\frac{1}{12}\right)$ different from the theoretical probability $\left(\frac{1}{6}\right)$?

```
                    X
                    X
              X     X
              X X   X X
              X X X X X     X
            X X X X X X X X X X
            2 3 4 5 6 7 8 9 10 11 12
```

Check Understanding

a. Discuss this statement: If the number of trials in a probability experiment increases, the experimental probability will be closer to the theoretical probability.

b. What is the theoretical probability of rolling a sum of 9, $P(9)$?

c. What is the theoretical probability of rolling a sum of 6 or 10, $P(6 \text{ or } 10)$?

d. What is the theoretical probability of rolling a sum that is even and greater than 8, $P(\text{even sum} > 8)$?

Practice

Use the cards to determine the theoretical probability of randomly drawing a given card. Write your answer in simplest form.

1. $P(\text{red})$ **2.** $P(\text{dotted})$

3. $P(\text{even})$ **4.** $P(\text{solid})$

5. $P(\text{striped})$ **6.** $P(\text{flowered})$

7. $P(\text{not blue})$ **8.** $P(\text{red or striped})$

9. $P(\text{blue and dotted})$ **10.** $P(\text{multiple of 3 or yellow})$

Apply

Determine theoretical probabilities for the spinner.

11. The pointer landing on C, $P(C)$

12. The pointer not landing on B, $P(\text{not B})$

13. The pointer not landing on orange, $P(\text{not orange})$

14. Two number cubes have been rolled 36 times and the results are recorded on the line plot. Using the chart in Construct Meaning, determine the theoretical probability of rolling a sum of 5.

15. Use the line plot to determine the experimental probability of rolling a sum of 5. Is it the same as the theoretical probability?

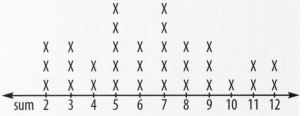

16. After rolling two number cubes for 60 turns, the sum of 10 occurred 5 times. How close is that to the predicted number based on the theoretical probability?

17. Tossing a coin has two possible outcomes: heads and tails.

     a. Predict the number of times heads will occur in 20 tosses.

     b. Toss a coin 20 times and record the results on a line plot.

     c. Calculate the experimental probability for tossing heads based on your results.

11.5 *Mutually Exclusive Events*

Construct Meaning

Have you ever had to make a decision to do one activity or another? Brian can either go to a drama production or practice basketball on Friday night with his friends. He cannot do both. These are **mutually exclusive events**. If either event occurs, the other cannot occur at the same time. Brian can choose to wear his jacket when he leaves the house on Friday night. Are wearing his jacket and practicing basketball mutually exclusive? Since Brian can do both at the same time, they are not mutually exclusive events.

When two events are mutually exclusive, the probability for one event <u>or</u> another occurring can be determined. There are five possible outcomes when using this spinner.

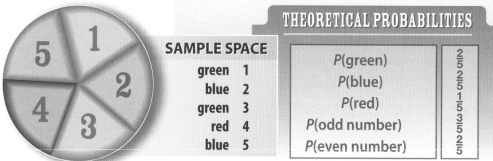

SAMPLE SPACE			THEORETICAL PROBABILITIES	
green	1		P(green)	$\frac{2}{5}$
blue	2		P(blue)	$\frac{2}{5}$
green	3		P(red)	$\frac{1}{5}$
red	4		P(odd number)	$\frac{3}{5}$
blue	5		P(even number)	$\frac{2}{5}$

Determine the theoretical probability of spinning a green <u>or</u> an even number.

- Find the number of favorable outcomes.

  <u>green</u> 1   blue②   <u>green</u> 3   red④

  $$P(\text{green or even}) = \frac{4 \text{ favorable outcomes}}{5 \text{ possible outcomes}} = \frac{4}{5}$$

- Find the individual probability for each event and add them together.

  $$P(\text{green or even}) = P(\text{green}) + P(\text{even}) = \frac{2}{5} + \frac{2}{5} = \frac{4}{5}$$

> **If two events A and B are mutually exclusive,**
> **the probability of A or B is the sum of their individual probabilities.**
> $$P(A \text{ or } B) = P(A) + P(B)$$

Check Understanding

a. Why does <u>adding</u> the probabilities of two mutually exclusive events make sense if you are trying to determine the probability of one <u>or</u> the other happening?

b. Consider the spinner on the previous page. Are spinning green and spinning an odd number mutually exclusive events?

c. What is the probability of rolling a 3 or a 5 on a ten-sided die numbered 1 through 10?

Practice

Consider using the spinner shown below for each probability.

1. P(green)   **2.** P(red)   **3.** P(not red)

4. P(green or red)   **5.** P(green) + P(red)

6. Are spinning a green and spinning a red mutually exclusive? Explain.

Apply

Now consider all the possible combinations for spinning the spinner and rolling a tetrahedral die for a single turn. Copy and complete the sample space. Use it for determining the following theoretical probabilities.

7. How many possible outcomes are there?

8. P(R1)   **9.** P(G4)

10. P(2 in the outcome)   **11.** P(blue in the outcome)

| | | **Spinner** | | | | |
		Red	Green	Red	Green	Blue	Green
Die	1	R1	G1	R1			
	2	R2	G2				
	3	R3					
	4						

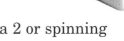

12. Using your sample space, determine the probability for rolling a 2 or spinning a blue in a single turn.

13. Find P(2) + P(blue).

14. Why is the P(2 or blue) you determined in problem 12 not the same as P(2) + P(blue) in problem 13?

Review

Simplify each expression.

1. $\frac{1}{2} + \frac{5}{6} - \left(-\frac{1}{3}\right)$ **2.** $-6.1 + 3.97$ **3.** $19(5.2 + 4.8)$

4. 25% of 144   **5.** $2(-3) + 15$ **6.** 120% of 50

Independent and Dependent Events

Construct Meaning

Deyla is at a point in a Scrabble® game where she wants to use her turn to exchange two of her letter tiles for two new tiles. She randomly draws two tiles from a pile containing the following letters. A **compound event** is a combination of two or more events.

Suppose Deyla replaces the first tile before drawing the second. What is the probability that she draws N O in that order?

The probability that the first draw is an N is $\frac{2}{8}$ or $\frac{1}{4}$. $P(\text{N}) = \frac{1}{4}$
The N is replaced and the second tile is drawn.
The probability that it will be an O is $\frac{4}{8}$ or $\frac{1}{2}$. $P(\text{O}) = \frac{1}{2}$

The probability of drawing an N on the first draw and an O on the second draw are **independent events**. The outcome of one event does not affect the probability of the other event.

> If two events, A and B, are independent, the probability of both occurring is the product of their individual probabilities. $P(A \text{ and } B) = P(A) \cdot P(B)$

Therefore, $P(\text{N and O}) = P(\text{N}) \cdot P(\text{O}) = \frac{1}{4} \cdot \frac{1}{2} = \frac{1}{8}$.

Suppose Deyla does not replace each tile after it is drawn.

What is the probability that she draws N O in that order?
$P(\text{N}) = \frac{1}{4}$ Individual probability of drawing N is 2 out of 8 tiles.
$P(\text{O on second draw}) = \frac{4}{7}$ Because the N is not replaced, 4 out of 7 tiles are O.
$P(\text{N, then O}) = \frac{1}{4} \cdot \frac{4}{7}$ Given that N is drawn first, multiply individual probabilities.
$P(\text{N, then O}) = \frac{1}{7}$

What is the probability that she draws N N in that order?
$P(\text{N}) = \frac{1}{4}$ Individual probability of drawing N is 2 out of 8 tiles.
$P(\text{N on second draw}) = \frac{1}{7}$ Because the N is not replaced, 1 out of 7 tiles is N.
$P(\text{N, then N}) = \frac{1}{4} \cdot \frac{1}{7}$ Given that N is drawn first, multiply individual probabilities.
$P(\text{N, then N}) = \frac{1}{28}$

Since the first tile drawn was not replaced, the first event affects the probability of the second event. With **dependent events**, the occurrence of the first event affects the probability of the second event.

> If two events, A and B, are dependent, the probability of both occurring is the product of the probability of A and the probability of B after A occurs. $P(A \text{ and } B) = P(A) \cdot P(B \text{ following } A)$

Check Understanding
Tell whether the events are *independent* or *dependent*.
  a. Having two children: having a boy and then having a girl
  b. Drawing a card from a deck, not replacing it then drawing another card
  c. Rolling a number cube twice: rolling a 2 and then rolling a 5
  d. Rolling a 6 on a number cube and spinning a red on the spinner

Practice
In a bag are 5 blue color tiles, 4 red color tiles, 4 yellow color tiles, and 3 green color tiles.

  1. $P(\text{yellow})$ **2.** $P(\text{blue})$ **3.** $P(\text{green})$

Find the following probabilities (in the indicated order), if two tiles are drawn with replacement.

  4. $P(\text{yellow, blue})$ **5.** $P(\text{red, red})$

If two tiles are drawn without replacement, determine the individual probabilities of each tile drawn and the probability that both tiles are drawn in that order.
  6. A yellow tile is drawn first and then a blue tile is drawn.

  7. A red tile is drawn first and then another red tile is drawn.

Apply
  8. The probability of a couple having a boy or a girl for a child is the same as tossing a heads or tails on a penny. Use the formula to determine probability that their first child is a boy and their second child is a girl. Draw a sample space to check your answer.

  9. Jayken is exchanging two of his Scrabble® letter tiles for two new letter tiles. He randomly draws two tiles from a pile containing the following letters.

  a. What is the probability that his first draw is an E?
  b. What is the probability that his next draw is a D, if the first letter, E, is not replaced?
  c. What is the probability of drawing a 4-point letter tile?
  d. What is the probability of drawing a D <u>or</u> an 8-point letter tile? Are these events mutually exclusive?
  e. What is the probability of drawing an F, replacing it <u>and</u> then drawing an H? Are these events dependent or independent?

Problem Solving

Construct Meaning

The table shows the distribution of letters in Scrabble®. There are 100 tiles in the game. Determine the theoretical probability of randomly drawing a tile that is a vowel.

$$P(A, E, I, O, or\ U) = \frac{Number\ of\ favorable\ outcomes}{Number\ of\ possible\ outcomes} = \frac{9 + 12 + 9 + 8 + 4}{100} = \frac{42}{100} = \frac{21}{50}$$

What is the probability of randomly drawing a blank tile?

$$P(blank) = \frac{2}{100} = \frac{1}{50}$$

Determine the experimental probability of drawing an E, based on randomly drawing seven tiles: O, F, E, L, G, E, E.

$$P(E) = \frac{Number\ of\ times\ event\ occured}{} = \frac{3}{7}$$

Jill has four letters on her rack J U I H. How many different ways can she arrange the four letters? First, determine if this is a permutation or a combination. Since order matters, each arrangement is a permutation.

$$4! = 4 \times 3 \times 2 \times 1 = 24\ permutations$$

Jill randomly draws two of her four tiles with replacement. What is the probability that the tiles drawn are I and J in that order? Are these independent or dependent events? Since the tiles are replaced, the events are independent.

$$P(I, J) = P(I) \cdot P(J) = \frac{1}{4} \cdot \frac{1}{4} = \frac{1}{16}$$

Letter	Number of tiles	Letter	Number of tiles
A	9	N	6
B	2	O	8
C	2	P	2
D	4	Q	1
E	12	R	6
F	2	S	4
G	3	T	6
H	2	U	4
I	9	V	2
J	1	W	2
K	1	X	1
L	4	Y	2
M	2	Z	1
BLANK	2		

Check Understanding

Use the distribution chart for the Scrabble® tiles for the following problems.

a. If Casey draws one tile, what is the probability of drawing an X, Y, or Z?

b. If Casey draws two tiles with replacement after each draw, what is the probability of drawing an I followed by a T?

c. If Casey draws two tiles without replacement, what is the probability of drawing an M followed by a G?

d. Casey draws three tiles with replacement. What is the probability of drawing a C, then an A, followed by a T?

Apply

In the game of Clue® there are 6 suspects, 6 weapons, and 9 rooms. A crime has been committed by one of the suspects, using one weapon, in one room. As the game progresses, players must eliminate the possibilities in order to solve the mystery. Herb has eliminated some of the suspects, weapons, and rooms as shown by an X marked in the chart.

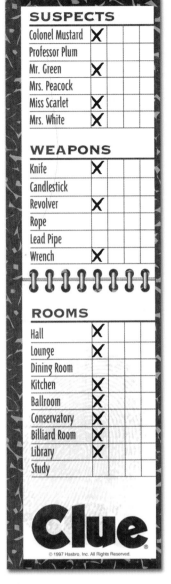

SUSPECTS			
Colonel Mustard	X		
Professor Plum			
Mr. Green	X		
Mrs. Peacock			
Miss Scarlet	X		
Mrs. White	X		

WEAPONS			
Knife	X		
Candlestick			
Revolver	X		
Rope			
Lead Pipe			
Wrench	X		

ROOMS			
Hall	X		
Lounge	X		
Dining Room			
Kitchen	X		
Ballroom	X		
Conservatory	X		
Billiard Room	X		
Library	X		
Study			

Clue

© 1997 Hasbro, Inc. All Rights Reserved.

1. How many different ways could the crime have been committed? (Hint: Consider the remaining possible arrangements.)

2. What is the probability that the crime was committed by Professor Plum? (Hint: Since 4 suspects have been eliminated only 2 remain as possibilities.)

3. What is the probability that the crime was committed using the candlestick?

4. What is the probability that the crime was committed by Professor Plum with the candlestick?

5. What is the probability that the crime was committed with the rope or the candlestick?

6. What is the probability that the crime was committed by Mrs. Peacock with the rope in the study?

7. If Herb has determined that the crime took place in the dining room, what is the probability that the crime was committed by Professor Plum with the lead pipe in the dining room?

Review

1. $\sqrt{169}$ 2. $-5\frac{2}{3} - \frac{1}{3}$ 3. $\left(-\frac{5}{9}\right)\left(-\frac{3}{25}\right)$ 4. $-2\frac{1}{3} \div 3\frac{1}{2}$

5. Find the LCM for 8 and 10.

6. Find the GCF for 16 and 24.

Simulations

Construct Meaning

A card store has randomly inserted one of four different coupons in each packet of baseball cards. The entire set of four coupons can be redeemed at the store for a $20 gift certificate. The card store will not redeem the coupons individually. Ken wants to collect the entire set so he can redeem them for the $20 gift certificate. Suppose there is an equally large supply of each of the four coupons. The probability of getting any one coupon in a packet of baseball cards is $\frac{1}{4}$.

How many packets of baseball cards would Ken have to purchase in order to get at least one of each coupon?

Perform a simulation. A **simulation** is an experiment that models outcomes of a real-world situation. What is the advantage of simulating this situation instead of actually purchasing the packets of baseball cards?

Ken uses a spinner with four numbers to simulate this situation. Each of the four numbers on the spinner represents one of the four cards. Landing on each number at least once simulates that each different coupon has been obtained at least one time. Ken spins the spinner and places a tally mark in the tally box until each number has at least one tally mark. The chart shows the results of Ken's ten simulations.

	Simulation 1		Simulation 2		Simulation 3		Simulation 4		Simulation 5		Simulation 6		Simulation 7		Simulation 8		Simulation 9		Simulation 10
1	l	1	l	1	ll	1	l	1	l	1	lll	1	ⅢⅡ	1	l	1	ll	1	l
2	ll	2	ⅢⅡ l	2	ll	2	ll	2	l	2	ll	2	l	2	l	2	l	2	ll
3	lll	3	lll	3	l	3	ll	3	l	3	ll	3	llll	3	l	3	ⅢⅡ	3	l
4	l	4	llll	4	ll	4	l	4	ll	4	l	4	ll	4	l	4	l	4	ll
Number of packets	7	Number of packets	14	Number of packets	7	Number of packets	6	Number of packets	5	Number of packets	8	Number of packets	12	Number of packets	4	Number of packets	9	Number of packets	6

Determine the average number of packets to purchase using the simulated results.

$$\frac{(7 + 14 + 7 + 6 + 5 + 8 + 12 + 4 + 9 + 6)}{10} = \frac{78}{10} = 7.8 \approx 8$$

Ken would probably need to purchase 8 packets of baseball cards to get at least one of each coupon.

If one packet of baseball cards cost $4.95, should Ken go ahead and purchase the cards?

Check Understanding

a. In the simulation, why was it necessary to continue to spin the spinner until all the numbers had been checked at least once?

b. If there were six coupons to be collected instead of four, how could a simulation be performed?

Apply

Puff Puff Breakfast cereal has randomly inserted one prize in each cereal box. There are six prizes available to collect, and you want to collect the entire set. Suppose there are thousands of boxes of cereal with prizes. How many boxes of cereal would you have to purchase in order to get at least one of each of the six prizes?

1. What is the theoretical probability of getting any one prize in a given box?

2. What is the advantage of simulating this situation instead of actually purchasing the cereal boxes?

3. How could a simulation be performed?

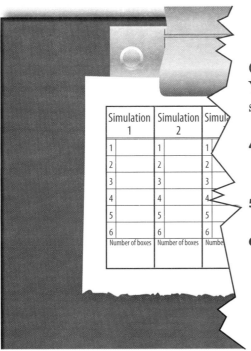

Copy and complete the chart for six simulations. You may use a number cube or the spinner with six numbers to fill out the chart.

4. What is the average number of boxes of cereal you need to purchase to collect all six prizes?

5. Why perform more than six simulations?

6. If you use the simulation results obtained by two other classmates, how many simulation results would you have including your own?

Review

1. $2 \cdot 3^3$

2. Which is greater, $\frac{3}{16}$ or $\frac{1}{5}$?

3. Twelve is what percent of 60?

4. Graph $x > -2$ on a number line.

5. Define supplementary angles.

Pascal's Triangle/Study Guide

Construct Meaning

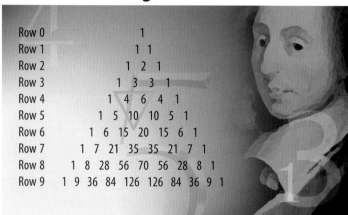

Row 0	1
Row 1	1 1
Row 2	1 2 1
Row 3	1 3 3 1
Row 4	1 4 6 4 1
Row 5	1 5 10 10 5 1
Row 6	1 6 15 20 15 6 1
Row 7	1 7 21 35 35 21 7 1
Row 8	1 8 28 56 70 56 28 8 1
Row 9	1 9 36 84 126 126 84 36 9 1

Blaise Pascal, a French mathematician, described this arrangement of numbers in 1653. Each number in Pascal's Triangle is the sum of the two adjacent numbers in the previous row. For example, the orange triangle shows $4 + 6 = 10$. Each number in Pascal's Triangle is referred to by row number and entry number. The top row is Row 0 and the first number in each row is the zeroth entry. For example, the number 20 is the third entry in Row 6.

Many patterns can be seen in Pascal's Triangle.

▶ The sum of the numbers in each row are 1, 2, 4, 8, 16, 32, 64, 128, 256, ... What is the pattern?

▶ The set of consecutive triangular numbers {1, 3, 6, 10, 15, 21, …} form a straight line in Pascal's Triangle. Find the diagonal containing this pattern on the triangle.

▶ The rows can be used to determine the number of possible combinations. In how many ways can you select 4 items from a group of 5?

Using a mathematical expression:

$$\frac{5 \cdot 4 \cdot 3 \cdot 2}{4 \cdot 3 \cdot 2} = 5$$

5 combinations

Using Pascal's Triangle:

1   5   10   10   **5**   1

Entry 0th 1st 2nd 3rd 4th 5th

5 combinations

> Use Row 5 from Pascal's Triangle to represent the group of 5 items.

> Consider the fourth entry in the row since 4 items are taken at a time.

Use Pascal's Triangle to determine how many ways to select 3 people at a time from a group of 9 people.

▶ Different patterns can be seen by coloring all the numbers in the triangle that are evenly divisible by a number, n, with one color and coloring the remaining numbers in the triangle with a different color.

The pattern seen here is Pascal's Triangle taken to 64 rows with $n = 2$. A number is left white if it is evenly divisible by 2 and colored blue if it is not. This pattern is linked to what is called Sierpinski's Gasket and fractal mathematics.

Use triangular grid paper to write out Pascal's Triangle, one number per triangle, through Row 10. Choose two colors for shading in the triangle. Use one color to shade in the triangles with numbers evenly divisible by two (and every blank adjacent triangle). Use the other color to shade in the remaining triangles. The resulting pattern will resemble Sierpinski's Gasket.

1. How many different outfits can be made from 6 shirts and 5 pairs of shorts? *Lesson 11.1*

2. In how many ways can the letters ENGLISH be arranged? *Lesson 11.2*

3. Complete the sample space to show all possible arrangements of three numbers chosen from 1234 if order is important. How many arrangements are possible? *Lesson 11.3*

123	213	312	412
124			
134	234	324	423

4. If order is <u>not</u> important, how many arrangements of three numbers are possible? *Lesson 11.3*

5. Write *permutation* or *combination*. *Lessons 11.2 and 11.3*

a. Choosing two toppings for a pizza
b. Awarding first, second, and third place
c. Arranging four different books on a shelf

6. Joe tossed a penny 200 times and recorded 110 heads. *Lesson 11.4*

a. What is his experimental probability for tossing heads?
b. Why does this value differ from the theoretical probability?

7. For a single spin of this spinner, are these events mutually exclusive? *Lesson 11.5*

a. Spinning a red; spinning an even number
b. Spinning a blue; spinning an odd number

8. For a single spin, determine the probability. *Lesson 11.5*

a. A red <u>or</u> an even number.
b. A blue <u>or</u> an odd number. (Hint: Use a sample space.)

9. A bag contains 6 red marbles, 5 white marbles, and 9 blue marbles. Write *independent* or *dependent* for each set of events. *Lesson 11.6*

a. Drawing a red marble, replacing it, and then drawing a white marble.
b. Drawing a red marble and without replacement drawing a white marble.

10. Consider the same bag of marbles as in problem 9. *Lesson 11.6*

a. What is the probability of drawing a blue marble, replacing it, and then drawing a red marble?
b. What is the probability of drawing a white marble first and then a red marble given that a white was drawn first and <u>not</u> replaced?

11. Katrina has 7 letters LUIHJEL on her rack in a game of Scrabble®. If she randomly chooses two tiles without replacement, what is the probability that L and then J are drawn in that order? *Lesson 11.7*

12. John wants to determine how many school days will pass before both he and his friend are randomly chosen from a group of six students to raise the flag before school. Propose a simulation John could perform to predict an answer. *Lesson 11.8*

13. How many combinations are possible if four items are drawn from a group of seven different items? You may use Pascal's Triangle. *Lesson 11.9*

Predictable Probabilities

Write the letter of the correct answer. Each letter may be used only once.

1. A ___ is an arrangement of items in which the order of items does not matter.
2. Two events are ___ when the outcome of one event does not affect the probability of the next event.
3. ___ is the ratio of the number of times an event actually occurs to the total number of trials.
4. A ___ is an arrangement of items in which order matters.
5. A ___ is a table or list that shows all the possible outcomes of a given situation.
6. With ___ events, if either event occurs, the other cannot occur at the same time.
7. ___ is the ratio of the number of favorable outcomes to the number of possible outcomes.
8. The ___ states that the total number of possible outcomes is the product of the number of items in each category.
9. Two events are ___ when the occurrence of the first event affects the probability of the second event.
10. A ___ is an experiment that models outcomes of a real-life situation.

a. Combination
b. Experimental probability
c. Dependent
d. Independent
e. Mutually exclusive
f. Permutation
g. Sample space
h. Theoretical probability
i. Simulation
j. Fundamental Counting Principle
k. Factorial

Write *permutation* or *combination*.

11. Arranging the letters in the word G U E S T

12. Selecting two books from the library

13. How many ways can the letters S T I C K Y be arranged?

14. How many seven-digit phone numbers can be made if the first number cannot be 0 or 9?

15. How many different sundaes can be made if you may choose one of 7 ice cream flavors, one of 4 sauces, and one of 4 toppings?

16. Consider four books, A, B, C, and D.
    a. Determine how many ways 4 books can be chosen if order is important.
    b. Copy and complete the sample space for choosing 3 books from 4 books.
    c. If order is not important, how many arrangements are possible?

ABC	BAC	CAB	DAB
ABD		CAD	
ACD		CBD	

17. Are these events mutually exclusive? Write *yes* or *no*.
    a. Dressing for school one morning: wearing gym shoes, wearing sandals
    b. Dressing for school one morning: wearing pants, wearing a shirt

18. Write *dependent* or *independent*.
    a. Drawing a red tile from a bag, not replacing the tile, and then drawing a blue tile
    b. Spinning a red on a spinner and rolling a 5 on a number cube

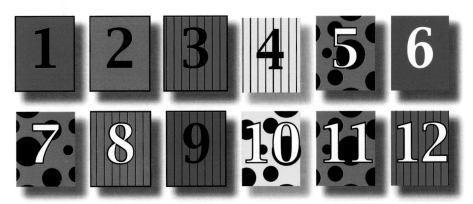

Use the cards above to determine the theoretical probability of randomly drawing the following. Write your answer in simplest form.

19. $P(7)$ **20.** P(dotted)   **21.** P(not striped)

22. P(dotted and prime)   **23.** P(blue or prime)   **24.** P(less than 5 and striped)

A bag contains 4 red marbles, 3 green marbles, 5 blue marbles, and 4 yellow marbles.

25. Draw two marbles, replacing the first marble before the second draw.
   a. P(red, blue)
   b. P(green, green)
   c. P(green, yellow)

26. Draw two marbles from the bag. The first is drawn, not replaced, and then the second is drawn.
   a. P(red, then blue)
   b. P(green, then green)
   c. P(green, then yellow)

Shaylee rolled a six-sided number cube 144 times and rolled 30 fours.

27. Determine her experimental probability of rolling a four.

28. How many fours would you predict if you rolled a number cube 144 times?

29. Do you think the number cube used in this experiment was fair? Explain.

30. A cracker manufacturer randomly places one of four different prizes in each box of crackers. To determine about how many boxes of crackers Dayton may need to purchase in order to collect one of each prize, he performed a simulation.

Simulation 1	Simulation 2	Simulation 3	Simulation 4	Simulation 5
Tally 卌 卌	Tally 卌	Tally 卌 卌 ||	Tally 卌 |||	Tally 卌 卌 ||||
1 ✓	1 ✓	1 ✓	1 ✓	1 ✓
2 ✓	2 ✓	2 ✓	2 ✓	2 ✓
3 ✓	3 ✓	3 ✓	3 ✓	3 ✓
4 ✓	4 ✓	4 ✓	4 ✓	4 ✓
Number of Boxes 10	Number of Boxes 6	Number of Boxes 12	Number of Boxes 8	Number of Boxes 14

a. According to his simulation results, how many boxes of crackers might Dayton need to purchase?

b. If Dayton wants his results to be more accurate, what can he do?

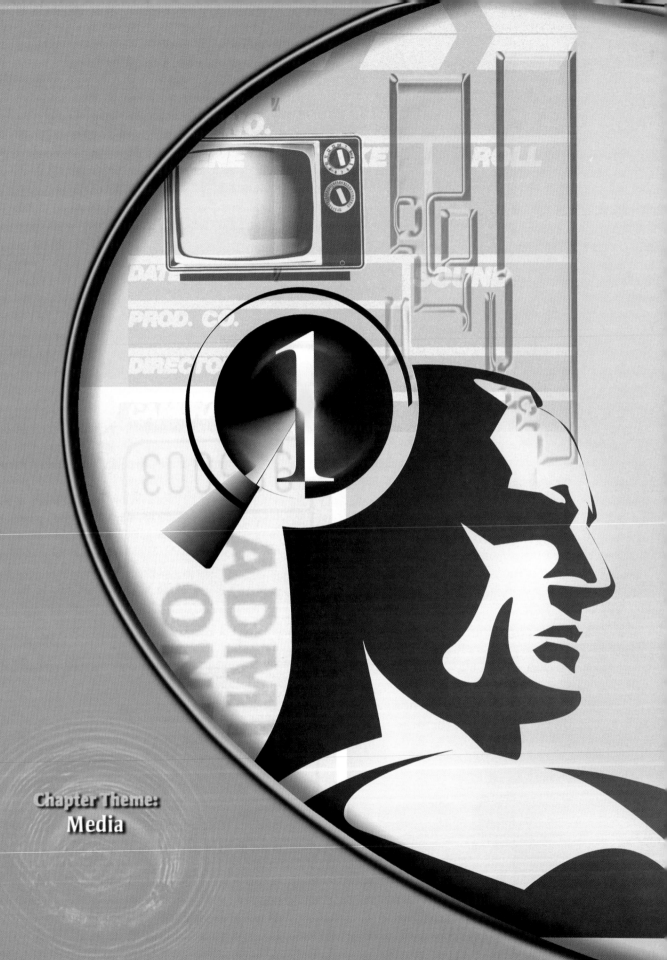

Chapter Theme:
Media

12.1 Displaying Data

Construct Meaning

The members of Miss Purdy's math class took a pet survey. These are the data they compiled:

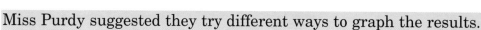

Dogs	Cats	Rodents	Birds	Reptiles

Miss Purdy suggested they try different ways to graph the results.

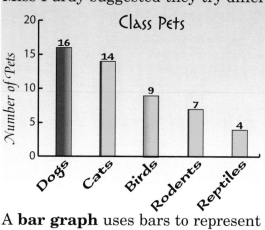

A **bar graph** uses bars to represent the values of a set of data.

A **circle graph** compares parts of a whole.

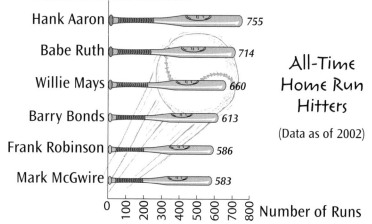

All-Time Home Run Hitters

(Data as of 2002)

World Religious Affiliation

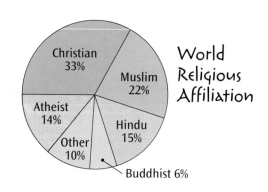

A **line graph** uses line segments to represent increases or decreases over a period of time.

Check Understanding

a. What percentage of pets belonging to Miss Purdy's students are not cats or dogs?

b. How many home runs did Babe Ruth hit in his lifetime? Who hit more home runs?

c. What percentage of the world's population claims no affiliation with the leading four religions?

d. What was Bradley Motors' best month for auto sales? worst month?

e. What was Bradley Motors' best month for truck sales?

f. What was Bradley Motors' best month for overall sales?

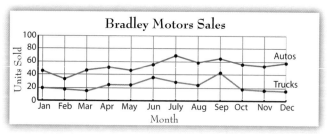

Practice

Refer to the bar graph at right.

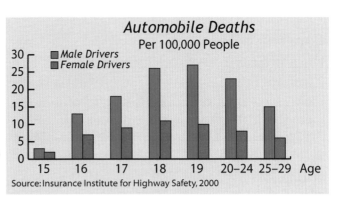

Automobile Deaths
Per 100,000 People

■ Male Drivers
■ Female Drivers

Source: Insurance Institute for Highway Safety, 2000

1. What does the graph show with respect to gender of young drivers?

2. At what ages are automobile deaths the highest?

3. Based on these statistics, would you expect insurance rates to be higher for males or females? for 17-year-olds or 26-year-olds?

Average Monthly Temperatures (°F)				
	Jan	Apr	Jul	Oct
Fairbanks, AK	−12.7	30.2	61.5	25.1
Honolulu, HI	72.6	75.7	80.1	79.5
Phoenix, AZ	52.3	68.1	92.3	73.4
San Francisco, CA	48.5	55.8	63.2	60.6

4. Make a line graph of the average monthly temperature data to track seasonal temperature variation for these four cities.

5. What does the relatively flat graph for Honolulu tell you?

6. Which city has the greatest variation between seasons?

7. Which city has the highest average winter temperature? the highest average summer temperature?

8. What inference could you make regarding coastal cities (Honolulu, San Francisco) and inland cities (Fairbanks, Phoenix)?

Federal Government Revenue
(Year 2000 Estimate)

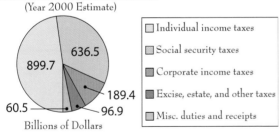

636.5
899.7
60.5
189.4
96.9
Billions of Dollars

☐ Individual income taxes
☐ Social security taxes
☐ Corporate income taxes
☐ Excise, estate, and other taxes
☐ Misc. duties and receipts

9. According to the circle graph, what is the largest source of federal government income? the second largest?

10. In 2000 how much money was collected from these two sources?

11. What was the total federal revenue in 2000?

12. In the summer of 2002, NBC's *Dateline* was the most popular news show with a rating of 8.2%, viewed by 8,643,000 households. TV ratings are calculated by dividing the number of viewing households by 105,500,000—the total number of TV households. Make a bar graph comparing the <u>ratings</u> for the following news shows.

SHOW	VIEWING HOUSEHOLDS
DATELINE	8,643,000
60 MINUTES	8,492,000
48 HOURS (Mon)	8,012,000
48 HOURS (Wed)	7,434,000
60 MINUTES II	6,533,000

13. Which show had the higher combined ratings, *48 Hours* or *60 Minutes*?

Construct Meaning

For a project in statistical sampling, Jewel and Nicolette purchased twelve identical packages of cookies, each with a labeled weight of 453 grams (one pound). Realizing the product was packaged by machine, they carefully weighed each one and found the actual net weights in grams: 447, 457, 463, 459, 455, 449, 457, 455, 452, 448, 457, and 459. They graphed the data on a line plot.

The students wanted to find the average weight of one package. They calculated the **mean**, the sum of the values of a set of data divided by the number of items in the set.

$$\frac{447\text{ g} + 457\text{ g} + 463\text{ g} + \dots + 459\text{ g}}{12} = \frac{5458\text{ g}}{12} = 454.8\text{ g}$$

MEAN

How does the mean compare to the weight printed on the packages?

A statistical **sample** is a selection of data randomly taken from a larger group for the purpose of analyzing information. There are other methods of finding the center of a sample. The **median** is the middle value in an ordered set of data. To find the median, Jewel wrote the weights in order from least to greatest. Then she counted inward from both ends to find the middle value. Because there were an even number of samples, she took the average of the two in the middle.

447 448 449 452 455 455 457 457 457 459 459 463

MEDIAN

$$\frac{445\text{ g} + 457\text{ g}}{2} = 456\text{ grams}$$

In this case, is the median the same as the mean?

The **mode** is the value (or values) that occurs most frequently in a set of data. From the line plot it is easy to see that 457 grams is the value that appeared most often.

The **MODE** is 457 grams.

Jewel and Nicolette concluded that the variation between weights of the packages was very small. A value widely separated from others in a set of data is called an outlier. If the lowest value they found had been 407 grams instead of 447 grams, how would each measurement have been affected?

Check Understanding

Round all answers to the nearest hundredth.
Use the data set: 5, 8, 7, 3, 5, 8, 4, 6, 5, 6. Find each of the following.
   a. Mean   **b.** Median   **c.** Mode

If the data value 14 is added to this data set, find the new value.
   d. Mean   **e.** Median   **f.** Mode

   g. Which measurement is affected the most? the least?
   h. With what term could you classify the data value 14?

Practice

For each of the data sets, find the mean, median, mode, and any outliers.
   1. $\frac{1}{2}, \frac{5}{8}, \frac{1}{8}, 2, \frac{3}{4}, \frac{1}{4}, \frac{1}{4}, \frac{1}{2}$
   2. 1.5, 2.1, 1.34, 1.9, 0.97, 1.6, 1.18, 2.33, 1.52, 1.71, 1.45

Five teenage boys compared how much money they were carrying in their wallets. Here's what they found:

Boy	$1	$5	$10	$20	$100	Amount
A	5	1	1			$20
B	1	2		1		$31
C				2		$40
D	2	3				$17
E		1		1	1	$125

   3. Find the average (mean) amount of money that the boys had.

   4. What is the median amount?

   5. If Boy E were excluded from the sample, recalculate the mean and the median.

   6. Which of the four measurements of the set of data above best represents the average? Explain why you think so.

   7. Draw a line plot showing the total number of each kind of bill carried by the five boys.

   8. Which bill was most commonly carried by the boys? Which measurement is this?

   9. Which bill appears as the median?

Apply

Cindy found houses in her area listing for the following dollar amounts: 93,600; 115,300; 111,200; 89,200; 135,400; 94,800; 106,700; 104,800; 126,300; 119,500; 121,900; 98,600; 246,800. Round all answers to the nearest dollar.

   10. Use your calculator to find the mean price of the houses.

   11. Find the median price of the houses.

   12. Which data value is an outlier?

   13. Remove the outlier and recalculate the mean and median prices.

   14. Which measurement does the outlier affect more, the mean or the median?

Analyzing Data

Construct Meaning

Brenda and Makayla are in the same Girl Scout troop as Hannah and Ashley. During this year's cookie sales event, the two pairs of girls competed to see who could sell the most cookies. They worked every afternoon for two weeks. Each evening they recorded the day's sales and determined the sales winner for that day. The troop leader promised awards for the most packages sold on any one day and for the highest number of sales overall.

Here is the record of the girls' daily sales.

	Mo	Tu	We	Th	Fr	Sa	Mo	Tu	We	Th	Fr	Sa
Makayla & Brenda	23 ✓	28	39	27 ✓	12 ✓	48	36 ✓	37	45 ✓	34	20 ✓	43
Hannah & Ashley	21	31 ✓	43 ✓	14	9	55 ✓	22	40 ✓	27	43 ✓	11	54 ✓

Hannah and Ashley sold more cookies on 6 days out of 12; Makayla and Brenda sold more on the other 6 days. When they totaled their sales, however, they found that Makayla and Brenda had the greater overall sales (392 vs. 370). The girls decided to graph the data with a **stem-and-leaf plot**, a diagram that displays the distribution of data by ordering and grouping according to place value.

First they ordered their daily sales from least to greatest, grouping the data also by place value.

M & B: 12 | 20 23 27 28 | 34 36 37 39 | 43 45 48

H & A: 09 | 11 14 | 21 22 27 | 31 | 40 43 43 | 54 55

When they ordered the data they could see that, although Hannah and Ashley had fewer overall sales, they would win the award for the most packages sold on a single day (55). Then they drew the diagrams.

First each team made a "stem" using the digits from the tens place of their data values.

M & B		H & A
4		5
3		4
2		3
1		2
		1
		0

Then they arranged the digits in the ones place to make the "leaves." They ordered the ones place digits from least to greatest outwardly from each stem.

M & B		H & A
4	3 5 8	5	4 5
3	4 6 7 9	4	0 3 3
2	0 3 7 8	3	1
1	2	2	1 2 7
		1	1 4
		0	9

The diagram allowed the girls to see the distribution of data. Although the means for the teams were very close (32.67 and 30.83), Makayla and Brenda's figures tended to cluster around the middle of the spread of values. Hannah and Ashley's numbers were distributed toward the extremes.

Check Understanding

Ashley suggested it would be easier to compare their results if they graphed the data from both teams on the same stem on a double stem-and-leaf plot. They plotted Hannah and Ashley's data as before, then made a mirror image of Makayla and Brenda's data on the left side of the stem. On either side, the ones place data are ordered outwardly from the stem.

M & B		H & A
	5	4 5
8 5 3	4	0 3 3
9 7 6 4	3	1
8 7 3 0	2	1 2 7
2	1	1 4
	0	9

a. Examine the double stem-and-leaf plot. What was the least number of packages that Hannah and Ashley sold in one day?

b. What was the least number that Brenda and Makayla sold? What was the greatest number?

c. What team had the most consistent daily sales?

Practice

Match the data with the best type of graph.

1. Percentages of different apple varieties sold by a supermarket

2. Stats for top ten NHL point scorers

3. A car salesman's weekly sales figures

4. Height comparisons for 13-year-old boys and girls

a. Bar graph
b. Circle graph
c. Line graph
d. Double stem-and-leaf plot

These are recent test scores from Mrs. Purdy's 3rd and 5th period math classes.

3rd Period: 83, 72, 95, 96, 88, 100, 75, 89, 92, 94, 88, 86, 75, 78, 92, 94, 86, 85, 75, 86

5th Period: 93, 100, 98, 78, 82, 100, 88, 85, 94, 98, 99, 96, 74, 86, 92, 95, 96, 83, 78

5. Find the median score for each class.

6. Use a calculator to determine the mean score (to the nearest hundredth) for each class.

7. What is the mode for the combined test scores?

8. Make a double stem-and-leaf plot comparing the scores of the two classes.

Apply

The table lists speed statistics for the Indianapolis 500 automobile races from 1980 to 1999.

9. Round average speeds to the nearest mile per hour, then make a double stem-and-leaf plot comparing the winning speeds from 1980 to 1989 with the speeds from 1990 to 1999.

10. In what year was the highest average speed recorded? What was the speed?

11. By looking at the graph, predict which decade was faster, the 1980s or the 1990s. Then use the rounded speeds to calculate the mean average speed for both decades. Was your prediction correct?

Year	Winner	Car	Average Speed (mph)
1980	Johnny Rutherford	Chapparral-Cosworth	142.862
1981	Bobby Unser	Penske-Cosworth	139.029
1982	Gordon Johncock	Wildcat-Cosworth	162.029
1983	Tom Sneva	March-Cosworth	162.117
1984	Rick Mears	March-Cosworth	162.962
1985	Danny Sullivan	March-Cosworth	152.982
1986	Bobby Rahal	March-Cosworth	170.722
1987	Al Unser, Sr.	March-Cosworth	162.175
1988	Rick Mears	P.C. 17-Chevrolet	144.809
1989	Emerson Fittipaldi	Penske-Cosworth	167.581
1990	Arie Luyendyk	Lola-Cosworth	185.987
1991	Rick Mears	Penske-Cosworth	176.460
1992	Al Unser, Jr.	Valvoline-Chevrolet	134.477
1993	Emerson Fittipaldi	Penske-Chevrolet	157.207
1994	Al Unser, Jr.	Penske-Mercedes	160.872
1995	Jacques Villeneuve	Reynard-Ford	156.616
1996	Buddy Lazier	Reynard-Ford	147.956
1997	Arie Luyendyk	G Force-Aurora	145.827
1998	Eddie Cheever	Dallara-Aurora	145.155
1999	Kenny Brack	Dallara-Aurora	153.176

Examining Range

Construct Meaning

This table compares the average daily temperatures for Raleigh, North Carolina, and San Francisco, California. Tristan found the mean temperatures to be 59.25°F for Raleigh and 57.25°F for San Francisco. From his calculations it appeared that the temperatures for the two cities are very similar.

Average Daily Temperature °F

	Raleigh	San Francisco
January	39	49
February	42	52
March	50	53
April	59	56
May	67	58
June	74	62
July	78	63
August	77	64
September	71	65
October	60	61
November	51	55
December	43	49

He made a line graph to get a picture of the data. Although the means are similar, Tristan could see that the ranges of data for the two cities are very different. Range measures the spread of data. **Range** is the difference between the greatest value and the least value in a set of data.

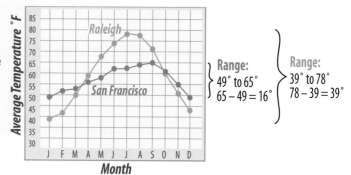

Range:
49° to 65°
65 − 49 = 16°

Range:
39° to 78°
78 − 39 = 39°

A **box-and-whisker plot** gives a precise display of the spread of data. It divides an ordered set of data into four equal parts. Tristan created the plot for Raleigh by first ordering the temperatures and finding the median. Then he found two more measurements: the median of the lower half of the data, called the **lower quartile**; and the median of the upper half, called the **upper quartile**. The lower quartile, median, and upper quartile divide a set of data into four equal parts. Tristan used these points, together with the greatest and least values of the data set, to draw a box-and-whisker plot.

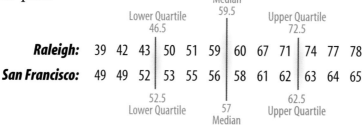

Median
59.5

Lower Quartile
46.5

Upper Quartile
72.5

Raleigh: 39 42 43 | 50 51 59 | 60 67 71 | 74 77 78

San Francisco: 49 49 52 | 53 55 56 | 58 61 62 | 63 64 65

52.5
Lower Quartile

57
Median

62.5
Upper Quartile

These are box-and-whisker plots for both cities.

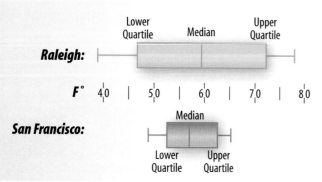

Raleigh:

San Francisco:

The "box" of each plot shows the range of the central half of the data values. It is drawn between the lower and upper quartiles and is divided by a line representing the median. The "whiskers" extend to the lowest and highest values of each set of data. The box-and-whisker plot shows the entire range of data divided into four parts, each containing one-fourth of the data.

Check Understanding

a. Why is the plot for Raleigh much larger than the plot for San Francisco? Are there more data values for Raleigh?

b. The central half of the data values for San Francisco range between 53° and 62°. What is the range of the central half of the data values for Raleigh?

c. Tell how you would find the median, lower quartile and upper quartile for the following data set. Determine each value.

10 11 12 13 15 16 17 19 19

Practice

This box-and-whisker plot represents the average spelling scores for Miss Eller's English class.

1. What is the range of scores?
2. What range of scores was achieved by the upper half of the class?
3. Between what two numbers did the central 50% of the students score?
4. What is the median score?

These were the test scores on a math midterm exam.
90, 85, 92, 84, 83, 93, 86, 84, 90, 91, 84, 93, 99, 86, 86, 91, 88 , 94, 93, 91, 85

5. Order the data values from least to greatest. Circle and label the median value.
6. Circle and label the values that represent the upper and lower quartiles.
7. Give the range of the test scores.
8. Make a box-and-whisker plot of the test scores. Include the measurements for each of the five points.
9. What is the range of the top half of the scores? the central half?

Apply

This stock table shows one-day changes in the dollar price per share for a sample of NYSE corporations.

Airborne Ex	+0.48	Coca Cola	−1.63	Gucci	−0.63	Pepsi	−0.90	Toyota	+0.02
AutoZone	+0.53	Disney	−0.93	Hasbro	−0.26	Reebok	+0.02	Tupperware	−0.35
Avon	−1.13	Fed Ex	+1.96	Hershey	−1.29	Revlon	−0.25	UPS	+0.80
Best Buy	+0.15	Ford	−0.39	Mattel	−0.22	Six Flags	−0.63	WalMart	−0.68
Blockbuster	−0.25	Gap	−0.25	Nike	+0.96	Sony	−1.71		
Borders	−0.54	GM	−1.29	Penneys	−0.41	Target	−1.39		

10. Order the data from least to greatest. Then find the median, lower quartile, and upper quartile.
11. Draw a number line from −2.00 to +2.00. Above the number line make a box-and-whisker plot of the data. Include the five measurements on the graph.
12. What is the range of the central half of the data?

Finding Frequency

Construct Meaning

For an assignment in probability, Ryan rolled two number cubes and kept a tally of the sums he rolled. Instead of adding all the sums together to calculate the mean, he made a frequency table. He multiplied each possible sum (from 2 to 12) by its frequency– the number of times it occurred in 50 rolls. Then he totaled the products and divided by 50 to find the mean.

$$\text{Mean} = \frac{\text{Total of all sums rolled}}{\text{Number of rolls}} = \frac{358}{50} = 7.16$$

Frequency is the number of times a particular value appears in a set of data.

	Frequency Table		
Sum	Tally	Frequency	Product
2	I	1	2
3	II	2	6
4	III	3	12
5	IIII	5	25
6	IIII III	8	48
7	IIII IIII	9	63
8	IIII IIII	9	72
9	IIII I	6	54
10	III	3	30
11	II	2	22
12	II	2	24
Totals	**50**	**50**	**358**

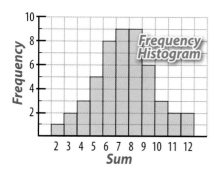

Ryan made a histogram of the data. A **histogram** is a type of bar graph that shows the number of values that appear in each of a series of equal intervals. How would you describe the distribution of data as they are displayed by the histogram's shape? Is the shape of the graph consistent with a mean value of 7.16?

Check Understanding

This histogram shows the age distribution of the population of the United States as recorded in the 2000 census.

a. What percentage of the US population is elementary and middle-school age?

b. Observe the shape of the histogram. Between what ages does the large majority of the population lie?

c. What percentage of the population is over 84 years old?

d. Can you tell from the graph what percentage of the population is age 13?

e. At the time of the 2000 census, what was the most numerous age group in the US?

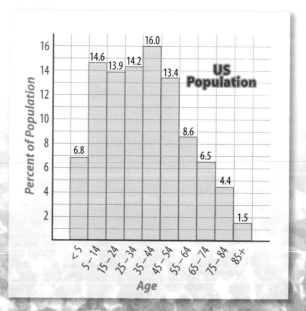

Practice

The histogram at the right shows the average annual income earned by people living in the United States. The data were gathered from each of the 50 states, ranging from Mississippi with the lowest average income of $20,900 to Connecticut with the highest average income of $40,702.

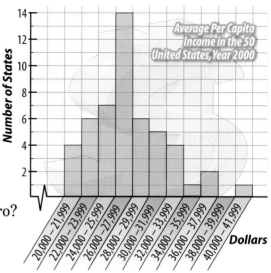

1. What is the most typical range of incomes earned by people in most states?

2. What income range has a frequency of zero?

3. What else can you learn from looking at the graph?

Apply

For a report that Tom wrote about summer jobs, he conducted a survey of the students at his school. He compiled the following data representing the dollar amounts earned by each student over the summer.

438	449	0	0	290	89	1918
256	577	0	1500	1568	680	1375
1284	0	100	1337	1730	1580	2159
200	150	1423	800	1250	2250	847
2366	2045	1883	0	755	2110	1500
375	1495	2250	265	488	670	1898
0	340	885	300	900	1555	2006
836	250	1100	550	1355	2280	240

4. Make a frequency table of the data. Use intervals of $250, starting with $0–$249, $250–$499, etc., and ending with the interval $2250–$2499. Use tally marks to find the frequency for each interval. You do not need to find the products.

5. From the data in the frequency table draw a histogram. Label the axes of the graph and give it a title.

6. What interval has the greatest frequency? the least?

7. What might be misleading about the data included in the first interval of earned income ($0–$249)?

Construct Meaning

Scatterplots are often used in scientific research. A **scatterplot** is a graph of points that shows a relationship between two sets of data.

Cultures of bacteria are studied in scientific disciplines such as immunology. Cultures are grown under various conditions, then counted by measuring the optical density of the growth medium. This scatterplot shows the numbers of bacteria grown experimentally at different temperatures.

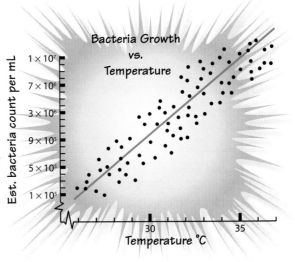

The data points, which show the relationship between temperature and the number of bacteria, reveal a trend. The green line shows this trend more clearly. It is called a **trend line**, a line to which the points of a scatterplot tend to conform. It shows that, as the temperature increased in this experiment, the number of bacteria increased. What conclusion might you draw from this finding? What conclusion would you make if the points of the scatterplot were randomly distributed over the graph?

Trend lines can be used to estimate values for data not specifically recorded in a data sample. This scatterplot shows increasing postage rates since 1968. Use the trend line to estimate what the one-ounce postage rate was raised to in 1985. By extending the trend line, predictions can also be made about values beyond the range of the data sampled. At the current rate of increase, estimate what year the one-ounce postage rate will reach $0.50.

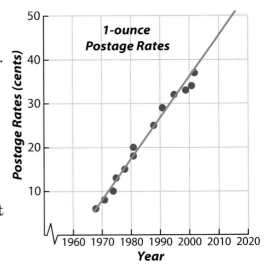

Each of the graphs above shows a *positive* trend. That is, as the value of one data set increases, the value of the other also increases. The scatterplot to the left shows data relating the weight of automobiles to mileage performance. Notice that its trend line goes *down*. This graph shows a *negative* trend. That is, as the value of one data set increases, the value of the other decreases.

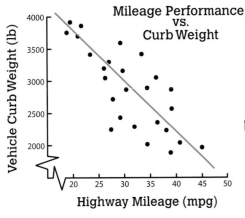

Check Understanding

The manatee is a large, slow-moving marine mammal that can be found in the coastal waters of Florida. Each year so many manatees are killed as a result of watercraft collisions that they have become an endangered species.

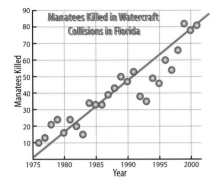

a. Why is the green line called a trend line?

b. Does the plot show a negative or positive trend?

c. Observe the data points to determine which year showed the greatest increase in manatee deaths compared to the previous year.

d. Discuss factors that might affect the accuracy of these data or the validity of the trend they display.

Practice

Last summer Seth took scuba diving lessons. For a science experiment, he borrowed a pressure gauge from his instructor and measured the pressure at various depths, recording the data in a table. Then he graphed his data on a scatterplot.

Depth (ft)	Pressure (psi)
0	14.7
1	15.0
2	15.2
3	15.6
4	15.9
5	16.2
6	16.5

1. Make a scatterplot on a piece of graph paper. Along the horizontal axis mark the depth from 0 to 20 feet. Up the vertical axis mark the pressure in pounds per square inch (psi) from 14 to 24 psi. Then plot the data Seth collected.

2. Without diving, Seth wanted to know what the pressure would be at a depth of 20 feet. Draw a trend line through the data points on your graph, extending the line to the edge of the graph. Draw a vertical line from the 20-foot mark on the horizontal axis so that it intersects the trend line. Then follow the point of intersection to the vertical axis. Estimate the pressure at this depth.

Mr. Branigan looked up the overall grade point averages of the students in his third-period math class. Then he took a survey of the students in that class to determine the number of hours a week each of them studied on average. Here is a table of his findings.

3. Make a scatterplot of the data and draw a trend line.

4. What conclusions can you draw from the graph?

Hours	GPA	Hours	GPA	Hours	GPA	Hours	GPA	Hours	GPA
0	0.7	4	1.5	7	2.6	11	2.3	13	3.5
1	0.5	5	1.3	8	2.5	11	3.0	14	3.5
2	1.1	5	2.0	9	3.2	11	3.5	15	3.6
3	1.2	5	2.8	10	3.2	12	3.2	15	4.0
3	1.5	6	2.0	10	4.0	12	4.0	16	4.0

Review

1. Use a calculator to find the mean overall GPA of the students in Mr. Branigan's class. Round your answer to the nearest tenth.

2. What is the median GPA?

3. Draw a box-and-whisker plot of the GPAs.

Construct Meaning

Spreadsheets are computer-generated tables of data used for organizing information, performing calculations, and even making graphs. Spreadsheets typically have columns lettered from A to Z and rows numbered 1, 2, 3, etc. Data and formulas are entered into the grid spaces, called **cells**. In the spreadsheet below, cell C5 is highlighted. Spreadsheets are highly versatile tools because they can be easily updated. When one number is changed, the computer recalculates the entire spreadsheet and displays the new results.

	A	B	C	D	E	F
1	**Third Quarter Sales Commissions**					
2	Account Exec	Jul	Aug	Sept	Total	Average
3	Joshua Judd	$3110	$2590	$3255	$8955	$2985
4	Alyssa Autumn	$3085	$2775	$3370	$9230	$3077
5	Zachary Zook	$3275	$2885	$3960	$10120	$3373
6	Austin Awesome	$2940	$3215	$3375	$9530	$3177
7	Olivia Orange	$2650	$2175	$2545	$7370	$2457
8						
9	TOTALS	$15060	$13640	$16505	$45205	
10						

The formula for cell E3 is =(B3+C3+D3).

The formula for cell F5 is =E5/3.

The formula for cell B9 is =B3+B4+B5+B6+B7.

Businesses use spreadsheets to record income and expenses, to track sales, and to forecast demand for their services and products. Bradley Motor Company employs five salespeople on its new car lot. Julie, the company accountant, keeps track of their sales commissions using spreadsheets. Julie formatted the spreadsheet above, typing in the appropriate headings, formulas, and names of the employees. At the end of each month, she enters the sales commission figures for each person. The software automatically calculates the sales commission total in column E for each salesperson based on the formula she entered in the spreadsheet. Julie uses column F to display the quarterly average for each employee. The bottom row is used to calculate monthly totals.

Check Understanding

a. How much did Alyssa Autumn make in commissions in August?

b. Who had the highest sales commission for the third quarter?

c. What does the amount in cell B9 represent?

d. How much did Olivia Orange make in commissions during the third quarter?

e. What is the formula for cell D9?

f. How much did Bradley Motors pay its sales staff in commissions during the third quarter?

Chapter 12 Study Guide

Match the data with the best type of graph. *Lesson 12.1*

1. Average points per game for NBA's ten top players
2. Daily high and low temperatures for April in Kansas City
3. Percent of students enrolled at each grade level at Holcomb High

a. Line graph
b. Circle graph
c. Bar graph

Answer the following using the graph at left.

4. Which part of the week shows a warming trend? *Lesson 12.1*

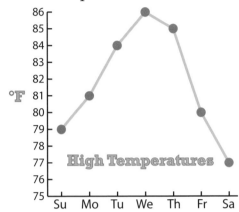

5. Which day shows the greatest increase in high temperature compared to the previous day? *Lesson 12.1*
6. Calculate the average (mean) high temperature (to the nearest tenth). *Lesson 12.2*
7. Determine the median high temperature. *Lesson 12.2*
8. Write the range for the high temperatures this week, both as a single number and as a comparison of two values. *Lesson 12.4*

The double stem-and-leaf plot shows the test scores for Mr. Allen's math classes.

2nd Period		3rd Period
	5	00
88553200	4	1336779
874	3	5888
83	2	9
	1	6

9. What is the mode of the third-period test scores? *Lesson 12.2*
10. Which class had the higher average (mean)? *Lesson 12.3*
11. Determine the median score for each class. *Lesson 12.3*

Analyze this box-and-whisker plot of scores on a 100-question test. *Lesson 12.4*

12. Overall, would you say the students did well or poorly?
13. About what percent of the students scored 50 or higher?
14. What range of scores represents the top quarter of the students?

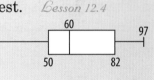

Use the histogram of employee salaries to answer the following questions. *Lesson 12.5*

15. Which range of salaries has the greatest frequency?
16. Does the histogram show the exact range of salaries at this company? Explain.
17. How many employees make less than $50,000?

18. Using the postage rate scatterplot on page 262, predict the 1-ounce rate for the year 2010. *Lesson 12.6*

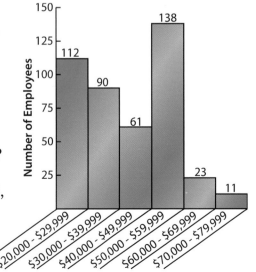

Stacks of Stats

Write *true* or *false*.
1. A trend line rarely intersects all data points on a scatterplot.
2. Generally, an outlier affects the median more than the mean.
3. Two data sets with identical means sometimes differ with respect to spread.
4. Spreadsheet data are found in cells.
5. A scatterplot showing the relationship between the distance from a radio station and the strength of the signal received will show a negative trend.

Write the letter of the <u>best</u> answer. Letters may be used more than once.

a. Stem-and-leaf plot　　**b.** Box-and-whisker plot　　**c.** Circle graph
d. Line plot　　　　　　 **e.** Histogram　　　　　　　**f.** Line graph
g. Scatterplot　　　　　　**h.** Spreadsheet

6. Displays data in numbered rows and lettered columns
7. The data points on this plot may reveal a trend.
8. The median, as well as the high and low data values, are written on this plot.
9. Shows frequency of data values by using marks above a number line
10. Most often used to display changes in a quantity over time
11. Divides data into four equal parts called quartiles
12. If data change, it can be easily updated.
13. Shows the number of values that appear in each of a series of equal intervals
14. Displays the whole divided into parts
15. Divides data according to place value

Write the term that fits the definition.
16. The median of the lower half of an ordered data set
17. The data tend to conform to this.
18. A data value that is widely separated from the others in a data set
19. The difference between the greatest and least data values
20. The value (or values) that appear most frequently in a data set
21. The middle value in a data set
22. The number of times a certain value appears in a set of data

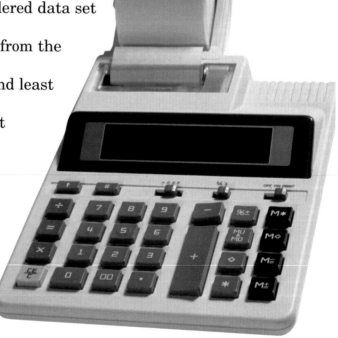

Refer to the stem-and-leaf plot to determine each of the following.

23. Median

24. Mean (to the nearest tenth)

25. Mode

26. Range (as a single figure)

```
2 | 2 5 5 5 6
1 | 0 0 2 5 8
0 | 8 9
```

27. Given the values for a set of data having a range of 82, copy and correctly label the box-and-whisker plot.
Median = 60; Lower quartile = 43
Upper quartile = 75; Lowest data value = 12

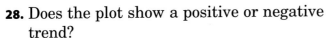

Robert measured the weight of a cup of various numbers of pennies and graphed the results as shown at right. Use the graph to answer the following questions.

28. Does the plot show a positive or negative trend?

29. Estimate the weight of the cup with 25 pennies.

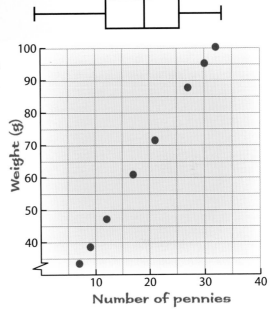

At a junior league batting practice, each player was thrown ten pitches. The results are recorded on the histogram.

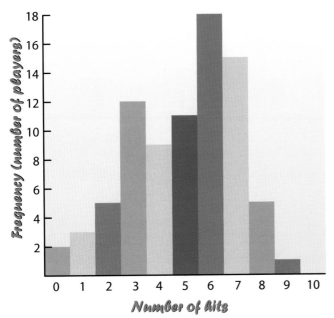

30. Complete the frequency table.

Hits	Frequency	Product
0		
1		
2		
3		
4		
5		
6		
7		
8		
9		
10		
Totals		

31. Calculate the mean to the nearest hundredth.

32. Find the median number of hits.

33. In this case, does the median represent the most frequent number of hits?

Chapter Theme:
Architecture

13 Chapter

Solid Geometry

Exploring Three-Dimensional Figures

Construct Meaning

The building blocks of structures are geometrical figures. These figures, modified by engineering and architectural limitations, combine to form the design of many buildings. With the use of computer software, an architect's initial concept for a structure comes to life in a three-dimensional model. 3-D models provide realistic visual presentations of what structures will look like after construction.

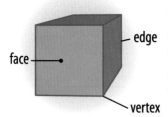

Unlike plane geometric figures, **three-dimensional figures** occupy space. A **polyhedron** is a three-dimensional figure made up of flat, polygonal surfaces. Each flat surface is called a **face**. An **edge** is a line segment where two faces of a polyhedron intersect. The **vertex** is the point at which edges of a polyhedron meet.

A **pyramid** is a polyhedron with triangular faces that meet at a common vertex and join to a polygonal base. The **base** of a pyramid is the face opposite its vertex. A pyramid usually takes its name from the base polygon. Another name for a triangular pyramid, which has four triangular faces, is a **tetrahedron**.

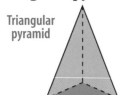

Triangular pyramid

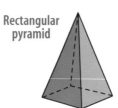

Rectangular pyramid

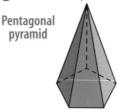

Pentagonal pyramid

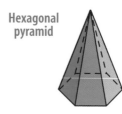

Hexagonal pyramid

A **prism** is a polyhedron with two congruent and parallel bases; all other faces are parallelograms. The **base** of a prism is one of the parallel and congruent faces from which its height is measured. A prism usually takes its name from the base polygon. A special rectangular prism is the **cube**, a prism in which all faces are squares.

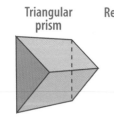

Triangular prism

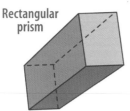

Rectangular prism

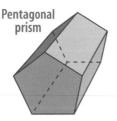

Pentagonal prism

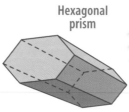

Hexagonal prism

Euler's formula relates the number of edges (E), faces (F), and vertices (V) in a polyhedron.
$$E = F + V - 2$$

Three-dimensional figures that are not polyhedrons include the cylinder, cone, and sphere, all of which have curved surfaces. A **cylinder** has two congruent and circular bases. A **cone** has one circular base and one vertex opposite the base. A **sphere** is the set of all points in space that are the same distance from its center.

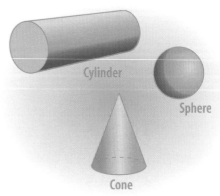

Cylinder

Sphere

Cone

Check Understanding

Consider a polyhedron that has 5 faces and 6 vertices.
  a. Determine the number of edges of the polyhedron.
  b. Identify the type of polyhedron.
  c. Which polyhedron has the fewest number of faces? How many faces does it have?
  d. How many edges does a cube have?
  e. Which prism has the fewest number of faces? How many faces does it have?
  f. How many vertices are on a hexagonal pyramid? on a hexagonal prism?

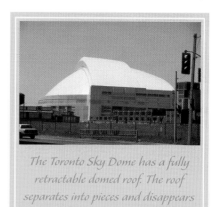

The Toronto Sky Dome has a fully retractable domed roof. The roof separates into pieces and disappears from sight in less than 20 minutes.

Practice

Copy and complete the chart.

	POLYHEDRON	NUMBER OF FACES	NUMBER OF VERTICES	NUMBER OF EDGES
1.	Cube			
2.		4	4	6
3.	Tetrahedron			
4.	Rectangular prism			
5.		7	10	
6.	Pentagonal pyramid			
7.		8		18

8. Describe one property that a pyramid and a cone have in common.
9. Describe one property that a prism and a cylinder have in common.

Determine the area of the base for each of the following.
(Round your answer to the nearest whole number.)
10. A cone with a base diameter of 6 centimeters
11. A rectangular pyramid with a base measuring 6 centimeters by 18 centimeters
12. A rectangular prism measuring 6 centimeters by 9 centimeters with a height of 8 centimeters
13. A cube with edges of 6 centimeters

Apply

14. The world's largest pyramid, the Great Pyramid of Khufu, once stood approximately 481 feet high. Due mainly to erosion over the years, it has lost nearly 10 meters in height. About how tall is this pyramid today?

15. Why are more structures built as prisms than pyramids today?

Construct Meaning

Cheeses come in many sizes and shapes. They are often sealed in plastic, wax, or other materials to prevent them from drying out or molding. Wax is applied either by brushing it on the cheese or by dipping the cheese in hot wax. The wax covers the whole surface by adhering to the cheese and conforming to its shape. The **surface area** of any three-dimensional figure is the sum of the areas of all the surfaces.

A cheese brick is an example of a rectangular prism. Its surface area is the sum of the areas of all the faces. The **height** of a prism or a cylinder is the perpendicular distance between the two bases. Determine the surface area of wax around a cheese brick of 7 inches by 2 inches by 3 inches.

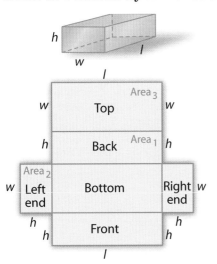

Surface Area = Sum of the areas of all the faces
$$= 2(\text{Area}_1) + 2(\text{Area}_2) + 2(\text{Area}_3)$$
$$SA = 2lh + 2hw + 2lw$$

> Surface area of a rectangular prism $= 2lh + 2hw + 2lw$

For the cheese brick: $l = 7$ in., $w = 3$ in., and $h = 2$ in.
Surface Area $= 2(7 \text{ in.})(2 \text{ in.}) + 2(2 \text{ in.})(3 \text{ in.}) + 2(7 \text{ in.})(3 \text{ in.})$
$$= 2(14 \text{ in.}^2) + 2(6 \text{ in.}^2) + 2(21 \text{ in.}^2)$$
$$= 28 \text{ in.}^2 + 12 \text{ in.}^2 + 42 \text{ in.}^2$$
$$SA = 82 \text{ in.}^2$$

Surface area of the cheese is 82 sq in.

A cheese wheel is an example of a cylinder. Its surface area is the sum of the areas of its curved surface and the circular bases. Determine the surface area of wax covering a cheese wheel with a diameter of 12 inches and height of 4 inches.

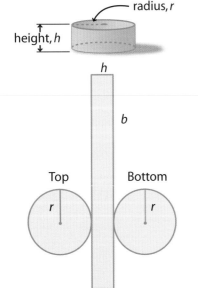

Surface Area = Sum of the areas of the bases and curved surface
$$= 2(\text{Area of circle}) + \text{Area of rectangle}$$
$$= 2(\pi r^2) + bh$$
$$SA = 2\pi r^2 + (2\pi r)h$$

(*think*) The base, b, of the rectangle equals the circumference of the circle. $C = 2\pi r$

> Surface area of a cylinder $= 2\pi r^2 + 2\pi rh$

For the cheese wheel: $r = 6$ in. and $h = 4$ in. Use $\pi \approx 3.14$.
Surface Area $= 2\pi(6 \text{ in.})^2 + 2\pi(6 \text{ in.})(4 \text{ in.})$
$$= 2\pi(36 \text{ in.}^2) + 2\pi(24 \text{ in.}^2)$$
$$= 72\pi \text{ in.}^2 + 48\pi \text{ in.}^2$$
$$= 120\pi \text{ in.}^2$$
$$\approx 120(3.14) \text{ in.}^2$$
$$SA \approx 376.8 \text{ in.}^2$$

Surface area of the cheese wheel is approximately 377 sq in.

Why is this surface area an approximation?

Check Understanding

Consider a cube with a side length of s.

a. Draw a net diagram of a cube.

b. Determine a formula for the surface area of the cube.

Consider a cylinder with radius r and height h.

c. Draw a net different from the one in Construct Meaning.

d. Using π and the variables r and h, determine a formula for the surface area of the cylinder without the top.

e. Determine the height of a 6 ft by 6 ft rectangular prism with a surface area of 120 ft².

f. Determine the approximate height of a cylinder with a diameter of 4 ft and a surface area of 90 ft². Use $\pi \approx 3.14$ and round your answer to the nearest tenth.

Practice

1. Consider the triangular prism.

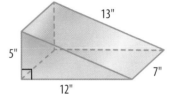

a. How many faces does the figure have?

b. Draw and label a net diagram of the prism.

c. Determine the surface area.

2. Determine the surface area of a rectangular prism measuring 3 ft by 2 ft by 2 ft.

3. Determine the surface area of a cylinder with a diameter of 8.8 cm and a height of 0.5 cm. Use $\pi \approx 3.14$ and round your answer to the nearest tenth.

4. Determine the ratio of the length of the edge of each cube to its surface area.

a. A cube with an edge of 1 inch

b. A cube with an edge of 2 inches

c. A cube with an edge of 3 inches

5. How does doubling the length of an edge of a cube affect the surface area? tripling the length?

6. Does doubling the height of a cylinder double its surface area? Explain your answer.

7. Does doubling the radius of a cylinder double its surface area? Explain your answer.

8. Which increases the surface area of a cylinder more, doubling its height or doubling its radius?

Apply

9. Michelle wants to wrap a box measuring 7 inches by 4 inches by 2 inches. Which of the three pieces of wrapping paper will be the best choice?

a. 15 in. by 15 in. **b.** 8 in. by 12 in. **c.** 11 in. by 13 in.

10. A can of soup has a diameter of 3 inches and a height of 4 inches. What is the area of the soup can's label? (Use $\pi \approx 3.14$.)

11. Claudia made a hat out of cardboard. She wants to paint the surface shown below. Calculate the area to be painted to the nearest square inch. (Use $\pi \approx 3.14$.)

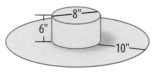

12. Mr. Riley wants to repaint the brown siding on his shed. How many gallons of paint should he buy? (Coverage is 300 ft²/gal.)

Surface Area of Pyramids

Construct Meaning

The Transamerica Pyramid is a 48-story office tower standing 853 feet tall (including a 212-foot spire). The shape of the structure was an important element in determining the amount of materials used in the construction of the building. The pyramid shape allows for varying space in floor plans. The "wings" toward the top of the pyramid are necessary for elevators and stairwells.

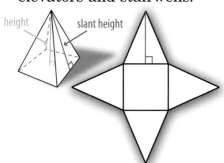

height   slant height

The surface area of a pyramid is the sum of the areas of all its faces, including the base. The **height** of a pyramid is the perpendicular distance from the base to the opposite vertex. The **slant height** of a pyramid is the height of a triangular face. It is the perpendicular distance from an edge of the base to the opposite vertex.

Determine the surface area of a square pyramid with a slant height of 6 inches and a base area of 25 square inches.

Surface Area = Sum of the areas of the base and the triangular faces
$\qquad$ = Area of the square + 4(Area of one triangular face)
$\qquad$ = 25 in.² + 4($\frac{1}{2}$ · 5 in. · 6 in.)
$\qquad$ = 25 in.² + 4(15 in.²)
$\qquad$ = 25 in.² + 60 in.²
Surface Area = 85 in.²

think
The area of the square is 25 in.² so each side is 5 in. The area of each triangle is $\frac{1}{2}bh$.

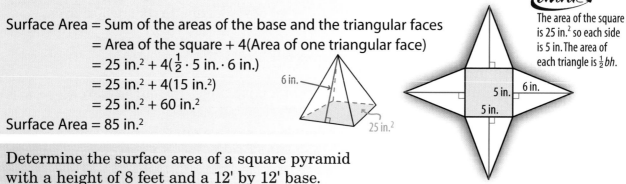

6 in.   5 in. | 6 in.   5 in.   25 in.²

Determine the surface area of a square pyramid with a height of 8 feet and a 12' by 12' base.

Surface Area = Area of the square + 4(Area of one triangular face)
$\qquad$ = (12 ft · 12 ft) + 4($\frac{1}{2}$ · 12 ft · 10 ft)
$\qquad$ = 144 ft² + 4(60 ft²)
$\qquad$ = 144 ft² + 240 ft²
Surface Area = 384 ft²

think The Pythagorean Theorem ($a^2 + b^2 = c^2$) is used to determine the slant height.
$\qquad$ $8^2 + 6^2 = c^2$
$\qquad\qquad$ $100 = c^2$
$\qquad\qquad\quad$ $10 = c$

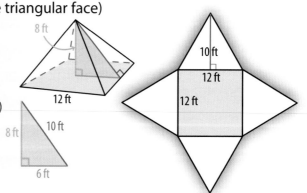

8 ft   10 ft   12 ft   12 ft   8 ft   10 ft   6 ft   12 ft   12 ft

Check Understanding

a. Define the terms height and slant height for a pyramid.

Consider a tetrahedron with all edges 10 meters in length.
b. Draw the tetrahedron with its measurements.
c. What is the slant height of this pyramid? Round your answer to the nearest tenth.
d. Draw a net diagram of the tetrahedron with the measurements labeled.
e. Calculate the surface area of the tetrahedron.

Practice

For each square pyramid find the (a) height, (b) slant height, and (c) surface area. Round decimals to the tenths place.

1.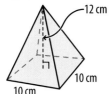

2.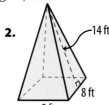

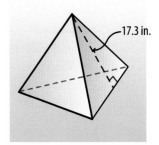

Consider a tetrahedron having all faces congruent, with a slant height of 17.3 inches. Its surface area is 692 square inches.

3. What is the length of each edge of the tetrahedron?

4. If the slant height of the tetrahedron is doubled and the base remains unchanged, what is its new surface area?

Consider the hexagonal pyramid at right. Round all answers to the nearest whole number.

5. The hexagonal base can be divided into six equilateral triangles with sides of 4 cm. Find the area of the base.

6. What is the area of one triangular face of the pyramid?

7. What is the surface area of this hexagonal pyramid?

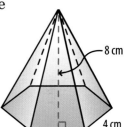

Consider a 6-centimeter square pyramid with a slant height of 5 centimeters.

8. What is the surface area of the square pyramid?

9. If the lengths of all the edges are doubled, what is the new surface area of the square pyramid?

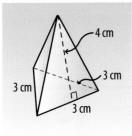

Apply

10. A candy manufacturer sells solid chocolate in the shape of a triangular pyramid with the dimensions shown. Each face of the pyramid (except the base) is coated with a different color of powdered sugar. What is the area of the surface to be covered with powdered sugar?

11. Annette is making a model of an Egyptian pyramid for a history project. Her model is one foot tall. The sides of its square base are 10 inches. She wants to paint the outside of the pyramid, excluding the base. What is the area of the surface to be painted in square inches?

12. A square pyramid candle with the scent of sandalwood has a height of 3 inches and a slant height of 5 inches.
a. Find the area of its base.   b. Find its total surface area.

Challenge

13. Consider a rectangular pyramid with the given dimensions. What is the surface area of the pyramid?

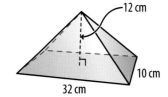

Construct Meaning

A jigsaw puzzle manufacturer has an option of packaging his product in two types of containers, a rectangular prism or a cylinder. Which option requires less cardboard?

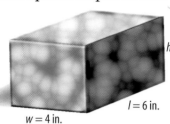

$h = 3$ in.
$l = 6$ in.
$w = 4$ in.

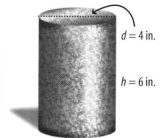

$d = 4$ in.
$h = 6$ in.

> Divide the problem into two smaller problems.

Surface area of a rectangular prism $= 2lh + 2hw + 2lw$
Surface Area $= 2(6 \text{ in.} \cdot 3 \text{ in.}) + 2(3 \text{ in.} \cdot 4 \text{ in.}) + 2(6 \text{ in.} \cdot 4 \text{ in.})$
$= 2(18 \text{ in.}^2) + 2(12 \text{ in.}^2) + 2(24 \text{ in.}^2)$
$= 36 \text{ in.}^2 + 24 \text{ in.}^2 + 48 \text{ in.}^2$
Surface Area $= 108 \text{ in.}^2$

> Compare the numbers to answer the question.

Surface area of a cylinder $= 2\pi r^2 + 2\pi rh$
Surface Area $= 2\pi(2 \text{ in.})^2 + 2\pi(2 \text{ in.})(6 \text{ in.})$
$= 2\pi(4 \text{ in.}^2) + 2\pi(12 \text{ in.}^2)$
$= 8\pi \text{ in.}^2 + 24\pi \text{ in.}^2$
$= 32\pi \text{ in.}^2$
Surface Area $\approx 100.48 \text{ in.}^2$

THE CYLINDRICAL CONTAINER REQUIRES LESS CARDBOARD.

The same manufacturer packages a wooden puzzle in the container shown. What is the surface area to be covered?

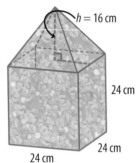

$h = 16$ cm
24 cm
24 cm
24 cm

think

Use the Pythagorean Theorem to calculate the slant height of the triangle. $12^2 + 16^2 = c^2$

Total surface area = Surface area of cubical base + Area of triangular faces
$= 5(\text{Area of one square}) + 4(\text{Area of one triangle})$
$= 5(s^2) + 4(\frac{1}{2}bh)$
$= 5(24 \text{ cm} \cdot 24 \text{ cm}) + 4(\frac{1}{2} \cdot 24 \text{ cm} \cdot 20 \text{ cm})$
$= 5(576 \text{ cm}^2) + 4(240 \text{ cm}^2)$
$= 2880 \text{ cm}^2 + 960 \text{ cm}^2$
Surface Area $= 3840 \text{ cm}^2$

THE SURFACE AREA TO BE COVERED IS 3840 CM².

Practice

1. Marcy wants to paint each of the following figures. What is the surface area to be painted for each one?

a.

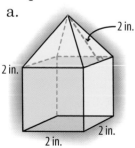

2 in.
2 in.
2 in.
2 in.

b.

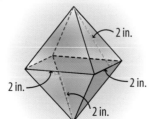

2 in.
2 in.
2 in.
2 in.

c.

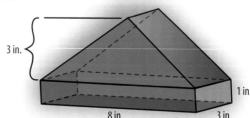

3 in.
1 in.
8 in.
3 in.

2. Mama's Munchies can package their cookies in one of two tin boxes. Which container will use less tin?

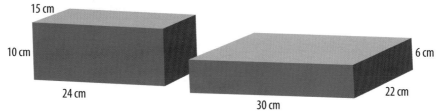

3. Two wastebaskets are made of the same type and thickness of plastic. Which wastebasket weighs less? (Note: The wastebaskets do not have a lid.)

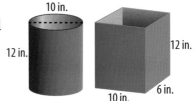

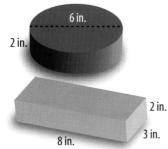

4. Sweet Tooth can package their assorted chocolates in one of two packages.
a. Which package will use less material?
b. Approximately how much less material is required? Round your answer to the nearest whole number.

5. Two cylindrical candles are wrapped individually in plastic packaging material. One candle is shorter than the other. Does the shorter candle require less packaging material than the tall candle? Explain.

6. Karissa wants to make a tiered cake that consists of three cylindrical layers. She plans on frosting the cake by frosting the top and sides of each layer and then placing the layers on top of each other. Each cup of frosting covers about 80 square inches.
a. What is the approximate surface area to be frosted? Use 3.14 for π, and round your answer to the nearest whole number.
b. About how many cups of frosting should Karissa make?

7. An ice-cream bar with the given dimensions is dipped in chocolate. Find the surface area of the chocolate coating. Use 3.14 for π, and round your answer to the nearest whole number.

8. The Thompsons purchased a mailbox with the given dimensions. They want to paint the outside surface white. Find the approximate area to be painted. Use 3.14 for π and round your answer to the nearest whole number. (Note: The top portion of the mailbox is half of a cylinder.)

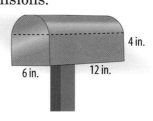

Construct Meaning

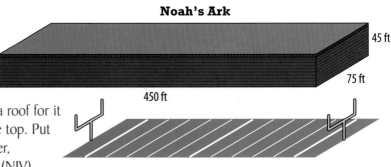

Noah's Ark

"So make yourself an ark of cypress wood. Make rooms in it and coat it with pitch inside and out. This is how you are to build it: The ark is to be 450 feet long, 75 feet wide and 45 feet high. Make a roof for it and finish the ark to within 18 inches of the top. Put a door in the side of the ark and make lower, middle and upper decks." Genesis 6:14–16 (NIV)

According to the Scriptures, Noah's ark was not constructed as some children's books have depicted it. It was actually a wooden rectangular prism, one and one-half times the length of a football field, six times as long as it was wide. Given the biblical dimensions of the ark, find its volume.

Volume is the amount of space a three-dimensional figure occupies, expressed in cubic units of measurement. The volume of a prism is the product of the area of its base B and its height h.

$$V = Bh$$

To determine the volume of the ark, first use the formula $A = lw$ to calculate the area of its base.

$B = (450 \text{ ft})(75 \text{ ft})$
$B = 33{,}750 \text{ ft}^2$

Then multiply the area by its height. Express your answer in cubic measurement.

$V = (33{,}750 \text{ ft}^2)(45 \text{ ft})$
$V = 1{,}518{,}750 \text{ ft}^3$

> The volume of the ark was sufficient to accommodate over 30,000 sheep-sized animals on each of its three decks.

The volume of cylinders and other types of prisms can be calculated in a similar manner. First find the area of the base. Then multiply by the height of the figure. Express your answer in cubic measurement.

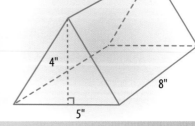

To find the area of the base of a triangular prism, use the formula $A = \frac{1}{2}bh'$ (where h' is the height of the triangle).

$B = \frac{1}{2}(5 \text{ in.})(4 \text{ in.}) = 10 \text{ in.}^2$
$V = (10 \text{ in.}^2)(8 \text{ in.}) = 80 \text{ in.}^3$

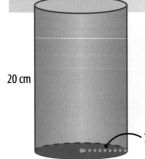

To find the area of the base of a cylinder, use the formula $A = \pi r^2$. Use $\pi \approx \frac{22}{7}$.
To calculate the volume of a cylinder, use the formula $V = Bh$.

$B \approx \frac{22}{7}(7 \text{ cm})^2 = 154 \text{ cm}^2$
$V \approx (154 \text{ cm}^2)(20 \text{ cm}) = 3080 \text{ cm}^3$

Check Understanding

Use a calculator to solve the problems in this lesson.

a. Find the volume of a rectangular prism whose base is 4 in. by $9\frac{3}{4}$ in. and whose height is 6 in.

b. Find the volume of a cylinder whose diameter is 8 cm and whose height is 22 cm. Use $\pi \approx 3.14$.

c. In the metric system, $1 \text{ cm}^3 = 1 \text{ mL}$. Is the volume of the cylinder in the previous problem greater than or less than one liter?

d. What is the height of a triangular prism whose base measures 2.5 square inches and whose volume is 20 cubic inches?

Practice

Find the volume.

1.
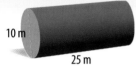
10 m
25 m

2.
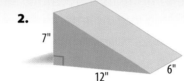
7"
12"
6"

3.
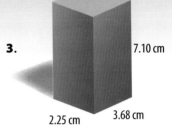
7.10 cm
2.25 cm
3.68 cm

4. A 2 cm regular hexagonal prism has a base area of 10.4 cm² and a height of 2 cm. What is its volume?

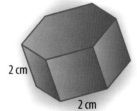
2 cm
2 cm

5. Use the Pythagorean Theorem to find the volume of a $5 \times 6 \times 5$-meter triangular prism that is 8 meters high.

5 m   5 m
6 m
8 m

Apply

6. Mrs. Wragg bought a package of sugar measuring $4\frac{1}{2}$ in. $\times 3\frac{1}{2}$ in $\times 8$ in. She would like to store her sugar in one of the containers at right. Which one is the best choice?

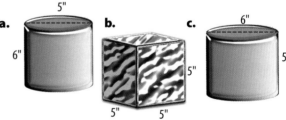
a. 5" 6"   **b.** 5" 5"   **c.** 6" 5"

7. A half-gallon milk container has a square bottom and is 20 cm high. It holds about 1900 mL (cm³). What is the width of the container? Round your answer to the hundredths place. Will it fit into a spot in the refrigerator that is 4 inches wide?

8. A five-gallon gas can measures 5 in. $\times$ 11 in. $\times$ 21 in. What part of one cubic foot is five gallons? (Hint: Think of a cubic foot as a cube that is one foot on each edge.)

9. A box of cereal has a volume of $192\frac{1}{2}$ cubic inches. If it takes up a $2\frac{1}{2}$" $\times$ 7" space on the cupboard shelf, how tall is the box?

10. A sugar cube is $\frac{1}{2}$" on each edge. What is its volume? Make a drawing of a cubic inch of sugar cubes.

Volume of Pyramids and Cones

Construct Meaning

"And this is eternal life, that they may know You, the only true God, and Jesus Christ whom You have sent." (John 17:3)

The Bible promises believers that they will one day inhabit a beautiful city that God even now is preparing for them in heaven. The ancient Egyptians, who worshiped the creation rather than the Creator, could only guess what would happen to them after they died. They built elaborate tombs for their kings with the hope that their bodies would survive through the centuries. These huge monuments to a mistaken notion of an "afterlife" are the Egyptian pyramids.

KHAFRE PYRAMID, GIZA PLATEAU, CAIRO

Through a geometric proof, the volume of a pyramid can be shown to be one-third that of a prism with the same base and height. Similarly, the volume of a cone can be shown to be one-third that of a cylinder with the same base and height. Therefore, the formula for finding the volume of a pyramid or cone is: $V = \frac{1}{3}Bh$.

Khafre's Pyramid, built on the Giza plateau around 2500 B.C. long before the Hebrews migrated to Egypt, had a square base 704 feet on each side and was 471 feet tall. Calculate its volume.

$V = \frac{1}{3}Bh$
$V = \frac{1}{3}(704 \text{ ft})^2(471 \text{ ft})$ Substitute.
$V = 77,811,712 \text{ ft}^3$ Multiply.

The Great Pyramid of Khufu originally had a height of 146.5 meters. Its original volume was 2,583,283 cubic meters—almost twice the size of the world's largest office buildings today. Calculate the length of its square base.

GREAT PYRAMID OF KHUFU, GIZA, EGYPT

$V = \frac{1}{3}Bh$	Use the volume formula.	
$2,583,283 \text{ m}^3 = \frac{1}{3}B(146.5 \text{ m})$	Substitute.	
$\dfrac{3(2,583,283 \text{ m}^3)}{146.5 \text{ m}} = B$	Use inverse operations.	
$52,900 \text{ m}^2 = B$	Simplify.	

$B = s^2$	Use the formula for the area of a square.
$52,900 \text{ m}^2 = s^2$	Substitute.
$\sqrt{52,900 \text{ m}^2} = \sqrt{s^2}$	Take the square root of both sides.
$230 \text{ m} = s$	

Find the volume of a cone with a base diameter of 4 inches and a height of 3 inches. The **height** of a cone is the perpendicular distance from the base to the vertex.

$V = \frac{1}{3}Bh$
$V = \frac{1}{3}(\pi r^2)h$
$V \approx \frac{1}{3}(3.14)(2 \text{ in.})^2(3 \text{ in.})$
$V \approx 12.56 \text{ in.}^3$

Check Understanding

a. The volume of a rectangular prism is 360 ft³. Find the volume of the pyramid with the same base and height.

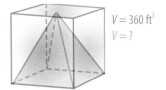

V = 360 ft³
V = ?

b. Find the volume of a pyramid whose base measures 7 inches by 18 inches and whose height is 10 inches.

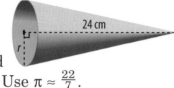

24 cm

c. Find the volume of a pyramid with a right triangular base as shown.

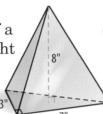

8"

3"

7"

d. Find the radius of the base of a cone whose volume is 1232 cm³ and whose height is 24 cm. Use $\pi \approx \frac{22}{7}$.

Practice

Find the volume. Use $\pi \approx 3.14$.

1.

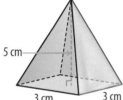

5 cm

3 cm   3 cm

2.

12"

8"

3.

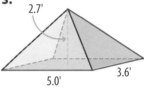

2.7'

5.0'   3.6'

4. Find the volume and total surface area of a square pyramid whose base measures 6 meters and whose height is 4 meters. (Use the Pythagorean Theorem to find the slant height.)

5. Find the volume of a 5-inch high pyramid whose base is a 4-inch equilateral triangle. Round your answer to the nearest tenth.

Apply

6. Matthew placed a solid brass cone with a base diameter of 14 cm and a height of 15 cm into a cylindrical glass beaker with the same base and height. Lauren poured water from a graduated cylinder into the beaker until it was filled to the brim. How many mL of water did she use? Use $\pi \approx \frac{22}{7}$. (1 cm³ = 1 mL)

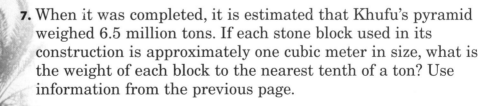

7. When it was completed, it is estimated that Khufu's pyramid weighed 6.5 million tons. If each stone block used in its construction is approximately one cubic meter in size, what is the weight of each block to the nearest tenth of a ton? Use information from the previous page.

8. Due to erosion and the loss of outer casing stones, Khufu's pyramid is now 449 feet high. Its present volume is 3,076,620 cubic yards. Aaron and Raizel toured the pyramid while visiting Cairo. The two walked around its base. How long was their walk? Is this greater or less than one-half mile?

Apply

Use a calculator to solve the following problems. Use $\pi \approx 3.14$.

1. A one-pound (453 g) box of granola measures 5.6 cm by 17 cm by 25 cm tall. The box is filled to within 2 cm of the top.

  a. Find the volume of the product to the nearest whole number.

  b. What is the average weight of the cereal per cm^3 to the nearest tenth of a gram?

2. A six-ounce, single-serving can of tomato juice is 5 cm in diameter and 9.5 cm tall. How many milliliters of juice does it contain? (1 cm^3 = 1 mL)

3. Emily, Ashley, and Sarah have each saved a jarful of dimes. Who saved the most money?

10 cm

Emily

├──8 cm──┤

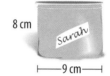

13 cm

Ashley

├─7 cm─┤

8 cm

Sarah

├──9 cm──┤

4. A cubic foot holds about 7.5 gallons of liquid. The fuel tank on Kevin's car measures 0.5 feet by 2 feet by 3 feet. When he pulled into the gas station, Kevin figured he only had a gallon left in the tank.

  a. How many gallons will it take for him to fill up the tank?

  b. At $1.699 per gallon, how much will it cost?

Bent Pyramid, Dashur, Egypt

5. A triangular cardboard mailing tube is 6 inches wide on each side and 36 inches long. Calculate its volume to the nearest cubic inch.

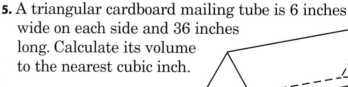

36"

6"

6. A two-liter plastic soft drink bottle is 10 cm wide at its base. To the nearest tenth, what is its minimum height?

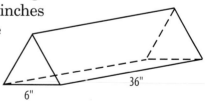

Cola

h

7. Ethan makes model rockets. Calculate the volume of the payload he can carry in the nosecone of his latest model to the nearest tenth of a cubic centimeter.

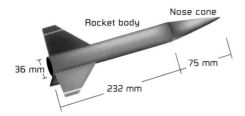

8. A church clock tower is a brick structure with a base 30 feet by 30 feet and a height of 210 feet. Atop this brick tower is a pyramid-shaped metal roof 32.2 feet high. Calculate the combined volume of the tower and roof.

9. Next month the roof of the clock tower will be repainted. If the paint coverage is 275 square feet per gallon, how many gallons should be purchased? (Round all calculations to the nearest tenth.)

10. A pint container of coffee creamer measures 7 cm by 7 cm by 9.7 cm tall. Use these container measurements to estimate the number of milliliters in a pint. Based on your calculations, about how many milliliters are in a fluid ounce? (Round your answers to whole numbers.)

11. A soup can has a diameter of 7 cm. Its contents are labeled 385 mL. About how tall must the can be?

12. Due to the loss of its outer casing stones, the Great Pyramid of Khufu is now 227 m long at its base and 137 m tall. When Aaron and Raizel visited the pyramid last summer, Aaron contemplated climbing to the top. What is the shortest distance to the top of the pyramid, to the nearest tenth of a meter?

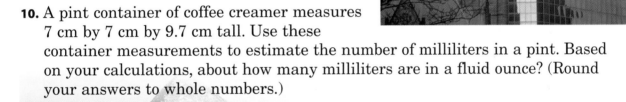

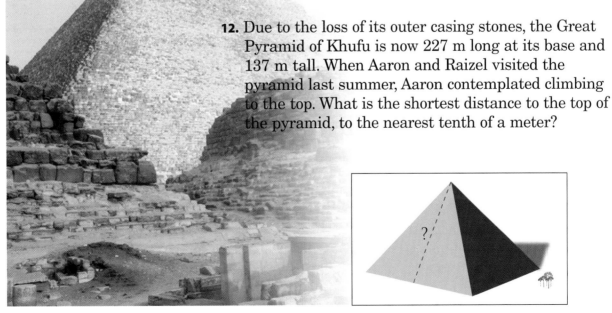

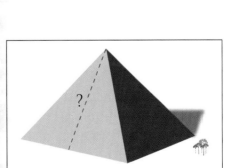

Construct Meaning

A circle is a plane geometric figure. It is defined as the set of all points in a plane that are equidistant from a given point, the center. Imagine a circle with a diameter drawn vertically. Hold the circle in space and spin it with the diameter as its axis. What do you have?

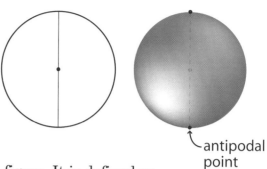

antipodal point

A sphere is a three-dimensional figure. It is defined as the set of all points in space that are equidistant from a given point, the center. How does this definition differ from that of a circle? A sphere is a three-dimensional surface, a shell. It is the peel of the orange—not the orange itself. A **hemisphere** is half of a sphere.

A line drawn through a sphere intersects it at two points in space. If this line also passes through the sphere's center, the points of intersection are called antipodal points.

If a plane intersects a sphere, what figure is formed?

If an intersecting plane passes through the center of a sphere, the figure formed at their intersection is called a **great circle**. The diameter of a great circle is the same as the diameter of the sphere. A great circle divides a sphere into two congruent hemispheres.

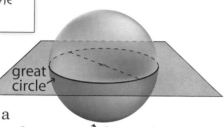

great circle

hemisphere

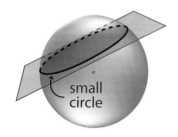

small circle

If an intersecting plane does not pass through the sphere's center, the resulting intersection is called a **small circle**.

The shortest distance between two points on the surface of a sphere follows the great circle on which both points lie.

Check Understanding

One of the most familiar spheres is the surface of the earth.

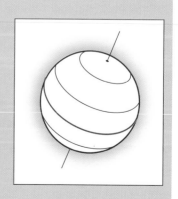

a. Name two well-known antipodal points on the earth.

b. Name the best known great circle on the earth.

c. Name a terrestrial hemisphere.

d. Do small circles form lines of latitude or longitude?

e. Why do transcontinental airline flights follow the path of great circles between cities in North America and Europe?

Use Euler's formula, if necessary, to find the following.   *Lesson 13.1*

1. The number of edges of a cube

2. The number of faces of an octagonal pyramid

3. The number of faces of a triangular prism

4. The number of vertices of a polyhedron with 6 faces and 10 edges

5. Name the polyhedron in problem 4.   *Lesson 13.1*

6. Wrapping paper is 36 inches wide. If you make a one-inch overlap, what length piece will you have to cut in order to wrap a box 14 inches by 22 inches by 10 inches?   *Lesson 13.2*

7. An empty oatmeal box has a height of 7.5 inches and a diameter of 4.0 inches. To the nearest tenth of an inch, what size sheet of paper is required to completely cover the curved surface of the container? Use 3.14 for π.   *Lesson 13.2*

8. Find the surface area of a triangular prism whose base measures 5 inches by 5 inches by 8 inches and whose height is 15 inches.   *Lesson 13.2*

9. Find the surface area to the nearest square inch of a tetrahedron whose edges are each 9 inches in length.   *Lesson 13.3*

10. A pup tent is 3 feet high, 4 feet wide, and 6 feet long. Including its floor, and an extra 5% overall to account for seams, how many square feet of material did it take to make the tent? Round your answer to the nearest tenth.   *Lesson 13.4*

11. Find the volume of a can that measures 10 centimeters in diameter and 20 centimeters in height. Use 3.14 for π.   *Lesson 13.5*

12. Find the volume of a cone with the same height and base as the cylinder in problem 11.   *Lesson 13.6*

13. The volume of a square pyramid is 4 cubic meters. If the pyramid is 3 meters tall, how wide is its base?   *Lesson 13.6*

14. Haley wants to store a liter of apple juice in one of two containers. Which container is the better choice?   *Lesson 13.7*

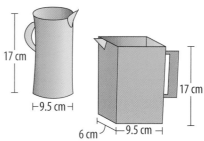

Chapter 13 Check-Up

Solid as a Rock

Draw each figure.

1. Rectangular pyramid   **2.** Cone   **3.** Triangular prism

Identify the number of faces, vertices, and edges for each figure.

4. Rectangular prism   **5.** Square pyramid   **6.** Tetrahedron

Write *perimeter*, *area*, *volume*, or *surface area* to indicate which geometric concept applies to each of the following.
   7. The amount of land in a national park
   8. The amount of space in a freezer
   9. The amount of cardboard to make a shoe box
   10. The distance around a chess board
   11. The amount of material to make a ball

Calculate the surface area of each figure. Use 3.14 for π.

12.

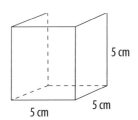

13.

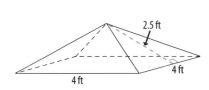

14.

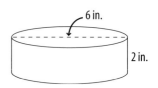

Match each volume formula to the appropriate figure. Each letter may be used only once.

15. $V = lwh$ **a.** Cylinder

16. $V = s^3$ **b.** Rectangular prism

17. $V = \frac{1}{3}\pi r^2 h$ **c.** Cube

18. $V = \pi r^2 h$ **d.** Cone

Calculate the volume of each figure. Use 3.14 for π.

19.

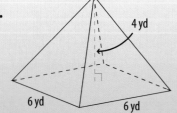

20.

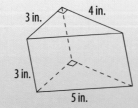

21.

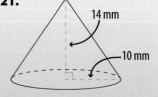

22. Tammy is making a three-layer chocolate cake for the holidays. Each layer is 10 inches by 4 inches by $1\frac{1}{2}$ inches high. She is frosting the top and sides of each layer and then placing the layers on top of each other. Each can of frosting covers about 80 square inches.
a. What is the surface area to be frosted?
b. How many cans of frosting should Tammy buy?

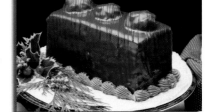

23. About how many gallons of water can a 30" by 12" by 18" fish tank hold? ($1 \text{ ft}^3 \approx 7.5$ gal)

24. A miniature candy bar measuring 2 cm by 4 cm by 1.5 cm weighs 10 grams. A full-size candy bar of the same type measures 3.5 cm by 10 cm by 2 cm. Estimate the weight of the full-size candy bar.

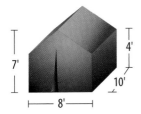

25. Consider a tent with the given dimensions.
a. How many square feet of canvas are required to make this tent including the floor?
b. What is the volume of the tent?

26. A trash can has a diameter of 1.3 feet and a height of 3 feet. What capacity trash bag (to the nearest gallon) does it require? ($1 \text{ ft}^3 \approx 7.5$ gal)

27. A 12-oz soft drink can measures 6.5 cm in diameter and is 10.75 cm tall.
a. How many milliliters can it hold? Use 3.14 for π and round your answer to the nearest whole number.
b. Based on your calculation, write a conversion factor for fluid ounces and milliliters.

28. A can of tomato sauce has a radius of 5 cm and a height of 11.5 cm. Use 3.14 for π and round your answers to the nearest whole number.
a. Find its volume.
b. Determine the amount of surface that needs to be covered by the label.

29. A can of vegetables is $4\frac{2}{3}$ inches tall. Its volume is 26 cubic inches. Find its diameter.

30. Vicky brought home a 5-pound bag of sugar in a sack measuring $3\frac{1}{2}$" $\times$ 5" $\times$ 8". Which of these canisters should she use for the sugar?

a.

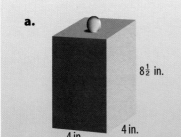

$8\frac{1}{2}$ in.

4 in.

4 in.

b.

5 in.

6 in.

c.

11 in.

4 in.

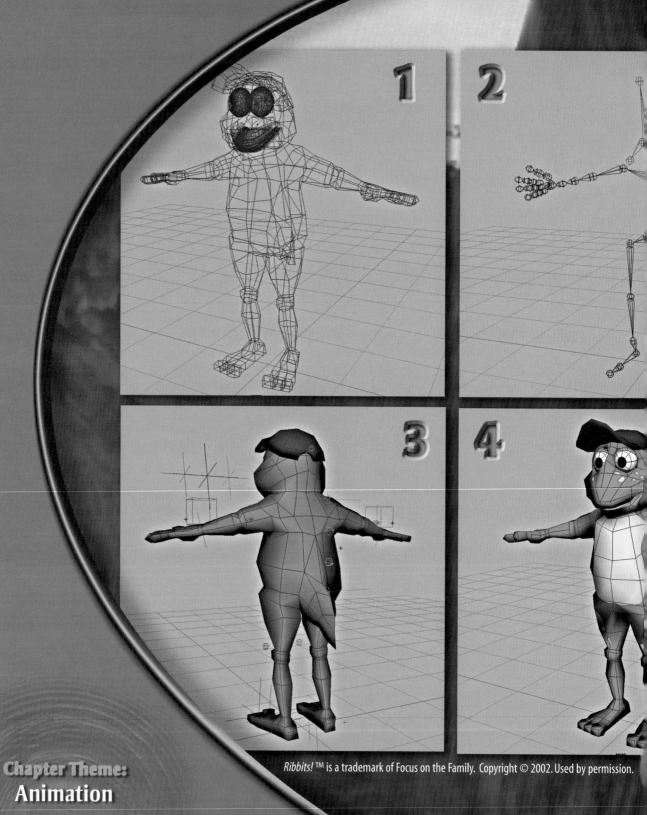

1

2

3

4

Ribbits! ™ is a trademark of Focus on the Family. Copyright © 2002. Used by permission.

Chapter Theme:
Animation

Chapter 14

Coordinate System

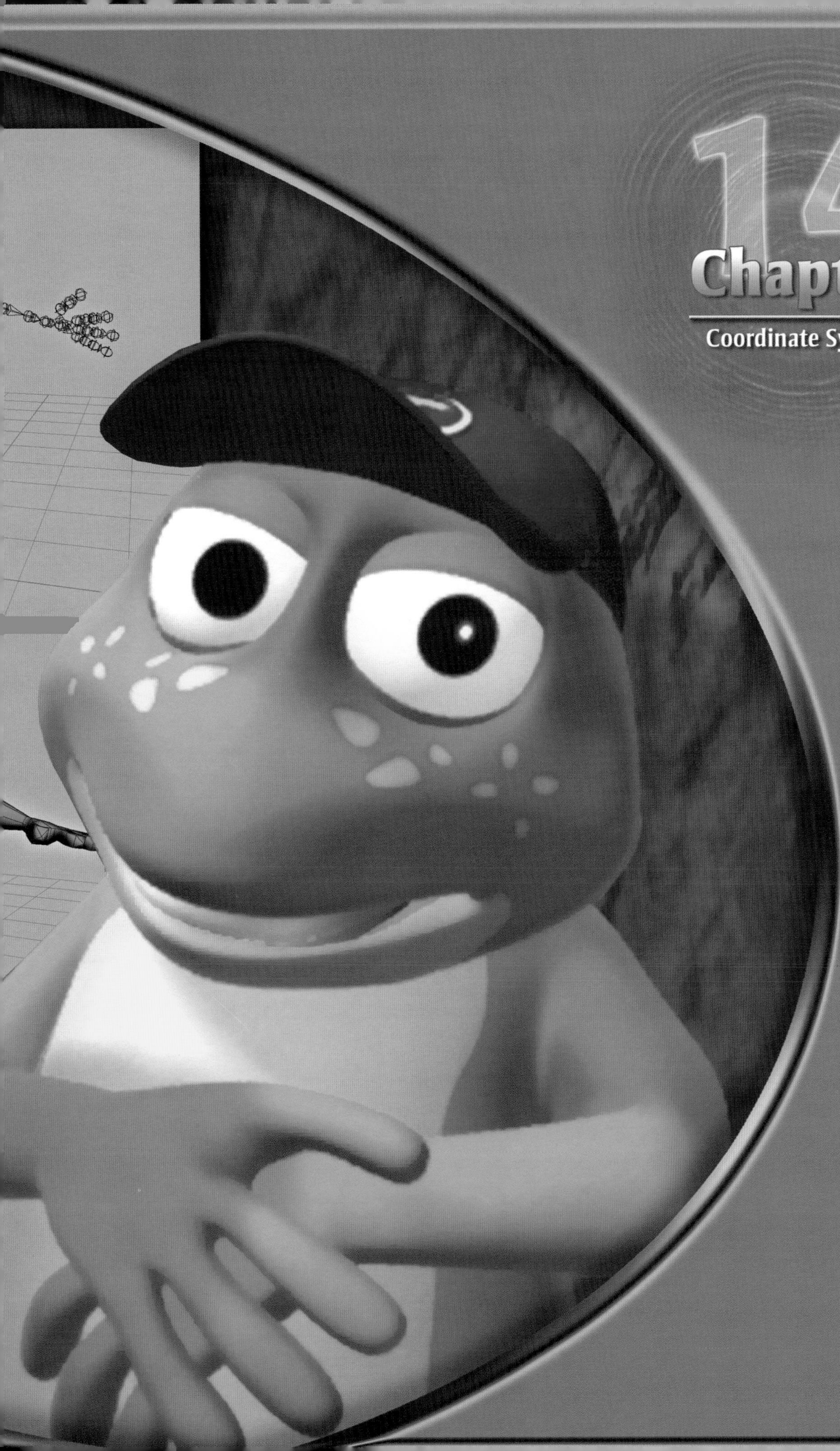

Construct Meaning

Does the dot seem to move smoothly across the grid as your eye travels from left to right? This ability of the human eye, persistence of vision, is the principle behind animation. A sense of movement is communicated as an object is drawn at slightly different locations on the same background. When viewed in rapid succession, the individual drawings result in an animated object. In traditional animation, the artist drew every frame one at a time. Use of computers allowed the development of more complex animation by generating motion through mathematical language.

A system of perpendicular horizontal and vertical number lines used to locate given points is called a **coordinate system**. The horizontal line is called the **x-axis** and the vertical line is the **y-axis**. They intersect at the **origin**, which has the coordinates (0, 0). The two axes divide the coordinate plane into four **quadrants**, or regions, as shown.

Each point is defined by an **ordered pair** of coordinates, (x, y). The first number is the **x-coordinate**, which indicates distance and direction along the x-axis from the origin. The second number is the **y-coordinate**, which indicates distance and direction along the y-axis.

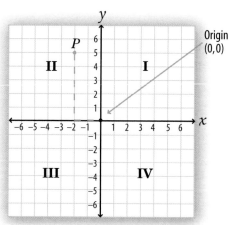

The point $P(-2, 5)$ is 2 units to the left of the origin since the x-coordinate is negative. Because the y-coordinate is positive, the point is 5 units up. In what quadrant would you place the point $(2, -2)$?

The nose of the cartoon dog is 6 units to the left of the origin and 5 units below the horizontal axis. Its coordinates are $(-6, -5)$.

Determine the coordinates of the tip of the cartoon cat's tail.

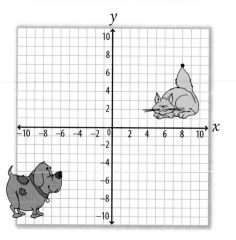

Check Understanding

Plot each point on a coordinate grid. Label each point on the graph with the appropriate letter.

a. $A(-3, 6)$ **b.** $B(0, 8)$ **c.** $C(2, -5)$

d. $D(-8, -3)$ **e.** $E(-5, 0)$ **f.** $F(3, 7)$

g. Give the quadrant for each point A through F.

h. If all points having the x-coordinate equal to the y-coordinate are plotted, what is the result?

Practice

Give the location of each object on the graph as an ordered pair.

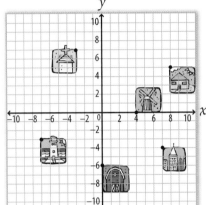

1. Barn

2. Church

3. Windmill

4. House

5. Office building

6. Lighthouse

Apply

Write your answer as an ordered pair.

7. Where am I? I am three units along the x-axis and four units from the x-axis in Quadrant III.

8. Where am I? I am five units along the x-axis and two units below the x-axis. I am not in Quadrant III.

9. Where am I? I am three units to the left of the y-axis. I am not in any quadrant.

10. Use a coordinate grid to plot the first point. For each successive point, join it to the previous point with a straight line.
$(0, -1)$ $(1, -1.5)$ $(2, -1)$ $(2, 1)$ $(1.5, 2)$ $(-0.5, 2)$ $(-2, 0)$ $(-3, 0)$ $(-3.5, 1)$ $(-3, 2)$
$(-4, 1.5)$ $(-5, 1)$ $(-4, 0.5)$ $(-3, -1)$ $(-2, -1.5)$ $(0, -1.5)$ $(1, -1.5)$
Lift your pencil. Plot the first point in this list and continue as before.
$(-1, -1)$ $(-1.5, -2)$ $(-2, -2)$ $(-1.5, -1)$ Plot the point $(0, 0)$ **What am I?**

11. On a coordinate grid, connect the following points in order. Connect the last point back to the first point. $(3, 3)$ $(0, 3)$ $(-2, -2)$ $(1, -2)$ **What am I?**

12. Predict the shape of the figure in problem 11 if each coordinate is doubled.

Translations

Construct Meaning

A change in the position or size of a figure is a **transformation**. A **translation** is a transformation that slides a figure in a straight line, changing the location but not the orientation. Translations in animation make an object appear to move across the screen.

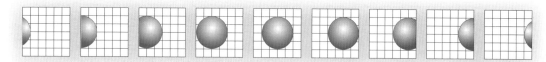

Sue plotted these points on a graph and connected the points to form a P.

She wanted to know how the graph would change if she subtracted six from each x-coordinate and subtracted eight from each y-coordinate. The point $(1, 1)$ became $(1 - 6, 1 - 8)$, or $(-5, -7)$.

(x, y)
$(1, 1)$
$(1, 7)$
$(3, 7)$
$(4, 6)$
$(4, 5)$
$(3, 4)$
$(1, 4)$

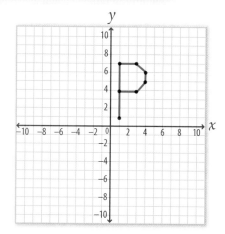

Original (x, y)	Translation $(x - 6, y - 8)$
$(1, 1)$	$(-5, -7)$
$(1, 7)$	$(-5, -1)$
$(3, 7)$	$(-3, -1)$
$(4, 6)$	$(-2, -2)$
$(4, 5)$	$(-2, -3)$
$(3, 4)$	$(-3, -4)$
$(1, 4)$	$(-5, -4)$

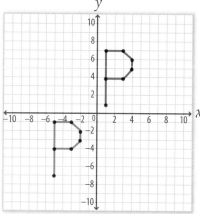

The P did not change size or shape. It shifted six units to the left and eight units down. This translation is represented by $T_{-6, -8}$.

If Sue performs a translation of $T_{5, -4}$ from the original blue P, what is the result?

Original (x, y)	Translation $(x + 5, y - 4)$
$(1, 1)$	$(6, -3)$
$(1, 7)$	$(6, 3)$
$(3, 7)$	$(8, 3)$
$(4, 6)$	$(9, 2)$
$(4, 5)$	$(9, 1)$
$(3, 4)$	$(8, 0)$
$(1, 4)$	$(6, 0)$

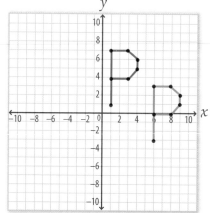

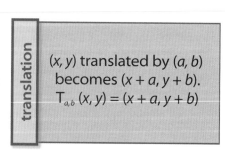

translation

(x, y) translated by (a, b) becomes $(x + a, y + b)$.
$T_{a, b} (x, y) = (x + a, y + b)$

Check Understanding

Use the original coordinates used to construct the original blue P in Construct Meaning. For each translation, describe what will happen to the figure.

a. $T_{3,-8}$ **b.** $T_{-4,6}$ **c.** $T_{2,0}$

d. Determine the set of points resulting from translating the P by $T_{2,-1}$. Draw a graph showing both figures.

e. Can translating an object ever change its size?

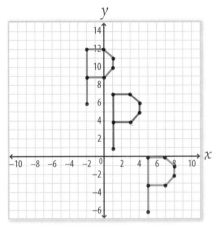

Practice

1. Determine the translation that will move the blue P to the position of the purple one.
2. Determine the translation that will move the blue P to the position of the green one.
3. Determine the translation that will move the purple P to the position of the green one.
4. Determine the translation that will move the green P to the position of the purple one.
5. What do you notice about the translations in problems 3 and 4?

Apply

6. Graph the following object on a coordinate grid by connecting each original point to the next one in the column.
7. Complete the second column of the chart by applying a translation of $T_{-6,3}$. How will this move the object?
8. Complete the third column of the chart by applying a translation of $T_{4,5}$ to the original set of points. How will this translation move the object?
9. Graph both translations on the same coordinate grid used for the original graph. Use different colors for each and label appropriately.

Original	$T_{-6,3}$	$T_{4,5}$
(4,−1)		
(2,3)		
(4,5)		
(6,3)		
(4,−1)		
(4,−2)		
(5,−3)		
(6,−3)		
(6,−2)		
(5,−2)		
(5,−4)		
(6,−5)		

10. Write the translation notation to represent a movement of three units down with no horizontal change.
11. What single translation would be the same as $T_{-5,3}$ followed by $T_{2,6}$?

Review

1. $1\frac{5}{6} - 3\frac{1}{2}$
2. $5^2 + 3(7-9)^2$
3. 20% of what number is 115.2?
4. What is 0.1% of 25?

Reflections

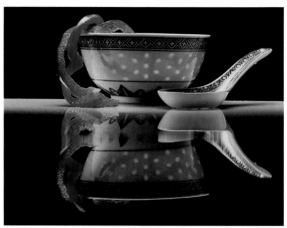

Construct Meaning

A **reflection** is a transformation that flips a figure over a line. The reflection is a mirror image of the figure. The two figures will match exactly if folded on the line of symmetry.

Chacko plotted points and connected them to draw the original blue P. He multiplied each *x*-coordinate by –1, recorded the new points, and connected them to form the orange P. The point (1, 2) became (1 · (–1), 2) or (–1, 2).

Original (x, y)	Reflection (–x, y)
(1, 2)	(–1, 2)
(1, 8)	(–1, 8)
(3, 8)	(–3, 8)
(4, 7)	(–4, 7)
(4, 6)	(–4, 6)
(3, 5)	(–3, 5)
(1, 5)	(–1, 5)

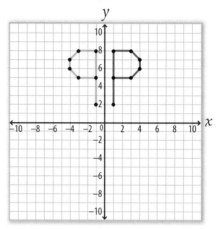

The P did not change size or shape. What is the change? The reflection is the mirror image of the original. It appears to have been flipped over the *y*-axis. Every point on the original figure is the same distance from the axis as the corresponding point on the reflection.

If Chacko wants to flip the original blue P over the *x*-axis he will multiply each *y*-coordinate by –1.

Original (x, y)	Reflection (x, –y)
(1, 2)	(1, –2)
(1, 8)	(1, –8)
(3, 8)	(3, –8)
(4, 7)	(4, –7)
(4, 6)	(4, –6)
(3, 5)	(3, –5)
(1, 5)	(1, –5)

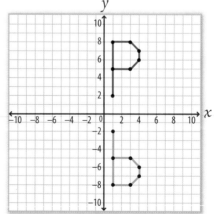

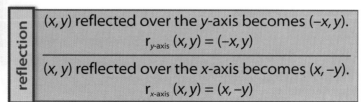

reflection

(x, y) reflected over the y-axis becomes (–x, y).
$$r_{y\text{-axis}}\,(x, y) = (-x, y)$$

(x, y) reflected over the x-axis becomes (x, –y).
$$r_{x\text{-axis}}\,(x, y) = (x, -y)$$

Check Understanding

Determine the color of the P described by each of the following.

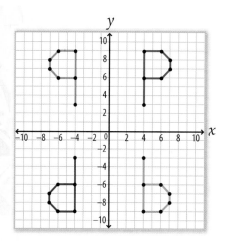

  a. The reflection of the purple P over the *y*-axis
  b. The reflection of the orange P over the *x*-axis
  c. The reflection of the blue P over the *x*-axis, followed by a reflection over the *y*-axis
  d. The reflection of the green P over the *x*-axis
  e. The reflection of the blue P over the *y*-axis

  f. Describe the relationship between the *x*- and *y*-coordinates of the points for the blue P and those of the purple P.
  g. Think of a geometric figure having a reflection that would appear to be a translation.

Practice

Write *true* or *false* for each statement. Explain your answer.

1. This graph represents a reflection over the *y*-axis.

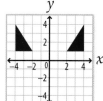

2. This graph represents a reflection over the *x*-axis.

3. This graph represents a reflection over the *y*-axis.

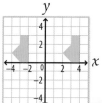

Apply

Original	Reflection over the y-axis	Reflection over the x-axis
(8, 2)		
(8, 3)		
(2, 3)		
(3, 1)		
(6, 1)		
(7, 3)		

4. Graph the following object by connecting each original point on the graph to the next one in the column.

5. Complete the second column in the chart to show a reflection over the *y*-axis. Graph the reflection on the same coordinate grid as problem 4. Use a different color and label.

6. Complete the third column in the chart to show a reflection of the original object over the *x*-axis. Graph this on the same coordinate grid and label.

Challenge

7. Determine the rule for what happens to the coordinates of the vertices of a figure that is reflected over a diagonal line through the origin of the coordinate grid.

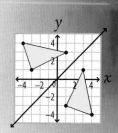

Dilations

Construct Meaning

A **dilation** is a transformation that results in a figure that is the same shape as the original, but has a different size. In animation, a series of dilations will make a character appear to come closer as it increases in size with the background remaining the same.

Emily plotted each ordered pair to form the the blue P.
She multiplied each coordinate by the same number and constructed a new P. The figure that resulted was the same shape but larger in size.

Original (x, y)	Dilation (2x, 2y)
(1, 2)	(2, 4)
(1, 8)	(2, 16)
(3, 8)	(6, 16)
(4, 7)	(8, 14)
(4, 6)	(8, 12)
(3, 5)	(6, 10)
(1, 5)	(2, 10)

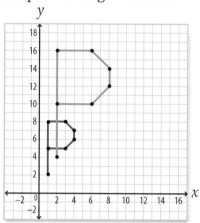

The **scale factor** k is the ratio of a dilated image to the original image. Each coordinate of the figure has been multiplied by the same scale factor to determine the set of coordinates for the orange P. This dilation is centered around the origin (0, 0). Observe what happens if Emily multiplies each coordinate by $\frac{1}{2}$.

Original (x, y)	Dilation $\left(\frac{1}{2}x, \frac{1}{2}y\right)$
(1, 2)	$\left(\frac{1}{2}, 1\right)$
(1, 8)	$\left(\frac{1}{2}, 4\right)$
(3, 8)	$\left(1\frac{1}{2}, 4\right)$
(4, 7)	$\left(2, 3\frac{1}{2}\right)$
(4, 6)	(2, 3)
(3, 5)	$\left(1\frac{1}{2}, 2\frac{1}{2}\right)$
(1, 5)	$\left(\frac{1}{2}, 2\frac{1}{2}\right)$

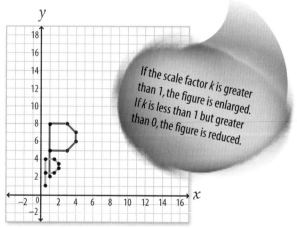

If the scale factor k is greater than 1, the figure is enlarged. If k is less than 1 but greater than 0, the figure is reduced.

How did the dilation affect the length of the side of the P?

dilation

(x, y) dilated by a scale factor of k becomes (kx, ky).
$$D_k(x, y) = (kx, ky)$$

Check Understanding

The blue P is the original.

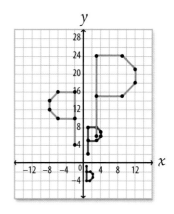

a. Which figure represents $D_3(x, y) = (3x, 3y)$?

b. Which figure represents a dilation with a scale factor of 2 and a reflection over the y-axis?

c. By what scale factor was the blue P dilated to result in the purple P? What other transformation took place before the dilation?

d. Does it matter whether dilation or reflection of a figure takes place first? Explain.

e. How can you enlarge a square so that each side length is five times the original?

Practice

1. On a coordinate grid, graph the following object by connecting each point to the next one in the list. $(-4, 4)$ $(0, 4)$ $(3, -6)$ $(-6, -6)$ $(-3, 4)$ $(-3, 7)$ $(0, 7)$ $(0, 4)$ $(1, 4)$

2. On the same grid, use a different color to draw a dilation of the object (in problem 1) with a scale factor of 2.

Apply

3. Construct a house on a coordinate grid by connecting the points $(-2, -2)$, $(-2, 0)$, $(0, 2)$, $(2, 0)$, $(2, -2)$, and $(-2, -2)$.

4. Perform a dilation of your house drawing using a scale factor of 3. Make a chart to record the coordinates. Plot them on the same grid using a different color.

5. Using the original house coordinates, multiply the x-coordinate by a scale factor of 6 and the y-coordinate by 3. Make a chart to record the coordinates. Plot them on the same grid using a different color.

6. What happens when the x-coordinate is multiplied by a different scale factor than the y-coordinate?

7. Joe has a 4-inch by 6-inch photo. Can it be enlarged to an 8-inch by 10-inch photo and be exactly the same? Explain.

8. Could a 4-inch by 5-inch photo be enlarged to an 8-inch by 10-inch photo and stay exactly the same? Explain.

Rotations

Construct Meaning

The use of rotations in animation can make an object such as a fan appear to spin. A **rotation** is a transformation that turns a figure around a fixed point called the **center of rotation**. The resulting figure has the same shape and size, but a different orientation.

Evan rotated the blue P in a counterclockwise direction and recorded the coordinates of each position after each change of 90°.

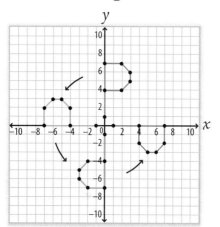

Original (x, y)	90° Rotation (−y, x)	180° Rotation (−x, −y)	270° Rotation (y, −x)
(0, 1)	(−1, 0)	(0, −1)	(1, 0)
(0, 7)	(−7, 0)	(0, −7)	(7, 0)
(2, 7)	(−7, 2)	(−2, −7)	(7, −2)
(3, 6)	(−6, 3)	(−3, −6)	(6, −3)
(3, 5)	(−5, 3)	(−3, −5)	(5, −3)
(2, 4)	(−4, 2)	(−2, −4)	(4, −2)
(0, 4)	(−4, 0)	(0, −4)	(4, 0)

Examine the coordinates for a counterclockwise rotation of 90° and compare them to the original. The original x-coordinate becomes the new y-coordinate. The original y-coordinate is multiplied by −1 and becomes the new x-coordinate.

For a counterclockwise rotation of 180°, both the x-coordinate and the y-coordinate are multiplied by a negative one.

Evan predicted that for a counterclockwise rotation of 270°, the original y-coordinate becomes the new x-coordinate and the original x-coordinate is multiplied by −1 and becomes the new y-coordinate. The points recorded in the chart verify his prediction.

rotations

(x, y) rotated 90° counterclockwise around the origin becomes (−y, x).

(x, y) rotated 180° around the origin becomes (−x, −y).

(x, y) rotated 270° counterclockwise around the origin becomes (y, −x).

Check Understanding

a. Give the coordinates of the point (6, 3) if it is rotated counterclockwise 90°, 180°, 270°, and 360° around the origin.

b. How can you tell the difference between a rotation of 180° and a reflection over a line?

c. When you are riding on a Ferris wheel, are you experiencing a rotation? Explain.

Practice

Determine the degree of counterclockwise rotation represented by each pair of figures. If it is not a rotation, write *not a rotation*.

1.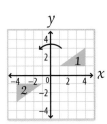

2.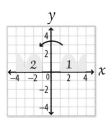

3.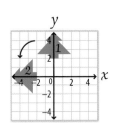

4.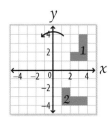

Apply

5. Copy and complete the chart for the counterclockwise rotation of the figure formed by connecting the points.

Original (x, y)	90° Rotation (−y, x)	180° Rotation (−x, −y)	270° Rotation (y, −x)
(8, 1)			
(8, 8)			
(3, 5)			
(1, 2)			

6. Graph each of the four figures above on the same coordinate grid. Connect the last point of each figure back to its first point. Use a different color for each rotation.

7. Are the four figures graphed in problem 6 congruent?

8. What is the center of rotation for the rotations in problem 6?

9. What clockwise rotation would have the same result as a 270° counterclockwise rotation?

10. John said that a reflection over the x-axis followed by a reflection over the y-axis is the same as a rotation of 180°. Is he correct? Explain.

Linear Equations

Construct Meaning

The coordinate system can be used to picture an algebraic equation. Begin by making a table of values for x and y that make the equation true. Plot each ordered pair on a coordinate grid and draw a line through the points.

Emmanuel wanted to know how the graph of $y = 2x - 1$ would look on a coordinate grid. He chose different values for x and solved for y.

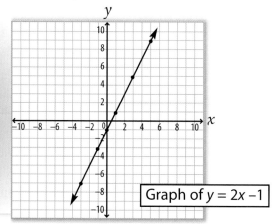

x	$2x - 1$	y	(x, y)
−3	$2(−3) − 1$	−7	$(−3, −7)$
−1	$2(−1) − 1$	−3	$(−1, −3)$
0	$2(0) − 1$	−1	$(0, −1)$
1	$2(1) − 1$	1	$(1, 1)$
3	$2(3) − 1$	5	$(3, 5)$
5	$2(5) − 1$	9	$(5, 9)$

Graph of $y = 2x - 1$

It is a good idea to choose some negative values as well as positive values for x. Although only two points are required to determine a straight line, plotting additional points serves to check your accuracy.

Emmanuel can use his graph to locate other ordered pairs that make the equation true. Use the graph to determine the value of y when x is 2. Find the value of x when y is −6. All points on the graph represent solutions of the equation. If all the points lie in a straight line, the equation is *linear*. A **linear equation** is an equation having a graph that is a straight line. Arrows on each end of the line indicate that the graph extends beyond the portion of the coordinate grid shown.

The truck Bonnie rented cost $40 per day plus $0.25 per mile. Construct a graph to show the relationship between total cost c and the distance d for one day.

$c = \$40 + \$0.25d$

d	$\$40 + \$0.25d$	c	(d, c)
0	$\$40 + \$0.25(0)$	40.00	$(0, 40.00)$
10	$\$40 + \$0.25(10)$	42.50	$(10, 42.50)$
40	$\$40 + \$0.25(40)$	50.00	$(40, 50.00)$
100	$\$40 + \$0.25(100)$	65.00	$(100, 65.00)$

Why does this graph not extend in both directions?

Use the graph to determine the maximum number of miles Bonnie can drive the truck and stay within her $70 budget.

Check Understanding

a. Joe made an *x-y* chart for the equation $y = -3x + 5$. When he drew the line on his coordinate grid, one of the points was not on the line. Find his error.

x	y
−3	14
−1	6
0	5
1	2
3	−4

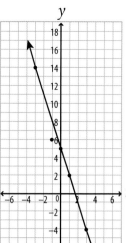
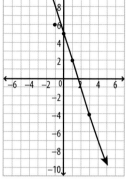

Determine if the point (4, 9) is on the graph of each line.

b. $y = 2x - 1$ **c.** $y = 3x - 3$

d. $y = 5x - 9$ **e.** $y = 2x + 1$

Practice

Make an *x-y* chart and draw the graph for each equation.
Use graph paper to construct the coordinate grid.

1. $y = 3x + 3$ **2.** $y = -3x + 4$ **3.** $y = x$

4. Use your graph for problem 1 to determine the value of *x* if *y* is equal to 15.

Apply

Joseph is trying to determine the equation which represents the pattern for the number of toothpicks used for each stage.

5. Copy and complete his chart.

Stage	Number of toothpicks
1	6
2	
3	
4	
5	

6. Which of the equations you graphed in Practice matches these points if they were graphed as ordered pairs (stage, number of toothpicks)?

7. Use the equation to predict the number of toothpicks Joseph will need for stage 30.

8. Jackie spent a total of $80 for her admission to the craft show and three wreaths. Jody spent $30 for her admission and one wreath. Julie spent $105 for admission and four wreaths. The wreaths were all priced the same. Use the graph at the right to determine the admission cost for the craft show.

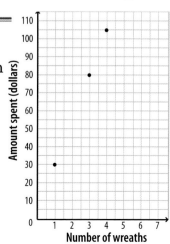

Construct Meaning

Joshua plotted the points $(-6, -5)$, $(1, -5)$, and $(4, -5)$ and drew a blue line through them. Notice that all points on this line have a y-coordinate of -5, no matter what the x-coordinate is. The equation of this horizontal line can be written as $y = -5$.

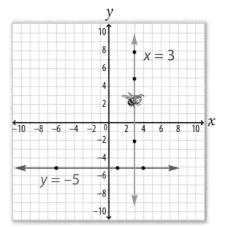

If the cartoon 🐝 moves along the line $x = 3$, its x-coordinate does not change. The value of y can change, moving the 🐝 up and down on the gold vertical line. All points on this line have an x-coordinate of 3.

Use the graph to determine the point of intersection for the line $y = -5$ and the line $x = 3$. Does the point $(3, -5)$ check when substituted into the equation $y = -5$? Try the equation $x = 3$.

> The equation of the horizontal line is $y = -5$.
>
> The equation of the vertical line is $x = 3$.

Check Understanding

Determine the equation for each line shown on the coordinate grid.

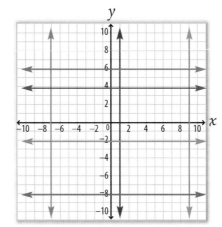

a. Blue
b. Purple
c. Pink
d. Grey
e. Brown
f. Green
g. Orange

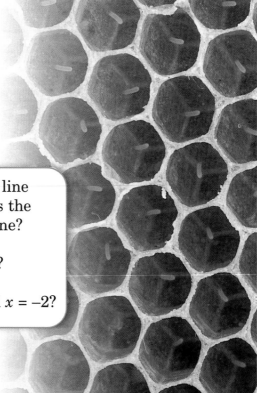

h. Spencer drew a horizontal line and a vertical line which intersected at the point $(-4, 6)$. What is the equation of the horizontal line? the vertical line?

i. What is the equation of the x-axis? the y-axis?

j. What is the point of intersection for $y = 5$ and $x = -2$?

Chapter 14 Study Guide

1. Write the quadrant in which each point is located. *Lesson 14.1*

$A(-7, 5)$ $B(6, 8)$ $C(0, -3)$ $D(8, -4)$

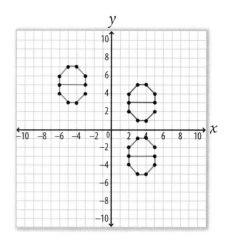

2. Determine the transformation that will move the blue e to the position of the purple e.   *Lesson 14.2*

3. Determine the transformation that will move the blue e to the position of the green e.   *Lesson 14.3*

---

4. Complete the following chart to determine the coordinates of a dilation using a scale factor k of 2. On a coordinate grid, plot the original points and connect them using a blue colored pencil. Use a red colored pencil to construct the dilation.   *Lesson 14.4*

Original (x, y)	Dilation (kx, ky)
(0, 4)	
(4, −2)	
(−2, −3)	

5. Which of the following represents a counterclockwise rotation of 270°?   *Lesson 14.5*

a.
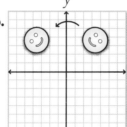

b.
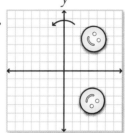

c.
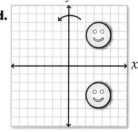

d.

For each picture, determine if a *translation*, *reflection*, *dilation*, or *rotation* is represented.   *Lessons 14.2-14.5*

6.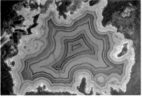

7.

8.

9.

---

10. Make an *x-y* chart for $y = 7 - 3x$ and construct a graph of the line on a coordinate grid.   *Lesson 14.6*

11. What is the equation of a horizontal line that passes through the point $(-2, -6)$? Graph the line on the coordinate grid used for problem 10.   *Lesson 14.7*

Plotting Perceptions

Write the letter of the correct word for each phrase.
1. Flips a figure over a line
2. The vertical axis on a coordinate grid
3. The first number in an ordered pair
4. Slides a figure in a straight line
5. Turns a figure around a fixed point
6. Results in a figure having a different size

a. Translation
b. Dilation
c. Reflection
d. y-axis
e. x-coordinate
f. Rotation
g. y-coordinate
h. x-axis

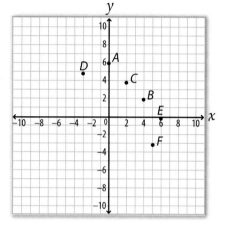

Match the given point with the letter of its location on the coordinate grid.
7. (2, 4)   8. (6, 0)   9. (−3, 5)

10. (0, 6)   11. (5, −3)   12. (4, 2)

Name the quadrant where each point is located.
13. D   14. F   15. A

16. Which of the following represents a reflection over the y-axis?

a. 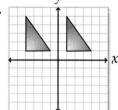   b. 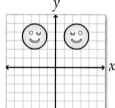   c. 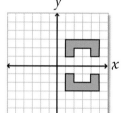   d.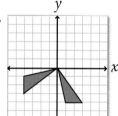

17. Copy and complete the following chart to determine the coordinates for a translation $T_{2, -3}$ applied to the original object.

Original	$T_{2, -3}$
(−2, 7)	
(−1, 5)	
(−2, 3)	
(−4, 3)	
(−5, 5)	
(−4, 7)	
(−2, 7)	

18. How will this translation move the object?

19. Graph the original object by connecting each original point on the graph to the next one in the column.

20. Graph the translation on the same coordinate grid. Use a different color and label appropriately.

21. Determine the coordinates of the vertices of the figure shown if it is reflected over the x-axis. Copy and complete the chart.

Original	$r_{x\text{-axis}}$
(2, −1)	

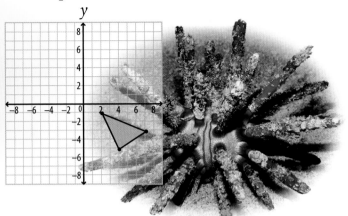

Pencil urchin, Hawaii

Determine the scale factor k for each dilation shown. The blue figure is the original in each case.

22.
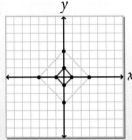

23.
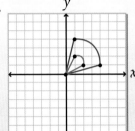

24.
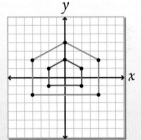

25. Which of the following represent a 90° counterclockwise rotation?

a.
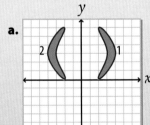

b.
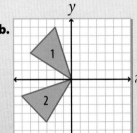

c.
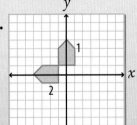

d.
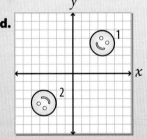

26. Make an x-y chart for the equation $y = 3x - 2$ and graph the line on a coordinate grid.

Write the letter of the correct graph at right for each equation.

27. $y = -2$

28. $x = 5$

29. $y = 5$

30. $x = -2$

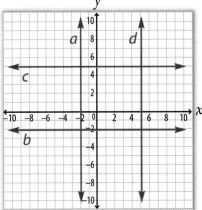

Chapter Theme:
Around
the World

15 Chapter

Cumulative Review

Identify which set or sets each number belongs to.

1. 0
2. $\frac{1}{4}$
3. −2
4. $\sqrt{2}$
5. $\frac{2}{3}$
6. 4
7. $-\frac{1}{5}$

a. Counting number
b. Whole number
c. Integer
d. Rational number
e. Irrational number

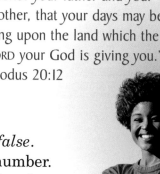

"Honor your father and your mother, that your days may be long upon the land which the LORD your God is giving you."
Exodus 20:12

Indicate whether each statement is *true* or *false*.

8. Every prime number is also a counting number.
9. A number can be both rational and irrational.
10. Every whole number is also a positive number.
11. Every composite number is also a whole number.
12. The number 1 is a prime number.
13. Every real number is also a rational number.

Copy and complete each chart.

Number	Factors	First four multiples	Prime factorization
12	14. _____	15. _____	16. _____
8	17. _____	18. _____	19. _____
25	20. _____	21. _____	22. _____

Pair of numbers	GCF	LCM
15 and 20	23. _____	24. _____
24 and 32	25. _____	26. _____

Write each number from the set {2, 3, 4, 5, 6, 9, 10} by which the given number is divisible.

27. 4000
28. 174,348
29. 78,615

30. Candice collected 320 old photographs. She wants to put the photographs in an album with a minimum of two and a maximum of eight photographs per page. Name all the ways the photographs can be grouped so that each page contains the same number of photographs.

31. Write $2 \times 2 \times 2 \times 3 \times 3 \times 4 \times 4 \times 4 \times 4 \times 4 \times 5 \times 5 \times 5 \times 5$ using exponential notation.

Simplify each of the following.

32. $\sqrt{144}$ 　　　　　　**33.** 5^3 　　　　　　**34.** $3^3 + 2^4$

35. $8 + 3(2 \cdot 6 - 1)$ 　　**36.** $9 \times \dfrac{45 - 3}{6}$ 　　**37.** $7 + 15 \div 3 - 6$

Write the letter of the correct match.

38. 895,237 　　**a.** 8.95237×10^1
39. 895.237 　　**b.** 8.95237×10^2
40. 89,523.7 　　**c.** 8.95237×10^3
　　　　　　　　d. 8.95237×10^4
　　　　　　　　e. 8.95237×10^5

Write one of the following numbers in each blank to make a true statement.

$$\frac{2}{3} \qquad \frac{3}{2} \qquad 3^2 \qquad 2^3$$

41. □ is an example of a fraction that is equivalent to a repeating decimal.
42. □ is an example of exponential notation with 2 as a base and 3 as the exponent.
43. □ is an example of a fraction that is equivalent to a terminating decimal.

Find each value of x.

44. $2^x = 64$ 　　　**45.** $x^3 = 343$ 　　　**46.** $6^3 = x$

47. For the study group at her house, Lindsey bought 75 cookies and 30 glasses of fruit punch so that each student could receive the same number of cookies and glasses of fruit punch. What is the greatest number of students for which Lindsey planned?

48. Use inverse operations to find the missing number in $(□ - 5) \cdot 5 = 25$.

Round each amount.
49. Twenty-seven quarters to the nearest dollar
50. 298.3648 to the nearest hundredth

Children's children are the crown of old men,
And the glory of children is their father.
Proverbs 17:6

Write the letter of the term that matches the definition.

1. A ratio comparing two amounts having different units of measure
2. A fraction with a fraction in the numerator and/or denominator
3. A rate that shows the cost of one item
4. An equation that shows that two ratios are equal
5. One of two numbers having a product of 1
6. For two ratios in a proportion, the product of one numerator and the other denominator

a. Improper fraction
b. Proportion
c. Cross product
d. Rate
e. Unit price
f. Reciprocal
g. Complex fraction
h. Property of Cross Products

Write the number that is not equivalent to the first number in the row.

7. $3\frac{3}{4}$ $\frac{11}{4}$ 3.75 $\frac{15}{4}$ 3.750

8. $\frac{5}{8}$ 0.625 $\frac{10}{16}$ $\frac{15}{24}$ 0.62

9. $10\frac{2}{5}$ $\frac{52}{5}$ $10\frac{4}{10}$ 10.25   10.4

Shanghai, China

Write >, < or = .

10. 0.096 ◯ 0.102

11. $7\frac{2}{5}$ ◯ $7\frac{1}{3}$

12. $\frac{2}{3}$ ◯ $\frac{10}{15}$

13. 5.07 ◯ 5.060

Simplify each ratio.

14. 20 cats:5 mice

15. $\frac{45 \text{ teachers}}{945 \text{ students}}$

16. 12 wins to 4 losses

17. $\frac{6.5 \text{ feet}}{13 \text{ feet}}$

Find the cross products.

18. $\frac{8}{10} = \frac{7.2}{9}$

19. $\frac{49}{7} = \frac{14}{2}$

Solve each proportion.

20. $\frac{x}{9} = \frac{7}{21}$

21. $\frac{12}{10} = \frac{a}{5}$

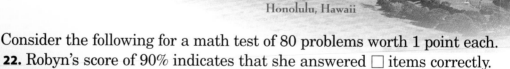

Honolulu, Hawaii

Montreal, Quebec

Consider the following for a math test of 80 problems worth 1 point each.

22. Robyn's score of 90% indicates that she answered ☐ items correctly.

23. If 68 items were answered correctly, the student's percentage score was ☐ .

24. A student who answered $\frac{3}{4}$ of the items correctly had ☐ correct answers.

25. The math teacher later gave another test. Natasha answered 46 problems correctly and received a score of 92%. How many items were on the test?

Determine the sum or difference.

26. $9\frac{1}{4} - 5\frac{7}{8}$ **27.** $\frac{5}{12} + \frac{2}{3}$ **28.** $8.98 + 103.6$ **29.** $200.25 - 50.75$

Determine the product or quotient.

30. $92.014 \div 0.02$ **31.** $3\frac{1}{3} \div \frac{1}{9}$ **32.** $\frac{3}{4} \cdot 15\frac{1}{2}$ **33.** $16.05 \cdot 83.5$

Determine the unknown value.

34. $\frac{1}{3} \cdot x = 36$ **35.** $x + 1.55 = 11.35$ **36.** $\frac{x}{5} = 13$ **37.** $x - 75.1 = 90$

Determine the unit price or rate.

38. $7.96 for 4 gallons   **39.** 6.2 miles in 31 minutes

Select the faster rate.

40. 246 items/2 hours or 2 items/minute

Write each percent as a decimal and as a fraction in simplest form.

41. 47%   **42.** 0.7%   **43.** $10\frac{1}{2}\%$

Rooftops of Seville, Spain

Student Donations to the Rescue Mission		
Items donated	Year 1	Year 2
Bibles	200	260
Clothing	75	90
Shoes	24 pairs	18 pairs

Use the chart to determine the percent increase or percent decrease from Year 1 to Year 2.

44. Bibles   **45.** Clothing   **46.** Shoes

Calculate the total cost of each item. Include a 6.5% state sales tax. Round the sales tax to the nearest cent if necessary.

47. $25.00 sweater

48. $80 sleeping bag discounted 15%

49. $17.00 compact disc

50. A cleaning solution calls for 6 cups of water to $\frac{1}{2}$ cup powder.
   Select the solution that does not have the same proportions.
   a. 24 cups water to 2 cups powder
   b. 3 cups water to $\frac{1}{3}$ cup powder
   c. 2 cups water to $\frac{1}{6}$ cup powder

Temple columns, Tunisia

Unless the Lord builds the house,
They labor in vain who build it;
Unless the Lord guards the city,
The watchman stays awake in vain.
Psalm 127:1

Write the letter of the example which best fits the given term.

1. Numerical expression

2. Equation

3. Algebraic expression

4. Additive inverses

5. Integers

a. $\{-6, -2, 0, 1, 15\}$

b. $3x - 2$

c. $16 + 5$

d. $2x - 6 = 20$

e. $\{-\frac{1}{2}, 0, \frac{3}{2}\}$

f. $5\frac{1}{2}$ and $-5\frac{1}{2}$

g. $\frac{3}{2}$ and $\frac{2}{3}$

GREAT BARRIER REEF

Write a numerical or algebraic expression for each phrase.

6. Four times the sum of six and five

7. One-half the sum of a number and 42

8. Nine divided by the sum of 5 and a number

9. Six less than the square of a number

Simplify each expression.

10. $(60 + 4)(8 \div 4)$

11. $2^3 + 16 \times 2$

12. $8 + 5(3 - 1)$

13. $16 - 4x + 6$

14. $n(14 - 2) \div 7$

15. $(3^2 + 7 \times 3)m$

Evaluate each expression if $a = 2$ and $b = 10$.

16. $(a + b)^2$

17. $a^2 + b^2$

18. ab^2

19. $(ab)^2$

Write *true* or *false* for each statement if x and y are whole numbers greater than zero.

20. $2xy < xy$

21. $x - 2 + y = x + y - 2$

22. $\frac{0}{x} < y$

23. $x^2 < x$

24. Use the formula $d = rt$ to determine how far Erin can travel in 6 hours if her average rate is 50 miles per hour.

Solve each equation for the given variable. Check your solution.

25. $6\frac{1}{2} = a - 5\frac{1}{4}$

26. $76.52 + b = 119.50$

27. $c - 16 = 59$

28. $d \div 4 = 100$

29. $16e = 80$

30. $2 = f \div 6.5$

31. Choose the correct rule for the pattern.

x	2	4	6	8	10
y	6	10	14	18	22

a. $y = x + 12$

b. $y = x^2 + 2$

c. $y = 2x + 2$

32. Copy and complete the table using the function $b = 6a^2 - 2$.

a	1	2	3	4	5
b					

NIAGARA FALLS

Compare using >, < or = .

33. $|23|$ ○ -23

34. $|6 - 12|$ ○ 6

35. $-|-15|$ ○ 15

Simplify each expression.

36. $30 + (-48)$

37. $15 - (-2) + 3$

38. $-100 + 14$

39. $-65 \div (-5)$

40. $72 \div (-6)$

41. $(-16)(-3)$

Solve each equation for the given variable. Check your solution.

42. $w - 6 = 14$

43. $x - 22 = -11$

44. $7 = 13 + y$

45. $-27r = 81$

46. $s \div 25 = -3$

47. $t \div (-10) = 200$

GRAND CANYON

48. Use the order of operations to evaluate $\dfrac{(8 - 12)5^2}{-16 + (-4)}$.

Write an equation and solve for the variable in each problem.

49. The height of Mount Everest has been determined to be 29,035 feet. This is 14,925 feet taller than Pikes Peak in Colorado which is climbed by thousands of hikers each year.
a. What is the height of Pikes Peak?
b. Matthew told his cousin that the elevation of Pikes Peak is 17 times the elevation of the town where his cousin lives. What is the elevation of the town?

Everest

Pikes Peak

50. If the Mountaineering Club purchases new sweatshirts for each of the 22 members, the balance in their account would be −$115.63. Each sweatshirt costs $25. What is the current balance?

Before the mountains were brought forth,
Or ever You had formed the earth and the world,
Even from everlasting to everlasting, You are God.
Psalm 90:2

1. Given the set $\left\{-\frac{3}{7}, -\frac{2}{5}, 0, \sqrt{3}, \pi, 3\frac{1}{4}\right\}$, list the numbers in this set that belong to the set of rational numbers.

Indicate whether each statement is *true* or *false*.

2. Every rational number is also an integer.

3. Every rational number is also a whole number.

4. Every rational number is also a real number.

5. Every rational number is also a negative number.

6. Order the numbers $-\frac{3}{4}$, $\frac{1}{5}$, $-1\frac{1}{2}$, $1\frac{1}{8}$, and 1.5 from least to greatest.

7. Indicate which of the following are equivalent forms of $-\frac{3}{7}x = 3$.

   a. $\frac{-3}{7}x = 3$ **b.** $\frac{3x}{-7} = 3$ **c.** $\frac{-3}{-7}x = 3$ **d.** $-\left(\frac{3}{7}\right)x = 3$ **e.** $\left(-\frac{3}{7}\right)x = 3$

Copy and complete the chart.

Number	Additive inverse	Multiplicative inverse
$2\frac{2}{3}$	**8.**	**9.**
-0.25	**10.**	**11.**

Match each inequality with its graph.

12. $x \leq -\frac{3}{4}$ or $x \geq \frac{1}{2}$

13. $-\frac{3}{4} \leq x < \frac{1}{2}$

14. $x < -\frac{3}{4}$ or $x > \frac{1}{2}$

15. $-\frac{3}{4} < x \leq \frac{1}{2}$

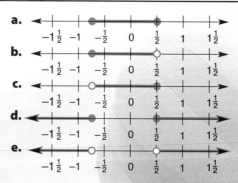

Use $>$, $<$ or $=$ to make each expression true.

16. $-\frac{5}{6} \bigcirc -\frac{1}{6}$ 17. $-\frac{2}{3} \bigcirc -\frac{1}{5}$ 18. $-3\frac{1}{4} \bigcirc -\frac{13}{4}$ 19. $-\frac{1}{2} \bigcirc -1\frac{1}{2}$

Given that a is a negative number and b is a positive number, fill in the blanks with *positive* or *negative*.

20. $-a$ is a ☐ number.

21. $-b$ is a ☐ number.

22. $a + a$ is a ☐ number.

23. $b + b$ is a ☐ number.

24. $a \cdot a$ is a ☐ number.

25. $b \cdot b$ is a ☐ number.

26. $\frac{a}{b}$ is a ☐ number.

27. $a \cdot b$ is a ☐ number.

Simplify.

28. $-\frac{3}{10} - \frac{1}{2}$

29. $-\frac{3}{10} - \left(-\frac{1}{2}\right)$

30. $\frac{3}{10} - \frac{1}{2}$

31. $0.7(-0.6)$

32. $-\frac{2}{3}\left(-2\frac{1}{4}\right)$

33. $\frac{2}{3} \div \left(-2\frac{1}{4}\right)$

Evaluate each expression when $x = -3$ and $y = -2$.

34. $\frac{3x}{2y}$

35. $\frac{x}{y} + \frac{x}{y}$

36. $(0.5)y^2 - x^2$

Solve each inequality and graph your solution.

37. $p - 3 \geq 15$

38. $6f < -240$

39. Is $x = -20$ a solution for the inequality $|13x| \leq 143$?

Solve each equation for the given variable.

40. $\frac{b}{2} - 4 = 9$

41. $-1\frac{3}{4} + a = -\frac{1}{2}$

42. $-\frac{2}{3}k = -\frac{5}{2}$

43. $5r + \frac{7}{2} = \frac{5}{6}$

44. $30.6t - 61.2 = -91.8$

45. $\left(-1\frac{3}{4}\right)h + \frac{3}{4} = -\frac{1}{2}$

Write each equation or inequality and solve.

46. Three times a number equals nine times the reciprocal of one-sixth.

47. The sum of three times a number and four is less than 22.

· ·

Write an equation or inequality to represent each problem. Solve. Check your answer.

48. Yesterday your stock posted a change of $-1\frac{1}{8}$ points, but today it shows a gain of $\frac{3}{4}$ of a point. Find the overall change for the two days.

49. Shawn purchased five identical shirts and two pairs of pants for his trip. The pants cost $30 each. If he spent a total of $176, how much was each shirt?

Trust in the LORD with all your heart,
And lean not on your own understanding;
In all your ways acknowledge Him,
And He shall direct your paths.   Proverbs 3:5-6

50. Janice wants to have at least $1500 in her savings account before leaving for college. She currently has $400 in the account. She wants to save $50 per month. How many months before she leaves does she need to start saving?

Write *permutation* or *combination* for each situation.
1. Selecting two shirts from a store
2. Entering a three-digit identification number
3. Choosing the first and second place winners in an essay contest

4. Make an organized list to show all the possible arrangements for two-topping pizzas made from five possible toppings: pepperoni, olives, sausage, mushrooms, and extra cheese.
5. A store advertises that there are 36 possible outfits that can be made from three skirts, three tops, and three jackets. Each outfit must have a skirt and top, but the jacket is optional. Explain why the advertisement is correct or incorrect.
6. How many different ways can the letters S A M P L E be arranged?

Are these events mutually exclusive for choosing a vehicle? Write *yes* or *no*.
7. Truck, sedan, van
8. Red exterior, power steering, five-passenger seating

Write *dependent* or *independent* for each pair of events.
9. Draw a red tile from a bag, replace it, and then draw a blue tile.
10. Draw a green marble from a bag and then a white marble without replacement.
11. Spin a red on a four-color spinner and roll a 2 on a number cube.

Use this set of cards for problems 12 through 27.

Determine the theoretical probability of randomly drawing the following if one card is drawn.
12. $P(3)$
13. P(striped)
14. P(even)
15. P(not purple)
16. P(striped and blue)
17. P(striped or blue)

Draw two cards, replacing the first before the second is drawn.
18. P(blue, blue)
19. P(green, purple)
20. P(blue, odd)

Draw two cards without replacing the first before drawing the second.
21. P(blue, then blue)
22. P(green, then purple)
23. P(purple, then green)

Myra had each of her classmates draw a card from the stack and return it. Thirteen drew a green card, ten drew blue, and seven drew purple.
24. What is the experimental probability of drawing a blue card?
25. Determine the theoretical probability of drawing a blue card.
26. Explain why the two probabilities are not the same.

27. If Myra's results had matched the theoretical probabilities, how many students would have drawn a blue card?

Write the letter of the best answer. Some letters may be used more than once.

28. Typically used to show frequency
29. Can be easily updated when data change
30. Shows the parts of a whole
31. Type of line used to interpret scatterplot data
32. Divides data into quartiles
33. Uses place value to display data
34. Its width indicates the range of data.
35. Displays data in rows and columns
36. Unconnected data points may show a trend.

a. Circle graph
b. Line graph
c. Trend
d. Quartile
e. Cell
f. Stem-and-leaf plot
g. Box-and-whisker plot
h. Scatterplot
i. Histogram
j. Spreadsheet

Write the term that fits the definition.
37. The number of times a particular data value appears in a data set
38. The middle data value in an ordered set
39. The point halfway between the lowest and middle data values
40. The average of the data values
41. A data value widely separated from the others
42. The difference between the greatest and least data values

43. List the scores for Team B in ascending order.
44. Find the median data value for Team B.
45. Compute the mean for Team B.
46. Express the range for Team A's scores as a single figure.

Team A		Team B
542	3	13
88761	2	245
0	1	19
	0	9

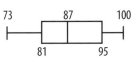

73   87   100

81   95

47. What is the median test score?
48. What is the upper quartile score?
49. Express the range of test scores as a single figure.

50. What type of trend is indicated by the graph?

But He said to them, "Why are you fearful, O you of little faith?" Then He arose and rebuked the winds and the sea, and there was a great calm. So the men marveled, saying, "Who can this be, that even the winds and the sea obey Him?"   Matthew 8:26–27

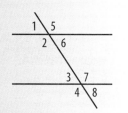

1. Name an obtuse angle.
2. Name an acute angle.
3. Name a straight angle.
4. Name a linear pair of angles.
5. Name two complementary angles.

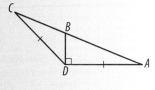

6. Relationship between ∠4 and ∠7
7. Relationship between ∠7 and ∠2
8. Relationship between ∠5 and ∠8
9. Relationship between ∠1 and ∠3
10. Relationship between ∠5 and ∠4

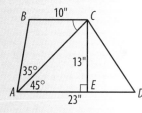

11. Name △DAB completely.
12. Name △CDA completely.
13. Name △CDB completely.

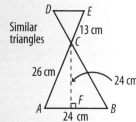

14. Find the area of the trapezoid ABCD.
15. Find the measure of ∠BCA.
16. Find the area of △CED.

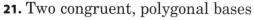

17. Find the length of $\overline{DE}$.
18. Find the area of △ABC.
19. Find the area of △CDE.
20. Name the angle whose measure is the same as ∠FBC.

Write the name of the three-dimensional figure that has:
21. Two congruent, polygonal bases
22. One polygonal base and one vertex opposite the base
23. Two congruent, circular bases

Tell the number of faces, edges, and vertices:
24. Of a cube
25. Of a tetrahedron
26. Of a hexagonal pyramid
27. Of a pentagonal prism

Match the formulas.
28. Surface area of a cube
29. Area of a triangle
30. Volume of a pyramid
31. Area of a parallelogram
32. Volume of a cylinder

a. $\frac{1}{2}h(b_1 + b_2)$
b. bh
c. s^3
d. πr^2
e. $\pi r^2 h$

f. $2\pi r^2 + 2\pi rh$
g. $6s^2$
h. $\frac{1}{2}bh$
j. lw
k. $\frac{1}{3}Bh$

33. Complete the statement with all of the terms that fit. A square is also a ☐.
34. Find the measurement of the angle formed by the clock hands at 6:30 P.M.
35. By what rule are two right triangles with congruent legs congruent?
36. Find the sum of the angle measures in a hexagon.
37. A 6-cm diameter circular disk is placed atop an 8-cm circular disk. What fraction of the larger disk is left uncovered?

Use $\pi \approx 3.14$. Round all answers to the nearest tenth unit.

38. How many milliliters can be poured into a glass jar 14 cm tall and 8 cm in diameter?
39. How tall must a 4-inch by 5-inch box be to hold all the cornmeal from a container 10 inches tall and 4 inches in diameter?

A triangular prism is 30 inches long, and its base is a right triangle with a 4-inch leg and a 3-inch leg.
40. Find the surface area.   **41.** Find the volume.

A square pyramid has a 10-cm base and a height of 12 cm.
42. Find the surface area.   **43.** Find the volume.

A cylindrical storage tank measures 2.6 meters in diameter and rises 3.3 meters above the ground.
44. Find the exposed surface area.   **45.** Find the volume.

46. Two 5-cm regular hexagons share a common side. What is their combined outside perimeter?

47. Find the area.
48. Find the perimeter.

8.5 yd

49. Find the area.
50. Find the perimeter.

12'   21'   15'

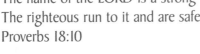

The name of the LORD is a strong tower;
The righteous run to it and are safe.
Proverbs 18:10

1. Convert 9504 feet to miles.
2. Convert 0.45 kilometers to meters.
3. About how many feet is 45 cm?
4. About how many kilometers is 5 miles?

5.
$$2\text{ ft }6\text{ in.}$$
$$+\ 3\text{ ft }8\text{ in.}$$

6.
$$8\text{ ft}$$
$$-\ 4\text{ ft }3\text{ in.}$$

7.
$$6\text{ yd }2\text{ ft}$$
$$\times\qquad 5$$

8. $36\text{ cm}\times 8 = \square\text{ m}$

$$F = \tfrac{9}{5}C + 32 \quad\Big|\quad C = \tfrac{5}{9}(F - 32)$$

9. Convert 68°F to °C.
10. Convert 100°C to °F.

11. How fast is 70 miles per hour in feet per second?
12. About how long is a meter in customary measure?
13. About how large is 2 liters in customary measure?
14. About how many pounds are in a kilogram?
15. What fraction of a gram is 250 milligrams?
16. How many kilograms make a metric ton?
17. How many pounds are in a customary ton?
18. How many fluid ounces are in a pint? in a quart?

19.
$$12\text{ lb }5\text{ oz}$$
$$-\ 3\text{ lb }8\text{ oz}$$

20.
$$3\text{ lb }10\text{ oz}$$
$$+\ 6\text{ lb }12\text{ oz}$$

21. $1\tfrac{1}{2}\text{ pt}\times 24 = \square\text{ gal}$
22. $453\text{ g}\times 25 = \square\text{ kg}$

23. Calculate the total cost of $4\tfrac{1}{2}$ lb of hamburger at \$2.88 per pound, two gallons of milk at \$2.49 per gallon, and five 2-liter bottles of cola at 4 for \$3.00.

24. Chloe paid \$13.53 plus tax for $2\tfrac{3}{4}$ yards of material to make a dress. What was the price of the material per yard?

25. A scarf pattern requires 2 feet 4 inches of material. Sydney wants to make four scarves as Christmas presents. If she buys 3 yards of material, will that be enough? Explain.

26. Mrs. Kinney figures she buys about 100 pounds of hamburger per year and serves it to her family of four an average of two nights per week. Estimate the average serving of hamburger to the nearest ounce.

27. Eight pallets of steel pipe each weighing 1650 pounds were loaded on a flatbed truck. How many tons will the truck be carrying?

28. At a health food market, bulk foods are sold by the pound. Bulk cinnamon is marked \$9.12 per pound. What will Kayla pay for two ounces?

29. Tyler is building a bookcase that requires two pieces of 1" × 8" pine 4' 8" long and five pieces 2' 10" long. How many 8-foot boards of 1" × 8" pine will he need to buy?

Match the given point with its location on the coordinate grid.

30. (4, 3)   **31.** (−4, 3)   **32.** (3, −4)

33. (−1, 6)   **34.** (−3, −2)   **35.** (4, 0)

Name the quadrant where each point is located.

36. A **37.** D **38.** F

39. Which of the following could represent a translation?

a. 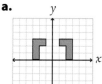   **b.**   **c.**   **d.**

Determine the coordinates of the vertices of the figure shown if it is reflected over the y-axis. Copy and complete the chart.

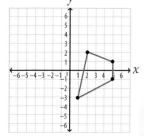

Original	$r_{y\text{-axis}}$
(2, 2)	**40.**
41.	**42.**
43.	**44.**
45.	**46.**

47. Graph the reflection in the above problem on a coordinate grid.

48. Which of the following represent a 180° rotation about the origin?

a. 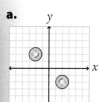   **b.** 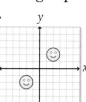   **c.**   **d.**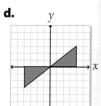

49. Make an x-y chart for the equation $y = x + 5$ and graph the line on a coordinate grid.

50. Would the equation of a horizontal line that contains the point (0, 3) be $y = 3$ or $x = 3$?

"Therefore do not worry, saying, 'What shall we eat?' or 'What shall we drink?' or 'What shall we wear?' For after all these things the Gentiles seek. For your heavenly Father knows that you need all these things. But seek first the kingdom of God and His righteousness, and all these things shall be added to you."
Matthew 6:31-33

Geometric Formulas

Rectangle 	**Square**
Area: $A = bh$ Perimeter: $P = 2b + 2h$	Area: $A = s^2$ Perimeter: $P = 4s$

Parallelogram 	**Trapezoid** 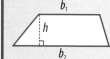
Area: $A = bh$ Perimeter: $P = 2a + 2b$	Area: $A = \frac{1}{2}h(b_1 + b_2)$

Triangle 	**Right Triangle**
Area: $A = \frac{1}{2}bh$ Perimeter: $P = a + b + c$	Pythagorean Theorem $a^2 + b^2 = c^2$

Circle 	**Sphere**
Area: $A = \pi r^2$ Circumference: $C = \pi d = 2\pi r$	Volume: $V = \frac{4}{3}\pi r^3$

Rectangular Prism 	**Cube**
Volume: $V = lwh$ Surface Area: $SA = 2lh + 2hw + 2lw$	Volume: $V = s^3$ Surface Area: $SA = 6s^2$

Triangular Prism 	**Pyramid**
Volume: $V = Bh$ (B = Area of base)	Volume: $V = \frac{1}{3}Bh$ (B = Area of base)

Cylinder 	**Cone**
Volume: $V = \pi r^2 h$ Surface Area: $SA = 2\pi rh + 2\pi r^2$	Volume: $V = \frac{1}{3}\pi r^2 h$

Measurement Conversions

Customary

Length
12 inches (in.) = 1 foot (ft)
36 inches = 1 yard (yd)
3 feet = 1 yard
5280 feet = 1 mile (mi)
1760 yards = 1 mile

Weight
16 ounces (oz) = 1 pound (lb)
2000 pounds = 1 ton (T)

Area
144 square inches (in.^{2}) = 1 square foot (ft^2)
9 square feet = 1 square yard (yd^2)
43,560 square feet = 1 acre (A)

Capacity
3 teaspoons (tsp) = 1 tablespoon (tbsp)
2 tablespoons = 1 fluid ounce (fl oz)
8 fluid ounces = 1 cup (c)
2 cups = 1 pint (pt)
2 pints = 1 quart (qt)
4 quarts = 1 gallon (gal)

Temperature in Degrees Fahrenheit (°F)
32°F = freezing point of water
212°F = boiling point of water
98.6°F = normal body temperature
$F = \frac{9}{5}C + 32$

Metric

Length
1000 millimeters (mm) = 1 meter (m)
100 centimeters (cm) = 1 meter
10 decimeters (dm) = 1 meter
10 meters = 1 dekameter (dkm)
100 meters = 1 hectometer (hm)
1000 meters = 1 kilometer (km)

Mass
1000 milligrams (mg) = 1 gram (g)
1000 grams = 1 kilogram (kg)
1000 kilograms = 1 metric ton (t)

Area
100 square millimeters (mm^2) = 1 square centimeter (cm^2)
10,000 square centimeters = 1 square meter (m^2)
10,000 square meters = 1 hectare (ha)

Capacity
1000 milliliters (mL) = 1 liter (L)
1000 liters = 1 kiloliter (kL)

Temperature in Degrees Celsius (°C)
0°C = freezing point of water
100°C = boiling point of water
37°C = normal body temperature
$C = \frac{5}{9}(F - 32)$

Time
60 seconds (sec) = 1 minute (min)
60 minutes = 1 hour (hr)
24 hours = 1 day (d)
7 days = 1 week (wk)
365 days = 1 year (yr)
52 weeks = 1 year
12 months = 1 year
366 days in a leap year
10 years = 1 decade
100 years = 1 century
1000 years = 1 millennium

Symbols

+	plus or minus		•A	point A
−	minus or negative		$\overleftrightarrow{AB}$	line AB
×	times		$\overline{AB}$	line segment AB
·	times		$\overrightarrow{AB}$	ray AB
÷	divided by		AB	length of $\overline{AB}$, distance between A and B
±	positive or negative		$\angle B$	angle B
<	is less than		$\angle ABC$	angle ABC
>	is greater than		$m\angle ABC$	measure of angle ABC
≤	is less than or equal to		$\triangle ABC$	triangle ABC
≥	is greater than or equal to		$\mathcal{P}$	plane $\mathcal{P}$
=	is equal to		(a, b)	ordered pair with x-coordinate a and y-coordinate b
≠	is not equal to			
≈	is approximately equal to		x'	x prime
%	percent		x^n	x to the nth power
$a{:}b$	ratio of a to b or $\frac{a}{b}$		x^{-n}	$\frac{1}{x^n}$, one over x to the nth power
≅	is congruent to		$\sqrt{x}$	square root of x
~	is similar to		$|x|$	absolute value of x
°	degree(s)		$f(x)$	function, f of x
π	pi (approximately 3.14 or $\frac{22}{7}$)		$P(E)$	probability of event E
‖	is parallel to		$n!$	n factorial
⊥	is perpendicular to		$\sin A$	sine of angle A
∟	right angle		$\cos A$	cosine of angle A
			$\tan A$	tangent of angle A

Problem Solving

PROBLEM-SOLVING GUIDE

1. Read and analyze.
What information is given, what am I expected to infer, and what am I asked to find?

2. Select a strategy.
What method will help solve the problem?

3. Apply the selected strategy using the appropriate operations.
How are the numbers and operations used with the strategy?

4. Check for reasonableness.
How can math reasoning be used to check the answer?

PROBLEM-SOLVING STRATEGIES

- Build a model.
- Choose an operation.
- Collect and interpret data.
- Conduct a simulation.
- Draw a diagram/picture.
- Find a pattern.
- Identify the sub-goals.
- Make a table or graph.
- Make an organized list.
- Solve a simpler problem.
- Try and check.
- Use estimation.
- Use logical reasoning.
- Use a formula.
- Work backward.
- Write an equation.

Glossary

absolute value The distance a number is from zero on a number line. (p. 94)

abundant number A number having a proper factor sum greater than the number itself. (p. 36)

acute angle An angle that measures less than 90°. (p. 186)

acute triangle A triangle with all acute angles. (p. 192)

additive inverse The opposite of a number. (p. 96)

Additive Inverse Property The sum of a number and its opposite is zero. (p. 96)
$a + (-a) = 0$

algebraic expression A mathematical phrase that uses numbers, variables, and operation symbols. Contains at least one variable and one operation symbol. (p. 72)

alternate exterior angles A pair of angles formed outside two lines on either side of a transversal, one angle at each intersection. Alternate exterior angles are congruent if the lines are parallel. (p. 188)

alternate interior angles A pair of angles formed between two lines on either side of a transversal, one angle at each intersection. Alternate interior angles are congruent if the lines are parallel. (p. 188)

angle A figure formed by two rays with a common endpoint. (p. 186)

Angle-Side-Angle (ASA) A rule stating that if two angles of a triangle and the side between them are congruent to the corresponding angles and side of another triangle, the triangles are congruent. (p. 192)

area The number of square units that cover a surface. (p. 200)

Associative Property of Addition Grouping addends differently does not change the sum. (p. 11) $a + (b + c) = (a + b) + c$

Associative Property of Multiplication The grouping of factors may change without changing the product. (p. 11) $a(b \cdot c) = (a \cdot b)c$

average See *mean*.

bar graph A graph that uses bars to represent the values of a set of data. (p. 252)

base (**1**) The number used as a repeated factor. (p. 4) (**2**) One of the parallel sides of a quadrilateral from which its height is measured. (p. 200) (**3**) One of the sides of a triangle from which its height is measured. (p. 200) (**4**) One of the parallel and congruent faces of a prism or cylinder from which its height is measured. (p. 270) (**5**) The face opposite the vertex of a pyramid or cone. (p. 270)

bisect To divide into two congruent parts. (p. 186)

box-and-whisker plot A graph that divides an ordered set of data into four equal parts. (p. 258)

capacity The volume of an object expressed in liquid measurement. (p. 172)

cell The basic unit of a spreadsheet. A cell can contain data, formulas, or labels. (p. 264)

Celsius The metric scale for measuring temperature. Expressed as °C. (p. 180)

center The point at the exact middle of the circle. (p. 204)

center of rotation The fixed point about which a transformation rotates a figure. (p. 298)

centimeter (cm) A metric unit of length. 100 centimeters equal 1 meter. (p. 166)

central angle An angle formed by two radii of a circle. (p. 204)

check digit A number that is added to the sum of all the zip code digits to make the sum divisible by ten. (p. 38)

326

chord   A line segment joining any two points on a circle. (p. 204)

circle   The set of all points in a plane that are equidistant from a given point, the center of the circle. (p. 204)

circle graph   A graph that compares parts of a whole. (p. 252)

circumference   The distance around a circle. (p. 204)

coefficient   A number by which a variable is multiplied. (p. 82)

combination   An arrangement of items in which order does not matter. (p. 234)

Commutative Property of Addition   Changing the order of addends does not change the sum. (p. 11) $a + b = b + a$

Commutative Property of Multiplication   The order of factors may change without changing the product. (p. 11) $ab = ba$

compatible numbers   Numbers that can be paired together to facilitate mental math. (p. 14)

complementary angles   Two angles with the sum of their measures equal to 90°. (p. 188)

complex fraction   A fraction having a fraction in the numerator and/or the denominator. (p. 52)

composite number   A whole number that has more than two factors. (p. 28)

compound event   A combination of two or more events. (p. 240)

concave polygon   A polygon in which a line segment between any two points inside the polygon can pass outside the polygon. (p. 198)

cone   A three-dimensional figure with one circular base and one vertex opposite the base. (p. 270)

congruent   Having the same measure. (p. 186)

contour interval   The elevation difference represented by the distance between each contour line. (p. 158)

contour line   A line that connects points of equal elevation. (p. 158)

conversion factor   A fraction, equal to 1, in which the numerator and denominator are equivalent quantities with different units. (p. 164)

convex polygon   A polygon in which a line segment between any two points inside the polygon lies completely within the polygon. (p. 198)

coordinate system   A system in which a horizontal number line and a vertical number line intersect at the origin. (p. 290)

corresponding angles   A pair of angles in matching positions where a transversal intersects two lines. Corresponding angles are congruent if the lines are parallel. (p. 188)

counting numbers   Whole numbers beginning with 1 and continuing infinitely; also called natural numbers. (p. 12)

cross product   For two ratios in a proportion, the product of one numerator and the other denominator. If two ratios are equivalent, their cross products are equivalent. (p. 138)

cryptography   The study of the techniques of secret writing. (p. 26)

cube   A prism with six congruent, square faces. (p. 270)

cubed   Raised to the third power. (p. 4)

cup (c)   A customary unit of capacity equal to 8 fluid ounces. (p. 170)

cylinder   A geometric figure with two congruent and parallel, circular bases. (p. 270)

D

decagon   A polygon with ten sides. (p. 198)

decimeter (dm) A metric unit of length. 10 decimeters equal 1 meter. (p. 166)

deficient number A number having a proper factor sum less than the number itself. (p. 36)

degree Standard unit of measurement for angles or temperature.

dekameter (dkm) A metric unit of length equal to 10 meters. (p. 166)

dependent events Events for which the occurrence of the first event affects the probability of the second event. (p. 240)

diagonal A line segment, that is not a side, connecting two vertices of a polygon. (p. 197)

diameter The distance across a circle through its center. (p. 204)

dilation A transformation that results in a figure that is the same shape as the original, but has a different size. (p. 296)

Distributive Property The product remains the same whether the factor is multiplied by the sum of the addends or by each addend. (p. 11) $a(b + c) = ab + ac$

divisible A number is divisible by another number if it can be divided by that number with no remainder.

dodecagon A polygon with twelve sides. (p. 198)

E

edge A line segment where two faces of a polyhedron intersect. (p. 270)

endpoint A point at the end of a line segment or ray. (p. 186)

equation A mathematical sentence that contains an equal sign. (p. 70)

equidistant The same distance. (p. 204)

equilateral triangle A triangle with all sides congruent. (p. 192)

equivalent fractions Fractions that name the same number. (p. 44)

Euler's formula A formula that relates the number of edges, faces, and vertices of a polyhedron. (p. 270) $E = F + V - 2$

evaluate To find the numerical value of an expression by replacing variables with numerals. (p. 76)

event In the study of probability, a specific outcome.

experimental probability The ratio of the number of times an event actually occurs to the total number of trials during an experiment. (p. 236)

exponent The number of times a base number is used as a factor. (p. 4)

exponential notation A way to express a number as a base number and an exponent that indicates the number of times the base number is used as a factor. (p. 4)

expression A mathematical phrase containing operation symbols and numbers and/or variables. (p. 10)

face A flat surface of a polyhedron. (p. 270)

factor tree A diagram showing the steps resulting in the prime factorization of a number. (p. 30)

factorial For a given number n, the product of all the whole numbers from 1 to n, starting with n. It is written as $n!$ and read as n factorial. (p. 232)

Fahrenheit The customary scale for measuring temperature. Expressed as °F. (p. 180)

fluid ounce (fl oz) A customary unit of capacity equal to 2 tablespoons. (p. 170)

foot (ft) A customary unit of length equal to 12 inches. (p. 164)

frequency The number of times a particular value appears in a set of data. (p. 260)

frequency table   A table showing a set of data and the frequency with which each item occurs. (p. 260)

function   A rule that shows the relationship between a given number, input, and the resulting number, output, by defining the operation(s) performed. (p. 86)

Fundamental Counting Principle   The total number of possible outcomes is the product of the number of items in each category. (p. 230)

gallon (gal)   A customary unit of capacity equal to 4 quarts. (p. 170)

gram (g)   The basic unit of mass in the metric system. (p. 172)

great circle   A circle formed by the intersection of a sphere and a plane passing through the center of the sphere. (p. 284)

greatest common factor (GCF)   The largest common factor of two or more numbers. (p. 32)

H

hectometer (hm)   A metric unit of length equal to 100 meters. (p. 166)

height   (**1**) The perpendicular distance from the base of a quadrilateral to the opposite side. (p. 200) (**2**) The perpendicular distance from the base of a triangle to the opposite vertex. (p. 200) (**3**) The perpendicular distance between the two bases of a prism or a cylinder. (p. 272) (**4**) The perpendicular distance from the base of a pyramid or a cone to the opposite vertex. (pp. 274, 280)

hemisphere   One half of a sphere. (p. 284)

hendecagon   A polygon with eleven sides. (p. 198)

heptagon   A polygon with seven sides. (p. 198)

hexagon   A polygon with six sides. (p. 198)

histogram   A type of bar graph that shows the number of data values that appear in each of a series of equal intervals. (p. 260)

hypotenuse   The side opposite the right angle in a right triangle. (p. 194)

I

improper fraction   A fraction that has a numerator equal to or greater than its denominator. (p. 46)

inch (in.)   A customary unit of length. (p. 164)

independent events   Events for which the outcome of one event does not affect the probability of the other event. (p. 240)

inequality   A mathematical sentence that contains $<, >, \neq, \leq,$ or $\geq$. (p. 124)

integers   All whole numbers and their opposites including zero. (p. 12)

interval   The number of units between the lines on the scale of a graph.

inverse operation   The opposite of a mathematical operation. (p. 16)

irrational number   A real number that cannot be expressed as a terminating or repeating decimal. (p. 12)

isosceles triangle   A triangle with at least two congruent sides. (p. 192)

K

kilogram (kg)   A metric unit of mass equal to 1000 grams. (p. 172)

kilometer (km)   A metric unit of length equal to 1000 meters. (p. 166)

L

latitude   Angular distance north and south of the equator. (p. 158)

least common denominator (LCD)   The smallest common multiple of two or more denominators. (p. 44)

least common multiple (LCM)   The smallest common multiple of two or more numbers. (p. 34)

leg   One of the two sides of a right triangle that form the right angle. (p. 194)

line   A straight path of points that extends without end in opposite directions. (p. 186)

line graph   A graph that uses line segments to represent increases or decreases over a period of time. (p. 252)

line of symmetry   A line that divides a figure into congruent halves that are mirror images of each other.

line plot   A graph that uses an × above a number on a number line to represent each favorable outcome or data value. (p. 236)

line segment   The part of a line that lies between two endpoints. (p. 186)

linear equation   An equation having a graph that is a straight line. (p. 300)

linear pair   Two adjacent angles that form a straight line. (p. 188)

liter (L)   The basic unit of capacity in the metric system. (p. 172)

longitude   Angular distance measured east and west of the prime meridian. (p. 158)

lower quartile   The median of the lower half of an ordered data set. (p. 258)

magnetic declination   The angular distance between true north and magnetic north at a given location. (p. 112)

mass   The amount of matter in an object. (p. 172)

mean   The sum of the values of a set of data divided by the number of items in the set. Also called *average*. (p. 254)

median   The middle value in an ordered set of data. (p. 254)

meter (m)   The basic unit of length in the metric system. (p. 166)

metric ton (t)   A metric unit of mass equal to 1000 kilograms. (p. 172)

midpoint   The point halfway between the endpoints of a line segment. (p. 186)

mile (mi)   A customary unit of length equal to 5280 feet or 1760 yards. (p. 164)

milligram (mg)   A metric unit of mass. 1000 milligrams equal 1 gram. (p. 172)

milliliter (mL)   A metric unit of capacity. 1000 milliliters equal 1 liter. (p. 172)

millimeter (mm)   A metric unit of length. 1000 millimeters equal 1 meter. (p. 166)

mode   The value (or values) that occurs most frequently in a set of data. (p. 254)

multiple   The product of a given number and any whole number. (p. 34)

multiplicative inverse   A number by which a given number is multiplied to yield a product of 1. Also called *reciprocal*. (p. 222)

mutually exclusive events   If either event occurs, the other cannot occur at the same time. (p. 238)

net   A flat pattern that can be folded into a three-dimensional figure.

nonagon   A polygon with nine sides. (p. 198)

numerical expression   A mathematical phrase that contains numbers and operation symbols to represent a known quantity. (p. 70)

obtuse angle   An angle that measures greater than 90° but less than 180°. (p. 186)

obtuse triangle   A triangle with one obtuse angle. (p. 192)

octagon   A polygon with eight sides. (p. 198)

opposites   Numbers that are the same distance from zero on a number line, but on opposite sides. (p. 94)

order of operations   The rules for determining in what order to perform mathematical operations:
1. Complete operations inside parentheses and above or below a division bar.
2. Simplify exponents.
3. Multiply and divide from left to right.
4. Add and subtract from left to right. (p. 10)

ordered pair   The location of any given point (*x, y*) on a coordinate plane. (p. 290)

origin   The intersection of the *x*-axis and the *y*-axis on a coordinate grid; the point (0, 0). (p. 290)

ounce (oz)   A customary unit of weight. (p. 170)

outcome   In the study of probability, one possible result.

outlier   A value widely separated from others in a set of data. (p. 254)

parallel lines   Lines that lie in the same plane and have no points in common. (p. 186)

parallelogram   A quadrilateral with two pairs of parallel sides. (p. 196)

pentagon   A polygon with five sides. (p. 198)

percent   Means per one hundred. A ratio that compares a number to 100.

percent decrease   A percent change that describes a decrease in a quantity. (p. 154)

percent increase   A percent change that describes an increase in a quantity. (p. 154)

percentile   One of the numbers dividing an ordered set of data into one hundred equal parts.

perfect number   A number that is equal to the sum of its proper factors. (p. 36)

perfect square   The number that results when a whole number is multiplied by itself. (p. 6)

perimeter   The distance around a figure. (p. 200)

period   In standard notation, each group of three digits separated by commas. (p. 2)

permutation   An arrangement of items in which order matters. (p. 232)

perpendicular bisector   A line that intersects a line segment at a right angle and divides it into two congruent segments. (p. 186)

perpendicular lines   Lines that intersect at right angles. (p. 186)

pi (π)   The ratio of the circumference of a circle to its diameter. (p. 204) $\pi \approx \frac{22}{7}$ **or 3.14**

pint (pt)   A customary unit of capacity equal to 2 cups. (p. 170)

plane   A collection of all points extending without end in two dimensions in every direction. (p. 186)

point   A specific location in space. (p. 186)

polygon   A closed plane figure formed by line segments. (p. 198)

polyhedron   A three-dimensional figure made up of flat, polygonal surfaces. (p. 270)

pound (lb)   A customary unit of weight equal to 16 ounces. (p. 170)

precision   The degree of exactness of a measurement.

prime factorization   A way to express a number as the product of only prime numbers. (p. 30)

prime meridian   The imaginary line that runs from the North to the South Pole passing through Greenwich, England. (p. 158)

prime number   A whole number that has only two factors, 1 and the number itself. (p. 28)

prism   A polyhedron with two congruent and parallel bases; all other faces are parallelograms. (p. 270)

probability   The likelihood that a given event will occur.

proper factor Any factor of a number except the number itself. (p. 36)

proportion An equation that shows that two ratios are equal. (p. 142)

pyramid A polyhedron with triangular faces that meet at a common vertex and join to a polygonal base. (p. 270)

Pythagorean Theorem For any right triangle, the sum of the squares of the lengths of the legs is equal to the square of the length of the hypotenuse. (p. 208) $a^2 + b^2 = c^2$

Q

quadrant One of four regions defined by the x- and y-axes on a coordinate plane. (p. 290)

quadrilateral A polygon with four sides. (p. 196)

quart (qt) A customary unit of capacity equal to 2 pints. (p. 170)

quartile One of the numbers dividing an ordered set of data into four equal parts.

R

radius The distance from the center to any point on the circle. (p. 204)

range The difference between the greatest value and the least value in a set of data. (p. 258)

rate A ratio comparing two amounts having different units of measure. (p. 140)

ratio A comparison of two quantities. It can be written three ways, a to b, a/b, $a{:}b$. (p. 138)

rational number A real number that can be expressed as an exact ratio of two integers other than 0. Rational numbers include integers, fractions, and terminating and repeating decimals. (p. 12)

ray A part of a line that originates at a point and extends without end in one direction. (p. 186)

real numbers All rational and irrational numbers. (p. 12)

reciprocal One of two numbers having a product of 1. Also called *multiplicative inverse*. (p. 52) $\frac{a}{b} \times \frac{b}{a} = 1$

rectangle A parallelogram with four right angles. (p. 196)

reflection A transformation that flips a figure over a line. (p. 294)

regular polygon A polygon with congruent sides and congruent angles. (p. 198)

relative primes Two numbers having no common factors other than 1. (p. 32)

repeating decimal A decimal that repeats a pattern of digits. (p. 12)

rhombus A parallelogram with four congruent sides. (p. 196)

right angle An angle that measures 90°. (p. 186)

right triangle A triangle with one right angle. (p. 192)

rotation A transformation that turns a figure around a fixed point called the center of rotation. (p. 298)

S

sample A selection of data randomly taken from a larger group for the purpose of analyzing information. (p. 254)

sample space A table or list that shows all possible outcomes of a given situation. (p. 230)

scale Numbers that define the intervals along the vertical and horizontal sides of a graph.

scale factor The ratio of a dilated image to the original image. (p. 296)

scalene triangle A triangle with no congruent sides. (p. 192)

scatterplot A graph of points that shows a relationship between two sets of data. (p. 262)

scientific notation A way to express a number as a decimal between one and ten multiplied by a power of ten. (p. 8)

sector   The portion of a circle marked by a central angle. (p. 204)

sequence   An ordered list of numbers.

set   A finite or infinite collection of elements. (p. 12)

Side-Angle-Side (SAS)   A rule stating that if two sides of a triangle and the angle between them are congruent to the corresponding sides and angle of another triangle, the triangles are congruent. (p. 192)

Side-Side-Side (SSS)   A rule stating that if all three sides of a triangle are congruent to the sides of another triangle, the triangles are congruent. (p. 192)

similar triangles   Triangles having congruent angles. Similar triangles have the same shape but may not have the same size. (p. 194)

simplest form   A fraction is in simplest form when the greatest common factor of the numerator and denominator is one.

simplify   To find a numerical value of an expression or to make an algebraic expression less complex by applying the order of operations. (p. 74)

simulation   An experiment that models outcomes of a real-world situation. (p. 244)

slant height   On a pyramid, the perpendicular distance from an edge of the base to the opposite vertex. (p. 274)

small circle   A circle formed by the intersection of a sphere and a plane that does not pass through the center of the sphere. (p. 284)

solid   A three-dimensional figure. (p. 270)

solution   A value that makes an equation or inequality true. (pp. 80, 124)

solve   To determine the value(s) of the variable that will make an equation true. (p. 80)

sphere   A three-dimensional figure consisting of the set of all points in space that are the same distance from its center. (p. 270)

spreadsheet   A computer-generated table of data used for calculating and displaying financial and other types of information. (p. 264)

square   A parallelogram with four right angles and four congruent sides. (p. 196)

square root   A number which, when multiplied by itself, results in the given number. (p. 6)

squared   Raised to the second power. (p. 4)

standard notation   The usual way to express a number using the digits 0 through 9. (p. 8)

stem-and-leaf plot   A diagram that displays the distribution of data by ordering and grouping according to place value. (p. 256)

straight angle   An angle that measures 180°. (p. 188)

supplementary angles   Two angles with the sum of their measures equal to 180°. (p. 188)

surface area   The sum of the areas of all the surfaces of a three-dimensional figure. (p. 272)

$\boxed{T}$

tablespoon (tbsp)   A customary unit of capacity equal to 3 teaspoons. (p. 170)

teaspoon (tsp)   A customary unit of capacity. (p. 170)

terminating decimal   A decimal that ends. (p. 12)

tetrahedron   A polyhedron with four faces; a triangular pyramid. (p. 270)

theoretical probability   The ratio of the number of favorable outcomes to the number of possible outcomes. (p. 236)

three-dimensional figure   A geometric figure that occupies space. It does not lie in a single plane. (p. 270)

ton (T)   A customary unit of weight equal to 2000 pounds. (p. 170)

topographic map   A map that shows the shape of the earth's surface by contour lines. (p. 158)

transformation   A change in the position or size of a figure. (p. 292)

translation   A transformation that slides a figure in a straight line, changing the location but not the orientation. (p. 292)

transversal   A line that intersects two or more lines. (p. 188)

trapezoid   A quadrilateral with only one pair of parallel sides, called bases. (p. 196)

tree diagram   A diagram that uses lines as branches to represent all possible outcomes of a given situation. (p. 230)

trend line   A line to which the points of a scatterplot tend to conform. (p. 262)

triangle   A polygon with three sides. (p. 198)

U

unit price   A unit rate that shows the cost of one item. (p. 140)

unit rate   A rate having 1 as the denominator. (p. 140)

upper quartile   The median of the upper half of an ordered data set. (p. 258)

V

variable   A letter that represents a numerical value. (p. 10)

vertex   (**1**) The common endpoint of two rays. (p. 186) (**2**) The point at which two sides of a polygon meet. (**3**) The point at which edges of a polyhedron meet. (p. 270)

vertical angles   Opposite congruent angles formed at the intersection of two lines. (p. 188)

volume   The amount of space a three-dimensional figure occupies, expressed in cubic units of measurement. (p. 278)

W

whole numbers   The counting numbers and 0. (p. 12)

X

x-axis   The horizontal line that passes through the origin on a coordinate system. (p. 290)

x-coordinate   The first number of an ordered pair. (p. 290)

Y

yard (yd)   A customary unit of length equal to 36 inches or 3 feet. (p. 164)

y-axis   The vertical line that passes through the origin on a coordinate system. (p. 290)

y-coordinate   The second number of an ordered pair. (p. 290)

Index

Least common multiple (LCM), 34–35, 39

Line
constructing perpendicular, 187
defined, 186
intersecting, 186–187, 209
parallel, 186–187
perpendicular, 186–187

Line graph
defined, 252
double, 252, 258
interpreting, 252–253, 265
making, 253

Line plot, 236–237, 254

Line segment
bisector, 186
congruent, 186–187
defined, 186

Linear equation, 300–301, 303

Linear pair, 188–189

Lower quartile, 258–259

M

Maps, 64, 106, 107, 112, 158

Mean
defined, 254
determining, 254–255, 257, 265

Measurement. *See also* Area;
Surface area; Volume
comparing customary and
metric, 168–169, 174–175,
181
conversion factors, 164–167,
170–173, 176–177, 181
converting rates, 176–177, 181
converting units, 54, 181
customary units of capacity
and weight, 170–171, 181
customary units of length,
164–165, 181
indirect, 145, 194–195
metric units of capacity and
mass, 172–173, 181
metric units of length,
166–167, 181
temperature, 180–181

Median
box-and-whisker plot, 258–259
defined, 254
determining, 254–255, 257, 265

Mental math, 3, 9, 11, 14–15, 18, 21,
44, 59, 107, 152–153, 155–157,
166–167, 174

Metric system of measurement
capacity and mass, 172–173, 181
compared to customary,
168–169, 174–175, 181
length, 166–167, 181

Midpoint, 186–187

Mixed number
adding, 46–47, 216–219, 225
as improper fraction, 46–47, 50
as percent, 151
comparing, 44–45
dividing, 52–53, 65, 220–221,
225
model, 46
multiplying, 50–51, 220–223,
225
renaming to subtract, 48
subtracting, 48–49, 65, 216,
218–219, 225

Mode
defined, 254
determining, 254–255, 257
finding from line plot, 254

Multiple
common, 34, 39

Multiplication
decimals, 60–61
fractions and mixed numbers,
50–51
in order of operations, 10, 110
integer, 104–105, 113
measures of length, 165, 181
measures of weight and
capacity, 181
negative and positive rational
numbers, 220–221, 225

Multiplicative inverse, 222–224

Mutually exclusive events,
238–239

N

Negative trend, 262–263

Nonagon, 198–199

Number line
decimals on, 215
graphing inequalities on,
118–119, 126–129, 133
fractions on, 45, 214–215
integers on, 2, 94, 96–99

O

Obtuse angle, 186, 209

Obtuse triangle, 192–193

Octagon, 198–199

Octagonal pyramid, 285

Opposite
defined, 94–95
to subtract integers, 98

Order of operations
defined, 10
evaluating expressions with,
10–11, 21, 110–111, 216,
218, 225
in equations, 11, 21

Ordered pair, 290–303

Outcomes, 230–231, 236–237

Outlier, 254–255

Output, 86–87

P

Parallel lines, 186–187

Parallelogram
area, 200–201
base, 200
defined, 196
find angle measures, 196–197
height, 200
identifying, 196–197

Pascal's Triangle, 246

Pattern
finding, 84–85, 89, 104–105
with exponents, 5, 111

Pentagon, 198–199

Pentagonal prism, 270–271

Pentagonal pyramid, 270–271

Percent
converting to decimals,
146–147, 159
converting to fractions,
146–147, 159
discount, 152–153, 156–157
equations, 148–151
estimating with, 152–153
find the percent, 150–151, 159
find the whole, 150–151,
156–157, 159
greater than 100%, 146
increase and decrease,
154–157, 159
less than 1%, 146
model, 146
of a number, 148–149, 159
sales tax, 152–153, 156–157,
159
using proportion to solve,
148–151

Perfect number, 36

Perfect square, 6, 21

Perimeter

    defined, 200

    of quadrilateral, 200–202

    of rectangle, 200–201

    of square, 200–201

    of triangle, 200–201

Permutation, 232–233, 247

Perpendicular

    bisector, 186

    lines, 186–187

Pi (π)

    approximations, 13, 204

    defined, 204

Place value

    chart, 2

    using to compare whole
        numbers and decimals, 2–3

Plane, 186

Point

    defined, 186

    on a line, 187

    plotting on a coordinate plane,
        290–303

    vanishing, 188

Polygon

    angles in, 198–199

    area, 200–203, 209

    classification, 198–199

    concave, 198

    convex, 198

    defined, 198

    irregular figures, 202–203, 209

    perimeter, 200–203, 209

    regular, 198–199

Polyhedron

    classifying, 270–271

    defined, 270

    surface area of, 272–277

    volume of, 278–283

Positive trend, 262–263

Prime factorization

    defined, 30

    to find the GCF, 32

    to find the LCM, 34

    using factor trees, 30–31

    using repeated division, 30–31

Prime number

    defined, 28–29

    determining, 28, 39

    relative primes, 32, 39

    twin primes, 29

Prism

    classifying, 270

    defined, 270

    surface area, 272–273, 285

    volume, 278–279, 282–283, 285

Probability

    arrangement, 232–233, 242, 247

    combination, 234–235, 246–247

    compound events, 240–241

    defined, 236

    dependent events, 240–241,
        247

    experimental, 236–237, 247

    factorial, 232–235

    formulas, 232, 234, 236, 238, 240

    Fundamental Counting
        Principle, 230–231

    independent events, 240–241,
        247

    line plot, 236–237

    mutually exclusive events,
        238–239

    outcomes, 230–231, 236–237

    Pascal's Triangle, 246

    permutation, 232–233, 247

    prediction, 236–237

    sample space, 230, 247

    simulation, 244–245, 247

    theoretical, 236–237, 247

    tree diagram, 230–231

Problem solving

*Problem solving is an integral
component of this math textbook.
Examples from various strands are
listed.*

    adding fractions and mixed
        numbers, 47, 49, 54–55

    adding integers, 97

    angles, 187, 189, 191, 197, 199,
        207

    area, 5, 12, 51, 53, 201, 203,
        205–207

    bar graph, 253

    box-and-whisker plot, 259

    calculator used, 20, 77, 155, 231,
        255

    circle graph, 49, 253

    circumference, 13, 205, 207

    combination, 235

    comparing and ordering
        fractions, 45, 49, 54

    comparing and ordering
        integers, 95

    comparing measurements, 169,
        217

    converting measurements, 54,
        165, 167, 171, 173, 181, 221

    converting rates, 140, 176–177

    decimal, 3

    decimal products and
        quotients, 61, 63

    decimal sums and differences,
        59, 63

    dividing fractions and mixed
        numbers, 52–53

    dividing integers, 107

    equivalent decimals and
        fractions, 57, 146

    estimation, 14–15

    Fundamental Counting
        Principle, 231

    GCF, 32–33, 37, 39

    histogram, 261

    inequalities, 119, 125, 127,
        129–131, 133

    LCM, 35, 36–37, 39

    line graph, 253

    linear equation, 301

    mean, median, mode, 255, 257

    multiplying fractions and mixed
        numbers, 51, 54–55, 215

    multiplying integers, 105

    order of operations, 19

    parallel and perpendicular
        lines, 187

    percent, 147, 149, 151, 153,
        155–157, 215

    perimeter, 19, 51, 63, 201, 217,
        219

    permutation, 233, 235

    probability, 241, 243, 247

    products and quotients of
        rational numbers, 221, 223

    proportion, 143–145

    Pythagorean Theorem, 209, 279,
        281–283, 285

    rate, 141, 145, 215

    ratio, 139, 144–145

    scale drawing, 193

    scatterplot, 263

    scientific notation, 9, 167

    similar figures, 145, 195

    simulation, 245, 247

    square roots, 7

    subtracting fractions and mixed
        numbers, 48–49, 54–55

subtracting integers, 99, 101

sums and differences of rational numbers, 217, 219, 224

surface area, 273, 275–277

tables, 3, 8, 47, 54, 59, 63, 107, 139, 173, 178

transformations, 293, 295, 297, 299

two-step equations, 121, 123

unit conversion, 140

volume, 5, 279, 281–283

writing equations, 17, 19, 80–83

writing expressions, 78–79

writing inequalities, 125, 127, 129–131, 133

Problem-solving strategies

choose a method of computation, 144

choose a strategy, 18, 54

determine reasonable answers, 51, 167–169, 173, 175, 181

draw a diagram, 19, 53, 62, 189, 195, 203

find a pattern, 18, 21, 29, 63

identify sub-goals, 19, 54, 206

make a chart or table, 199, 293, 295, 299, 301

make a graph, 253, 255, 257, 259, 261, 263

make a model, 47

make an organized list, 19

solve a simpler problem, 18, 62

try and check, 18–19, 63

use a formula, 6, 54, 61, 199, 201, 203, 205–207, 221, 223, 273, 275–277, 281–283, 285

use a graph, 49, 253, 257, 259, 261, 263, 265, 301–302

use a problem-solving guide, 18, 54, 130

use estimation, 18, 167–169, 173–175, 181

use math reasoning, 3, 18, 47, 109, 155, 167–169, 173–175, 181

work backward, 18–19

write an expression or equation, 17–19, 48–49, 63, 78–79, 101, 103, 105,

109, 113, 131, 148–151, 218–219, 223–224

Properties

Associative, 11

Commutative, 11

Distributive, 11

Proportion

convert fraction to percent, 146–147

cross products to determine, 142–143

defined, 142

equations with a variable, 143–144, 159

in percent problems, 148–151

on a coordinate grid, 142, 296–297

Pyramid

classifying, 270

defined, 270

surface area, 274–276, 283, 285

volume, 280–281, 283, 285

Pythagorean Theorem, 208–209, 274, 276, 279, 281–283, 285

Q

Quadrant,

defined, 290

plotting ordered pairs, 290–303

Quadrilateral

angle measurements in, 196–197

classifying, 196–197

defined, 196

Quartile, 258–259

R

Radius

of a circle, 204–205

of a cone, 280–281

of a cylinder, 272–273

Range, 258–259

Rate

converting, 60, 176–177, 181

defined, 140

unit, 140–142, 159

Ratio

and cross products, 138–139

defined, 138

equivalent, 138–139

models, 138

scale factor, 296–297, 303

simplifying, 138–139, 159

Rational number

classifying, 12–13, 21

defined, 12

equivalent forms, 214–215, 225

negative, 214–217

ordering, 214–215, 225

products and quotients of, 220–221, 225

sums and differences of, 216–217, 225

Ray, 186–187

Real number, 12–13

Reciprocal

defined, 52

used to divide fractions, 52–53, 220–221

Rectangle

area, 200–201

defined, 196

perimeter, 200–201

Rectangular prism

attributes, 271

defined, 270

surface area, 272–273, 276–277, 285

volume, 278–279, 282–283, 285

Rectangular pyramid, 270, 274–276, 280–281, 283, 285

Reflection

defined, 294

on a coordinate grid, 294–295, 297, 299, 303

Review, 27, 29, 31, 47, 49, 53, 61, 81, 83, 111, 125, 149, 151, 165, 167, 169, 175, 207, 239, 243, 245, 263, 293

Rhombus, 196–197

Right angle, 186, 194

Right triangle

defined, 192

hypotenuse, 194, 208

legs, 194, 208

Pythagorean Theorem, 208

Rotation

defined, 298

on a coordinate grid, 298–299, 303

Rounding

decimals, 14–15, 152–153

percent, 152–153

whole numbers, 14–15, 152